GREEK AND ROMAN
ARTILLERY

—

HISTORICAL
DEVELOPMENT

GREEK AND ROMAN ARTILLERY

═══

HISTORICAL DEVELOPMENT

═══

E. W. MARSDEN

OXFORD
AT THE CLARENDON PRESS

OXFORD
UNIVERSITY PRESS

Great Clarendon Street, Oxford OX2 6DP

Oxford University Press is a department of the University of Oxford.
It furthers the University's objective of excellence in research, scholarship,
and education by publishing worldwide in

Oxford New York

Athens Auckland Bangkok Bogotá Buenos Aires Calcutta
Cape Town Chennai Dar es Salaam Delhi Florence Hong Kong Istanbul
Karachi Kuala Lumpur Madrid Melbourne Mexico City Mumbai
Nairobi Paris São Paulo Singapore Taipei Tokyo Toronto Warsaw

with associated companies in Berlin Ibadan

Published in the United States
by Oxford University Press Inc., New York

British Library Cataloguing in Publication Data
Data available
ISBN 0-19-814268-4

1 3 5 7 9 10 8 6 4 2

Printed in Great Britain
on acid-free paper by
Bookcraft (Bath) Ltd,
Midsomer Norton

TO
W. T. M.
E. V. M.
M. M.

PREFACE

OVER a period of about a century, ending in 1929, much work was done—almost entirely by German and French scholars—on the Greek and Latin treatises describing the construction of catapults and on a wide range of topics relating to ancient artillery. In 1929 General E. Schramm, in collaboration with A. Rehm, published an edition of Biton's handbook on the construction of war machines and artillery, thus completing more than a quarter of a century of practical and academic labour in this field. In spite of such an impressive record it appeared that there was still considerable scope for further exploration of the subject. For instance, Schramm revealed in the preface to his edition of Biton a certain understandable uneasiness with regard to his interpretation of a difficult mechanical treatise. More recently investigations into ancient artillery seem conspicuously absent, although A. G. Drachmann has made one or two small but valuable contributions.

Discussions with the late Reverend M. P. Charlesworth, then President of St. John's College, Cambridge, led me to embark upon a study of Greek and Roman artillery from the beginning once more, starting with the ancient technical descriptions of the machines themselves, their construction, and developments in design. Editions of these mechanical manuals will appear in another volume (*Greek and Roman Artillery: Technical Treatises*). The conclusions reached there are largely assumed in this present volume, sometimes with relatively brief explanation. I am most grateful for the advice and encouragement provided during the period of my early efforts by the Reverend M. P. Charlesworth, the late Sir Frank Adcock, Professor A. W. Lawrence, and Mr. R. L. Howland.

I wish to offer my grateful thanks to Mr. G. T. Griffith and to Professor F. W. Walbank for their most generous help in many diverse matters over a considerable number of years, for much constructive criticism, and for keeping me on as straight a course as anyone could have done. Also I am indebted to Mr. J. V. H. Eames, with whom I have had some provocative and inspiring discussions from time to time, and to Lektor Inge Dahlàn who introduced me to some of the treasures in that splendid Uppsala institution, Carolina, and drew my attention to various pieces of archaeological evidence. I should like to thank especially Dr. W. Barr for suggestions on a wide range of points and for his careful reading of the proofs.

It would have been impossible to study the ancient mechanical writings seriously without constructing at least a few models. My first efforts were small and insignificant, but useful within their obvious limitations. I recall with gratitude the encouragement and financial assistance provided through Mr. Paul Johnstone of the B.B.C. T.V. Talks Department, who prevailed upon me to produce two larger models which were used in T.V. programmes. The first was a full-scale replica of an arrow-shooting catapult of small calibre, the lesser scorpion of the Romans, the three-span catapult of the Greeks (Plate 4). Because this machine was constructed in a hurry, the metal washers which allow the springs to be tightened are altogether inaccurate, and the arms require much smoothing and finishing. Basically, however, the model conforms to ancient standards.

The second model represented an *onager*. This was a scale reproduction, but was nevertheless quite large and heavy (Plate 14). It was built for me by Mr. R. G. Milles (of R. M. Milles Ltd., of Bootle), who interpreted my drawings and explanations with skill and sympathy, producing an efficient and successful machine. Several difficulties relating to Heron's *Cheiroballistra* were cleared up when Messrs. Norman and Raymond Cooper of Upminster constructed a splendid full-scale model in accordance with my interpretation of Heron's manual (Plates 6–8). I learned a great deal from my association with these three practical experts and I am pleased to take this opportunity of expressing my thanks to them.

The figures in the text which illustrate catapults or components have not been designed as working drawings. I have simply tried to make the construction of various types of catapult as clear as possible. Sometimes a feature which is shown in, let us say, the side-elevation of a particular machine, and which would be visible in the front-elevation, has been omitted from the latter for the sake of clarity. I have not always mentioned such omissions in the captions, but hope that they will be obvious to the reader. The diagrams illustrating fortifications are based on my own sketches and observations, on my photographs and those provided by friends, and on drawings and photographs contained in the works cited in the footnotes to the chapter on fortifications.

I am indebted to the committee of the Liverpool University Research Fund for two grants of money, one enabling me to study Greek fortifications in South Italy and Sicily, the other contributing to the cost of the five figures in colour in this volume. My thanks are due to the Society of Antiquaries of London for permission to reproduce as Plate 5 here the skull found at Maiden Castle which is Plate LIIID in R. E. M. Wheeler, *Maiden Castle, Dorset* (Reports of the Research Committee of the Society of Antiquaries of London, No. XII, Oxford, 1943). Also I offer my sincere thanks to Walter de Gruyter & Co. of Berlin for permission to reproduce six illustrations. My Plate 3 is taken from *Alt. Perg.* ii, Taf. 45. 1, and my Plates 9, 10, 11, 12, and 13 have been derived from C. Cichorius, *Die Reliefs der Traianssäule*, Tafelband i (Berlin, 1896), abb. 104–5, 163–4, 165, 166, and 169 respectively.

Last but not least I wish to record my appreciative gratitude to the staff of the Clarendon Press for their unfailingly patient, sympathetic, and skilful handling of the many problems involved in publishing this book.

E. W. MARSDEN

Liverpool, 1969

CONTENTS

LIST OF FIGURES AND DIAGRAMS

CHAPTER VIII

APPENDIX I

LIST OF PLATES

(At the end)

ABBREVIATIONS AND BIBLIOGRAPHY

Abh. Bay. Akad. = *Abhandlungen der Bayerischen Akademie der Wissenschaften, phil.-hist. Abteilung.*

Abh. Berlin. Akad. = *Abhandlungen der Preussischen Akademie der Wissenschaften, Berlin, phil.-hist. Klasse.*

AJA = *American Journal of Archaeology.*

AJP = *American Journal of Philology.*

Alt. Perg. = *Altertümer von Pergamon.* Berlin, 1885–1937.

AM = *Mitteilungen des deutschen archäologischen Instituts, athenische Abteilung.*

Arch. Journ. = *Archaeological Journal.*

BCH = *Bulletin de correspondance hellénique.*

Bengtson, *Strategie* = H. Bengtson, *Die Strategie in der hellenistischen Zeit.* 3 vols. *Münchener Beiträge*, vols. 26, 32, and 36. Munich, 1937–52.

Blouet = A. Blouet (et ses collaborateurs—A. Ravoisié, A. Poirot, F. Trézel, F. de Gournay), *Expédition scientifique de Morée*, i. Paris, 1831.

BPhW = *Berliner philologische Wochenschrift.*

Cichorius, *Römische Studien* = C. Cichorius, *Römische Studien.* Zweite Auflage. Darmstadt, 1961.

CIL = *Corpus inscriptionum latinarum.*

ClRh = *Clara Rhodos.*

CP = *Classical Philology.*

CQ = *Classical Quarterly.*

Daremberg-Saglio = Daremberg-Saglio, *Dictionnaires des antiquité grecques et romaines.* Paris, 1877–1919.

Diels, *Antike Technik* = H. Diels, *Antike Technik.* Ed. 3. Leipzig, 1924.

Domaszewski, *Rangordnung* = A. von Domaszewski, *Die Rangordnung des römischen Heeres.* (*Bonner Jahrbücher*, 117.) Bonn, 1908.

A. G. Drachmann, 'Remarks on the Ancient Catapults'. In *Actes du Septième Congrès International d'Histoire des Sciences.* Jerusalem, 1953.

A. G. Drachmann, *The Mechanical Technology of Greek and Roman Antiquity.* Copenhagen, 1963.

Droysen, *Heerwesen* = H. Droysen, *Heerwesen und Kriegführung der Griechen.* (Hermann's *Lehrbuch der griechischen Antiquitäten* ii, 2.) Freiburg, 1889.

Ferguson = W. S. Ferguson, *Hellenistic Athens.* London, 1911.

FGH = F. Jacoby, *Die Fragmente der griechischen Historiker.* Berlin–Leiden, 1923– .

Frazer, *Pausanias* = J. G. Frazer, *Pausanias' Description of Greece.* 6 vols. London, 1898.

Gött. Abh. = *Abhandlungen der Gesellschaft der Wissenschaften zu Göttingen.*

Gött. Nachr. = *Nachrichten von der Gesellschaft der Wissenschaften zu Göttingen.*

IG² = *Inscriptiones graecae, editio minor.*

ILS = *Inscriptiones latinae selectae*, ed. H. Dessau. 3 vols. Berlin, 1892–1916.

JAI = *Journal of the Royal Anthropological Institute.*

Köchly = H. Köchly and W. Rüstow, *Griechische Kriegsschriftsteller*, i. Leipzig, 1853.

Krischen, *Herakleia* = F. Krischen, *Die Befestigungen von Herakleia am Latmos.* (*Milet*, iii, 2.) Berlin–Leipzig, 1922.

Krischen, *Stadtmauern* = F. Krischen, *Die Stadtmauern von Pompeji und griechische Festungsbaukunst in Unteritalien und Sizilien.* (*Die hellenistische Kunst in Pompeji*, vii.) Berlin, 1941.

Kromayer, *Antike Schlachtfelder* = J. Kromayer and G. Veith, *Antike Schlachtfelder*. 4 vols. Berlin, 1903–31.

Lanckoronski = K. Lanckoronski, *Städte Pamphyliens und Pisidiens.* 2 vols. Vienna, 1890–2.

Launey = M. Launey, *Recherches sur les armées hellénistiques.* 2 vols. Paris, 1949–50.

Lawrence, *Greek Architecture* = A. W. Lawrence, *Greek Architecture.* Penguin, 1957.

LS = Liddell–Scott–Jones, *A Greek–English Lexicon.* Ed. 9. Oxford, 1940.

Maier = F. G. Maier, *Griechische Mauerbauinschriften.* 2 vols. Heidelberg, 1961.

Mansel, *Side* = A. M. Mansel, *Die Ruinen von Side.* Berlin, 1963.

Michel = Ch. Michel, *Recueil des inscriptions grecques.* Brussels, 1900 (supplements, 1912 and 1927).

Mon. Ant. Lincei = *Monumenti antichi pubblicati per cura della R. Accademia dei Lincei.*

OCD = *Oxford Classical Dictionary.*

R. P. Oliver, 'A Note on the *De Rebus Bellicis.* In *CP* 50 (1955), 113 ff.

Payne-Gallwey, *The Crossbow* = Sir R. W. F. Payne-Gallwey, *The Crossbow, mediaeval and modern, military and sporting.* Its construction, history and management, with a treatise on the balista and catapult of the ancients and an appendix on the catapult, balista and the Turkish bow. Ed. 2. London, 1958.

Pöhlmann, *Untersuchungen* = M. Pöhlmann, *Untersuchungen zur älteren Geschichte des antiken Belagerungsgeschützes.* Diss. Erlangen, 1912.

Prou, *Chirobaliste* = V. Prou, 'La Chirobaliste d'Héron d'Alexandrie'. In *Notices et Extraits des manuscrits de la Bibliothèque nationale et autres bibliothèques*, 26, 2 (Paris, 1877), 1–319.

B. Rathgen, 'Die Punischen Geschosse des Arsenals von Karthago und die Geschosse von Lambaesis'. In *Zeitschrift für historische Waffenkunde*, 5 (Dresden, 1909–11), 236 ff.

RE = Pauly–Wissowa's *Real-encyclopädie der classischen Altertumswissenschaft.* Stuttgart, 1893– .

REA = *Revue des études anciennes.*

RM = *Mitteilungen des deutschen archäologischen Instituts, römische Abteilung.*

Robert, *Ét. Anat.* = L. Robert, *Études anatoliennes: recherches sur les inscriptions grecques de l'Asie Mineure.* Paris, 1937.

E. von Röder, 'Die Kaliber der antiken Geschütze'. In *Zeitschrift für historische Waffenkunde*, 5 (Dresden, 1909–11), 311 ff.

Ross, *Aristotle* = W. D. Ross, *Aristotle.* Ed. 5. London, 1949.

RS = A. Rehm and E. Schramm, 'Bitons Bau von Belagerungsmaschinen und Geschützen'. In *Abh. Bay. Akad.* 1929.

S.-B. Berlin = *Sitzungsberichte der Preussischen Akademie der Wissenschaften, phil.-hist. Klasse.*

Schambach, *Bemerkungen* = O. Schambach, 'Einige Bemerkungen über die Geschützverwendung bei den Römern besonders zur Zeit Cäsars'. In *Programme von dem Friedrichs-Gymnasium zu Altenburg*, nr. 618 (1883), 1 ff.

Schenk, *Vegetius* = D. Schenk, *Flavius Vegetius Renatus. Die Quellen der Epitoma Rei Militaris. (Klio,* Beiheft 22.) Leipzig, 1930.

Schläger = H. Schläger, 'Zu den Bauperioden der Stadtmauer von Paestum'. In *RM* 69 (1962), 21 ff.

R. Schneider, 'Herons Cheiroballistra'. In *RM* 21 (1906), 142 ff.

Schramm, Μονάγκων *und Onager* = E. Schramm, 'Μονάγκων und Onager'. In *Gött. Nachr.* 2 (1918), 259 ff.

Schramm, *Poliorketik* = E. Schramm, 'Poliorketik'. In J. Kromayer and G. Veith, *Heerwesen und Kriegführung der Griechen und Römer* (Müller–Otto, *Handbuch* iv. 3, 2; Munich, 1928), 209 ff.

Schramm, *Saalburg* = E. Schramm, *Die antiken Geschütze der Saalburg.* Berlin, 1918.

Schramm, *Vitruvius* = E. Schramm, 'Erläuterung der Geschützbeschreibung bei Vitruvius x. 10–12'. In *S.-B. Berlin* (1917), 718 ff.

Scranton, *Greek Walls* = R. L. Scranton, *Greek Walls.* Cambridge, Mass., 1941.

Syll. = *Sylloge inscriptionum graecarum,* ed. W. Dittenberger. Ed. 3. 4 vols. Leipzig, 1915–24.

Syme, *Roman Revolution* = R. Syme, *The Roman Revolution.* Oxford, 1960.

Tarn, *HMND* = W. W. Tarn, *Hellenistic Military and Naval Developments.* Cambridge, 1930.

TC = C. Cichorius, *Die Reliefs der Traianssäule,* Tafelband i. Berlin, 1896.

Thévenot = M. Thévenot (ed.), *Veterum mathematicorum Athenaei, Apollodori, Philonis, Bitonis, Heronis et aliorum opera Graece et Latine ex manuscriptis codicibus Bibliothecae Regiae pleraque nunc primum edita.* Paris, 1693.

E. A. Thompson, *A Roman Reformer and Inventor.* Oxford, 1952.

Tod = M. N. Tod, *Greek Historical Inscriptions.* 2 vols. Oxford, 1946 (vol. i, ed. 2), 1948 (vol. ii).

Vors. = H. Diels–W. Kranz, *Fragmente der Vorsokratiker.* 3 vols. Ed. 6. Berlin, 1951–2.

W = C. Wescher, *La Poliorcétique des Grecs.* Paris, 1867.

Walbank, *Polybius* = F. W. Walbank, *A Historical Commentary on Polybius,* i. Oxford, 1957.

Wheeler, *Maiden Castle* = R. E. M. Wheeler, *Maiden Castle, Dorset. (Reports of the Research Committee of the Society of Antiquaries of London,* xii.) Oxford, 1943.

Winter, *Ikria* = F. E. Winter, 'Ikria and katastegasma in the Walls of Athens'. In *Phoenix,* 13, 4 (Toronto, 1959), 161 ff.

Yadin = Y. Yadin, *The Art of Warfare in Biblical Lands.* London, 1963.

WEIGHTS AND MEASURES

THERE is a more detailed discussion of Greek and Roman weights and measures so far as they affect artillery in *Technical Treatises*, Note on Measurements and Weights, which is mainly based on the work of F. Hultsch, *Griechische und Römische Metrologie*² (Berlin, 1882). A summary here may be helpful.

For the weights of stone-shot and calculations based on them Greek artillerymen probably used as their standard the Attic–Euboic *mina* which was equivalent to 436·6 grammes or to 0·96 lb. (British) (N.B. 100 *drachmae* = 1 *mina*: 60 *minae* = 1 talent). The Roman standard pound (*libra*) was equal to 327·5 grammes or to 0·72 lb. (British).

The generally standard Greek foot (πούς) measured 308·3 mm. or 12·16 inches:

	mm.	inches	useful approximation in inches
1 dactyl	19·3	0·76	¾
1 palm (4 dactyls)	77·1	3·04	3
1 span (12 dactyls)	231·2	9·12	9
1 foot (16 dactyls)	308·3	12·16	12
1 cubit (24 dactyls)	462·4	18·21	18

The standard Roman foot (*pes*) and its subdivisions had the following equivalents:

	mm.	inches (British)
1 foot (*pes*), of 12 *unciae* or 16 digits:	295·7	11·64
1 inch (*uncia*):	24·6	0·97
1 palm (*palmus*), of 3 *unciae* or 4 digits:	73·9	2·91
1 digit (*digitus*):	18·5	0·73

I

INTRODUCTION AND ANALYSIS OF CONSTRUCTIONAL SOURCES

FOR the present purpose a piece of artillery is to be defined as a relatively complex engine powered by springs of resilient material, composed of several mechanical devices, and designed to hurl bolts or shot over the longest possible range. Such engines could greatly exceed the performance of the simple machines, the bow and the sling, both in the length or weight of their missiles and in maximum effective range. Ancient pieces of artillery, though invented and developed by the Greeks, are perhaps best known by their Latin names, *catapulta* and *ballista*. *Catapulta* meant an arrow- or bolt-shooting engine.[1] A *ballista* was a more powerful machine, primarily designed for discharging stone-shot.[2] Occasionally *ballistae* hurled extraordinary projectiles. For instance, in a sea battle between the fleets of Prusias of Bithynia and Eumenes of Pergamum in 184 B.C., Hannibal, Prusias' commander at the time, apparently caused numerous jars full of poisonous snakes to be shot at the Pergamene vessels. The arrival of the pots created amusement among Eumenes' sailors, but this soon turned to consternation when the snakes appeared, and the stratagem contributed to Bithynian victory.[3] We sometimes find ancient artificers modifying *ballistae* in order to project immense bolts over extreme ranges; but the *ballista* usually functioned as a stone-thrower.

However, at some time during the period from A.D. 100 to 300, a change occurred in the system of nomenclature. Thus, in the fourth century A.D., *catapulta* indicates a one-armed stone-throwing engine, while *ballista* means a piece of artillery which shoots bolts only. But it must be emphasized that this somewhat astonishing change in terminology only applies in the later Roman imperial epoch. The reasons for it will be discussed at the appropriate time.[4]

[1] The Greek term for this type of artillery was καταπέλτης ὀξυβελής, though ὀξυβελής occurs very often by itself. The earliest form, however, was καταπάλτης ὀξυβόλος. Small *catapultae* were generally called scorpions.

[2] The Greek equivalent was, in full, καταπέλτης λιθοβόλος or πετροβόλος, though the word καταπέλτης was normally omitted.

[3] Frontin. *Strat.* iv. 7. 10–11; Nep. *Hann.* 10. 4–11. 6; Just. xxxii. 4. 6–7; Gal. xiv. 231 (Kühn).   [4] Below, pp. 188 ff.

It is customary to divide ancient pieces of artillery into two broad classes according to the means by which propulsive force was provided. When an engine obtains its motive power from a bow similar to, but much stronger and generally larger than, an ordinary hand-bow, that engine is called a non-torsion catapult.[1] A torsion catapult, on the other hand, derived its power from springs (τόνοι) of rope manufactured from animal sinew, hair, or, rarely, from other resilient materials. The non-torsion type was produced first and continued in use for some time after the introduction of the potentially more effective torsion engines; but it appears to have been completely superseded by the latter towards the end of the third century B.C. After a long interval, however, non-torsion machines appeared once more in the fourth century A.D., when they were called *arcuballistae*. The *arcuballista*, from which the word arbalest developed, was the forerunner of the medieval cross-bow. In a general way, medieval cross-bows of various kinds resembled their non-torsion catapult ancestors, but there were several technical differences in detail. Above all, early non-torsion engines could be, and very often were, much larger than any medieval cross-bow.

The aim of this book is to investigate the historical employment of ancient artillery from its invention in 399 B.C. to the collapse of the Roman Empire in the west (*c.* A.D. 400). What influence did the introduction of artillery have on various types of warfare? Could catapults be used effectively in field operations? Where and for what purposes were certain calibres popular? Did significant improvements in the design of catapults have important consequences for their role in fighting? How was the artillery of states and monarchs organized? By what methods could ancient governments obtain artificers and train artillerymen? What was the effect of artillery on the design of fortifications? These are the sort of questions which are discussed in pursuance of our aim. The evidence is rarely sufficient to answer them as fully as we would wish, but often an illuminating comment, half-concealed in an ancient military anecdote, or an item in an epigraphic list of equipment awakens our interest even if it does not completely satisfy our curiosity.

As an essential prerequisite for the fulfilment of this aim it is necessary to study the major technical treatises on the construction of artillery which have come down to us from the ancient world, and also to examine a few non-technical descriptions which help to amplify our knowledge

---

[1] Here, as elsewhere, the word 'catapult', when it is not further defined, is used in a general sense, just as the Greeks employed καταπέλτης to indicate any piece of artillery, whether non-torsion or torsion, arrow-shooting or stone-throwing. The resilient materials forming the bow of a non-torsion catapult were wood, sinew, and horn.

and to bridge certain gaps. A remarkable series of five constructional handbooks enables us not only to discover how a standard catapult was made and how it worked, but even to detect a number of major and minor improvements in the design of catapults, which, over the centuries, rendered them more and more effective. Apart from their obvious value for the student of ancient artillery, the handbooks possess a much wider significance because they give us a unique insight into the applied mechanics of the Greeks.[1] Since the ancient constructional writings are studied in detail in another volume,[2] it is sufficient here to give a very brief account of the technical writers and their works and then to offer a summary analysis of the information which can be derived from these constructional sources.[3]

The first of the five principal documents, the artillery manual (Βελο-ποιικά) of Heron of Alexandria, has always been considered most valuable because it is couched in rather more general terms than any of the others. Although Heron flourished in the second half of the first century A.D., his manual seems to have depended very closely indeed on the lost writings of Ctesibius of Alexandria, a famous engineer who lived about the middle of the third century B.C. Heron is the only person to include any description at all of the earliest type of non-torsion catapult. He is the only writer to survey early efforts to produce torsion artillery. Also he supplies by far the clearest account of developed torsion machines. In spite of his own date, the technical content of his work belongs in the third century B.C.

The next handbook, that of Biton who dedicated it to a king of Pergamum probably about 240 B.C., transports us straight back into the workshop of an ancient artificer, his condensed lists of instructions and measurements being clearly intended for experienced mechanics. Its great value lies in the fact that it supplies the only description of non-torsion catapults of advanced design; two of Biton's four non-torsion machines were stone-throwers. The third work, written about 200 B.C., is the artillery manual of Philon of Byzantium, who obtained his information by frequenting the great arsenals at Rhodes and Alexandria and questioning the leading artificers at these prominent technical centres. This manual provides two useful, though abbreviated, lists of dimensions for standard torsion arrow-shooting and stone-throwing catapults, a good examination of the formulae for determining calibre, some interesting

---

[1] Cf. M. R. Cohen and I. E. Drabkin, *A Source Book in Greek Science* (Cambridge, Mass., 1958), 318, n. 2.

[2] E. W. Marsden, *Greek and Roman Artillery. Ancient Technical Treatises* (Oxford, forthcoming); hereafter abbreviated as *Technical Treatises*.

[3] For fuller discussion of the dates of these writers, see *Technical Treatises*, Introduction.

criticisms of standard artillery, and descriptions of three novel catapults. Though the three last-mentioned machines appear never to have gone into general production, Philon's account contains material which is important from the technological point of view.

The fourth writer, Vitruvius (c. 25 B.C.), included three chapters on artillery in the tenth book of his general work on architecture. They are no more than lists of dimensions, very detailed ones, however, for torsion arrow-shooting and stone-throwing engines, with a few remarks on tuning. Vitruvius, we feel, should be a particularly valuable source, because he served as a builder and repairer of catapults and *ballistae* under Julius Caesar and, later, in the army of Caesar's heir, Octavian (afterwards Augustus). Unfortunately, in a sense, there is reason to suspect that Vitruvius may have preferred to obtain his material from a Greek written source rather than from his own experience. Finally, Heron of Alexandria's second artillery treatise, the *Cheiroballistra*, provides a technical description of a very powerful, torsion, arrow-shooting engine which must have been first developed in his own time and which apparently proved itself in the Dacian Wars of Trajan (A.D. 101–6).

Anyone who studies the constructional development of ancient machines inevitably becomes involved in building models. In the first place, it is rather fascinating to construct a machine by following instructions written 2,000 years ago or more. Secondly, reconstruction provides the translator of a Greek or Latin technical document with the best of all touchstones by means of which to check his interpretations. It is not too difficult now to build a small working model of an ancient catapult, bearing a general resemblance to the prototype and operating in roughly the same way. But it is quite a different matter to construct an accurate full-scale model of even a small Greek or Roman catapult, of any given type or period, and then to tune it until it achieves a performance approaching that of the original. In the nineteenth century several efforts were made in France and Germany to reconstruct *catapultae* and *ballistae*; but, on the whole, they were unsuccessful. Then the German General Schramm, whose outstanding work in this field it is fitting to acknowledge at an early stage in a study of catapults, succeeded in producing full-scale models with which, in 1904, he convincingly demonstrated the enormous power of those machines which were the artillery of the Greek and Roman world.[1]

---

[1] For a list of all his models, both scale and full-size, see Schramm, *Saalburg*, 8 f.; on earlier efforts to reconstruct catapults, see *Saalburg*, 12 ff.; Diels, *Antike Technik*, 91 f.

§ 1. *The Earliest Artillery*

The very first piece of artillery ever invented was the true *gastraphetes* (belly-bow), and Heron is the only mechanical writer to describe its earliest form.[1] The machine owed its name to the fact that the operator stretched its bow by resting his stomach in a concavity at the rear end of the stock and pressing forward with all his strength.[2] The *gastraphetes* was made up of two principal parts, the stock, and the bow which supplied the propulsive power (see Fig. 1, p. 6).

The stock itself was in two sections, the lower one, which we have called the case (σῦριγξ), being fixed solidly to the bow. The upper section, the slider (διώστρα), had approximately the same dimensions as the case along the full length of which it could slide freely, backwards and forwards, in a dovetailed groove.[3] The case incorporated a straight ratchet along each side and also had, at its rear end, a withdrawal rest (καταγω-γίς) which included the above-mentioned concavity for the operator's stomach. The slider possessed two pawls designed to work in the ratchets,[4] a trigger mechanism,[5] and a groove for the missile. Hence the stock of the *gastraphetes* was a combination of several mechanical devices, all assisting a man to draw and discharge a bow which would have been far too powerful for him to work by hand in the ordinary way.

We have no conclusive information about the construction of the actual bow, which, after all, is a rather vital part of the machine. Schramm apparently assumed that the bows of all non-torsion engines were made of resilient steel in the palintone shape.[6] This is clear from his models, his remarks on them, and the diagrams attached to his edition of Biton's manual.[7] Such an assumption is, in my opinion, utterly wrong. One cannot believe that either the Greeks or the Romans could produce resilient steel to order in sufficient quantity. It is one thing to produce resilient swords of Celtic and Spanish type,[8] but quite another to manufacture an efficient steel spring even for a small non-torsion catapult. Philon mentions the resilient properties of Celtic and Spanish swords in his account of Ctesibius' so-called bronze-spring engine in order to convince the incredulous reader that iron or, rather, steel, if correctly prepared, can acquire resilience.[9] Surely, if the earlier catapults, the non-torsion variety, had possessed steel bows, Philon would only have required to refer to the resilience of steel in the bows of these? In fact,

---

[1] Heron, *Bel.* W 75–81. [2] Ibid. W 78–9, a very neat account of this operation.
[3] Ibid. W 75–6. [4] Ibid. W 79–81. [5] Ibid. W 76–7.
[6] The typical shape of a palintone bow is illustrated in Fig. 2, p. 9.
[7] Schramm, *Saalburg*, 1 and 47 ff.; RS, *Biton*, plates.
[8] Philon, *Bel.* 71. [9] Ibid. 70.

in that case, the springiness of one form of steel would have been so well known that proof would have been unnecessary.

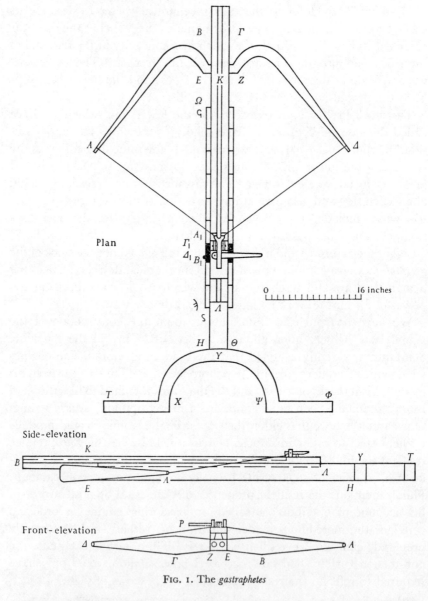

FIG. 1. The *gastraphetes*

The whole description of the bronze-spring engine, of course, is most curious. Whereas Philon, when discussing the machine itself, offers a careful recipe for bronze springs (which one cannot imagine being any use at all), he later seeks to show the resilient properties of metals by alluding to the above-mentioned swords, which he knows perfectly well were made of a form of iron, namely steel.[1] One might conclude that the Alexandrian disciples of the late Ctesibius, who passed on details of their former master's work to Philon, misled him as far as the recipe for the springs was concerned. But, however gullible he was, he surely could not have been deceived if the springiness of steel had been well known from its earlier application in the *gastraphetes* and the other more advanced non-torsion engines.

The significance of Philon's account of Ctesibius' bronze-spring machine seems to be this. No Greek artificer even contemplated employing metal springs as a source of propulsive power until the *gastraphetes* and its more developed derivatives were already obsolescent, having been superseded by torsion engines with springs of sinew- or hair-rope, and until the technique of manufacturing these torsion catapults had been virtually perfected. Only then did Ctesibius, for one, begin to appreciate the possibility of obtaining yet greater power by substituting metal springs in the place of sinew or hair. He may well have had moderately encouraging results at first, because he apparently thought it worth increasing the number of metal springs actuating each arm of his experimental machine.[2] But this in itself indicates that he had been unable to produce a really efficient metal spring, and there is nothing at all to show that any greater success was achieved with a multiplicity of springs or that the bronze spring was ever used to project a missile in anger. Looking at the question from another point of view, we might claim reasonably that, if the *gastraphetes* had had a steel bow, torsion artillery might well never have been invented or might, at least, have found it much harder to oust machines of the *gastraphetes* type.

At this point it will be advantageous to consider carefully what Heron has to say about the causes of the introduction of the *gastraphetes*:

Originally the construction of these engines developed from hand-bows. As men were compelled to project by their means a somewhat larger missile and at greater range, they increased the size of the bows themselves and of their springs—I mean the curved portions running inwards from the ends, that is to say, the resilient parts running inwards from the horns. As a result, they could hardly be persuaded to bend and required greater force than the pull exerted by the hand. Therefore, they devised something like this. Let the bow

---

[1] Philon, *Bel.* 71.
[2] Ibid. 72. Probably Ctesibius experimented in the main with alloys of iron for his springs; but he may have investigated the possibilities of bronze as well.

mentioned be *ABΓΔ*, with curved ends *AB* and *ΓΔ* too strong for withdrawal by the hand of man.[1]

This paragraph teems with implications. It shows that, at any rate just before the invention of the *gastraphetes*, some Greek technicians were fully aware of the considerable undeveloped potential of a hand-bow which they already possessed. They were unable to develop this bow further for the ordinary archer, because the arm and shoulder muscles of even the strongest bowman would have been unable to draw its bowstring. The passage shows, too, that the bow of the *gastraphetes* was of exactly the same construction as an existing hand-bow, though it would naturally be stronger and larger, particularly in girth. There is not the slightest suggestion that the Greeks had discovered a new elastic material which experience proved was too powerful for application in an ordinary hand-bow, and which, consequently, forced them to devise a machine to enable them to make use of it.

In these circumstances, then, indefatigable supporters of the theory that the *gastraphetes* was powered by a steel bow must necessarily maintain either that Heron's simple and logical account of the *gastraphetes'* origin is entirely misleading, or that the normal Greek hand-bow was made of steel! In reality, the most powerful weapon of an archer in the Greek world was the composite bow.

Greek knowledge of this magnificent instrument went back at least as far as Homer's time, for Odysseus' famous bow, its bowstring singing 'like the voice of the swallow',[2] plainly belonged to this type.[3] It would not be appropriate, though it would certainly be enthralling, to investigate here the story of Greek contact with, and employment of, composite bows. Suffice it to say for our present purpose that, though most Greek states paid very little attention to bows and archers, there undoubtedly existed a number of master bowyers in the fifth and fourth centuries B.C. capable of constructing first-rate bows of the composite or reflex type. It does not matter whether these master craftsmen were Greeks or foreigners in Greek pay; they were definitely available.[4]

Composite bows exhibit variations in construction according to the parts of the world from which they come and the period during which

---

[1] Heron, *Bel.* W 75.

[2] Hom. *Od.* xxi. 411.

[3] H. Balfour, 'The Archer's Bow in the Homeric Poems', in *JAI* 51 (1921), 289 ff.

[4] The Greeks, like the Medes and Persians (Hdt. i. 73. 3), probably acquired their knowledge of the composite bow from the Scythians. They had great respect for Scythian bows and skill in archery (Xen. *Mem.* iii. 9. 2).

they were made. But they conform to one basic design. The bow contains three principal layers.[1]

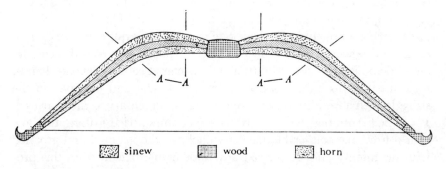

FIG. 2. The composite bow

The central strip of wood, though its relatively slight elasticity may contribute something to the total power of the bow, serves mainly as a base to which the other more resilient materials can be attached. On the back of the wooden layer, that is on the side facing away from the archer, the bowyer fastens a band of animal sinew. On the inner side he glues a series of pieces of horn. When the bow is bent the sinew is stretched and tries very hard to contract to its original size; the horn, on the other hand, is compressed and tries to expand to its original shape. The sum of these combined forces is considerable. They designed the composite bow in such a way that the handle and the tips of the arms had little or no resilience, but the two sections marked *A—A* in Fig. 2, which the Greeks called τόνοι (springs), possessed as much elasticity as possible.

The horn and, especially, the sinews exerted such pressure that the bow often curved excessively in precisely the wrong direction before the bowstring was attached (see Fig. 3).

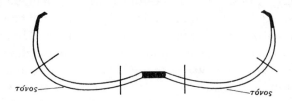

FIG. 3. Composite bow unstrung

---

[1] H. Balfour, 'On the Structure and Affinities of the Composite Bow', in *JAI* 19 (1890), 220 ff.; Payne-Gallwey, *The Crossbow*, app. 'The Turkish Composite Bow'. The horn was derived from the outer layers of animal horns, i.e. it was keratin and not the osseous core.

This characteristic position before stringing, with the springs pointing away from the archer, probably suggested the Greek description for this type of bow as παλίντονον (with the spring bending away, or back). It is easy to appreciate that it would be no mean feat of strength and skill just to string a bow like this. Penelope's suitors were quite unable even to string the powerful palintone bow (τόξον παλίντονον) of Odysseus, let alone demonstrate their ability as marksmen. Leiodes' delicate hands, unaccustomed to hard work, soon began to ache and he gave up the struggle with a rapidity that was most uncomplimentary to the charms of Penelope.[1] Antinous, with a certain low cunning, tried grilling the bow over a fire; but neither he nor Eurymachus, who grunted and groaned with his mighty efforts, derived any appreciable benefit from this procedure.[2] Odysseus, however, apparently without bothering to rise from his seat,[3] strung the bow with the ease and nonchalance of a bard stretching a string round a new peg in his lyre.

I have recalled this famous contest with Odysseus' bow in some little detail in order to emphasize that the inventors of the *gastraphetes* had not only to produce mechanical means for pulling back a powerful composite bow when already strung, but had also to consider how to stretch the bowstring from arm to arm in the first place. In fact, the stock of the *gastraphetes* can assist the operator to string the bow to which it is attached just as conveniently as it helps him to pull the bow back, when strung, ready to shoot the bolt. The *gastraphetes*, before its bow is strung, would appear as in Fig. 4a, p. 11 (from which unessential details have been omitted).

One first fits a bastard string of suitable length to clamps firmly fixed near the tip of each arm. Then, one pushes the slider forward until the bastard string can be locked in the trigger mechanism. The situation at this juncture is illustrated in Fig. 4a, p. 11. The forward end of the slider is next placed against a wall or the ground, and the operator presses with all his might against the withdrawal rest. The slider will move rearwards up the case (σῦριγξ) pulling the bastard string with it. This, in turn, will pull the arms of the bow back until they are in the usual position which they assume when the bow is strung. At this point, the ratchet and pawl systems will be allowed to lock the slider solidly to the case so that the artilleryman can fit the real bowstring into the notches prepared for it (see Fig. 4b, p. 11). Finally, the clamps and the bastard string can be removed, and the *gastraphetes* is ready for active service (see Fig. 4c, p. 11).

---

[1] Hom. *Od.* xxi. 144 ff.   [2] Ibid. 167 ff., 245 ff.
[3] Ibid. 404 ff. and 420: αὐτόθεν ἐκ δίφροιο καθήμενος.

One cannot pretend that there is any direct evidence for this procedure or that it may not have been accomplished in a rather different way as far as details are concerned; but I am certain it is right in principle.

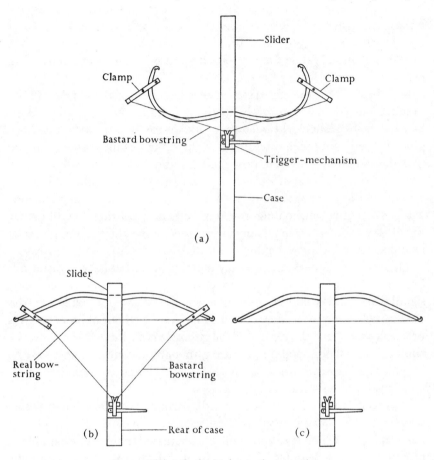

FIG. 4. Fitting the bowstring to the *gastraphetes*

Moreover, there is no doubt that a similar method of stringing with a bastard bowstring was used in connection with medieval cross-bows where the motive power was steel, and had probably been employed for earlier medieval machines with composite bows.[1]

In conclusion, I think that composite bows supplied the motive power for the *gastraphetes* and all the non-torsion machines later developed from it. The *gastraphetes* constituted an ingenious engine which enabled a man

[1] Payne-Gallwey, *The Crossbow*, 114 ff.

both to string and to shoot with a more powerful composite bow than any ordinary archer could possibly have manipulated. Any estimate of the increase in performance which it provided must be a pure guess. Composite hand-bows have been credited with extraordinary ranges.[1] Ignoring all extravagant claims, we find so many well-authenticated records of shots in the 400–500 yards bracket that we must accept 500 yards as the maximum range for a good composite bow in the hands of an expert.

But these long distances were achieved with special light arrows for practice only, and sometimes with the help of the horn groove.[2] War-arrows, being longer, heavier, and incapable of use with the horn groove, could not reach anything like the same distance. One estimates that the maximum effective range of a composite bow for military purposes was in the region of 150–200 yards. We may guess, therefore, that the earliest *gastraphetes* provided a maximum effective range of 200–250 yards, thus outshooting the most efficient existing hand-bow by about 50 yards. Naturally, at any given lesser range, the striking power of its bolts would be correspondingly greater than that of normal arrows.

This increase in performance may not appear particularly devastating; but an improvement of approximately 25 per cent has considerable significance, and would be impressive enough to the poor wretches who were struck down when they thought they were well out of bowshot. It is probable, too, that the design of the *gastraphetes* facilitated more precise aiming both for line and for elevation, though, of course, it possessed no formal sighting arrangement. In short, its original introduction must have produced a significant impact.

However, it would soon be realized (perhaps even in a few months) that the *gastraphetes* only enabled artillerymen to exploit a fraction of the potential force which great bows of composite design might be capable of providing. The power of the bow was limited for the moment because the power available for stringing and pulling back was still, after all, only the weight and thrust of one man. The size and weight of the instrument were also limited because the operator had to be able to manhandle it in the process of drawing the bow.[3] Incidentally, for these reasons, it does not seem probable that the earliest artificers would think it worth trying to adapt the machine to hurl small stones.

---

[1] Payne-Gallwey, *The Crossbow*, 27 ff. and app. 'The Turkish Composite Bow', 19 ff.
[2] Ibid., app. 'The Turkish Composite Bow', 11 (especially fig. 8). It was a device enabling the archer to draw the arrow back so far that its head was an inch or two behind the bow.
[3] Note particularly Heron, *Bel.* W 78–9.

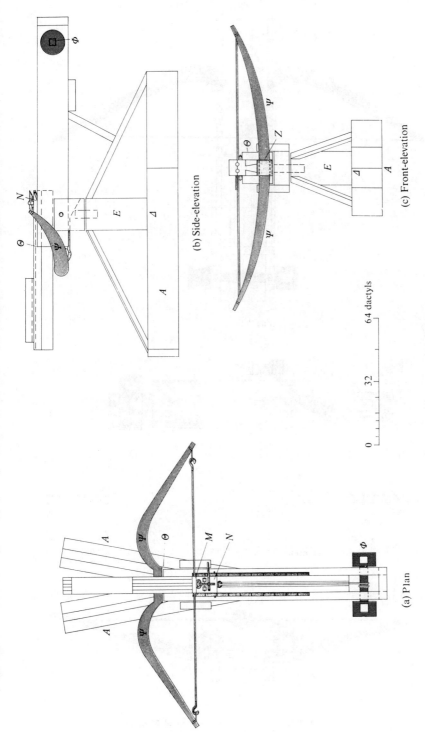

(a) Plan

(b) Side-elevation

(c) Front-elevation

0   32   64 dactyls

FIG. 1.5. Zopyrus' gastraphetes

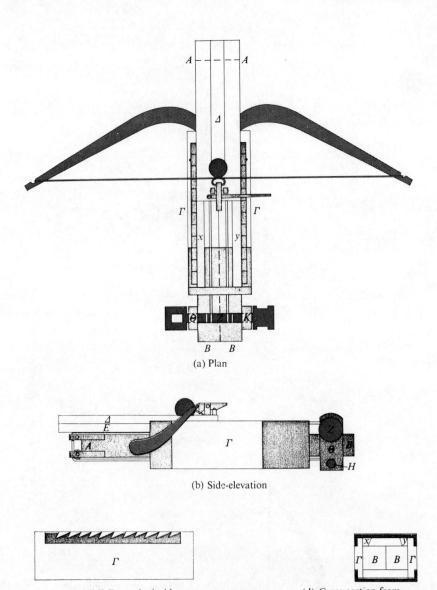

(a) Plan

(b) Side-elevation

(c) Γ From the inside

(d) Cross-section from rear to show ἀγκῶνες

(e) Front-elevation

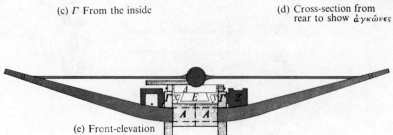

0   16   32 dactyls

FIG. 1.6. The Stone-thrower of Charon of Magnesia

§ 2. *Advanced Non-torsion Artillery*

Two additional contrivances, the winch and the base, enabled artillery-men to break through the limitations of the true *gastraphetes*. Unfortunately Heron's account, in his *Belopoeica*, of the introduction of these two devices may be somewhat misleading. Immediately after dealing with the *gastraphetes* proper, he embarks on a description of the earliest type of torsion artillery. Only after that does he proceed to explain the winch pull-back system, which is necessary 'since the force of the arms has become so powerful', and then the construction of the base 'so that the pull-back may be easier'.[1] Taken at its face value, this would suggest that winch and base were not introduced until the most primitive form of torsion catapult replaced the *gastraphetes*.

Biton, however, in his descriptions of four non-torsion engines, highly developed versions of the original *gastraphetes* type, incorporates winch pull-back systems in all machines and bases in connection with two of them.[2] But we must remember that Biton almost certainly wrote for King Attalus I of Pergamum and probably early in his reign, that is, almost a century after torsion catapults first appeared for certain.[3] It is possible, therefore, that the winch and base were brought in after, or at the same time as, the invention of torsion artillery and were then, and then only, applied to non-torsion machines by people who continued to build the latter.

Nevertheless, it is most unfair to argue in this way solely from consideration of the time at which Biton himself wrote. Every one of his machines was originally designed by some other artificer, who may have lived and worked very much earlier. We can at least be certain of this in the case of Poseidonius who created the *helepolis* for Alexander the Great, that is to say, about 330 B.C.[4] Nothing definite is known about the other engineers quoted by Biton, but there is a distinct possibility that Zopyrus of Tarentum, who produced the last two pieces of artillery mentioned in Biton's treatise, may be identical with the Pythagorean Zopyrus and may have flourished about 350 B.C., or possibly earlier.[5] If this could be proved, one would feel fairly sure that the *gastraphetes* was improved by the addition of winch and base well before the first torsion catapult was

[1] Ibid. W 84 and 86.
[2] Biton W 47: Charon of Magnesia's stone-thrower has a winch for pulling back and possibly one for pulling forward also; Biton W 50–1: Isidorus' stone-thrower certainly possesses winches for pulling the slider both backwards and forwards; Biton W 62 mentions the base, and W 63 refers to the winch, of Zopyrus' *gastraphetes*; Biton W 65 shows the base, and W 66 the winch, of Zopyrus' mountain *gastraphetes*.
[3] Cf. *IG*² ii. 2. 1467, B, col. ii. 48–56 for evidence of early torsion machines (*c.* 326 B.C.).
[4] Biton W 52. [5] See *Technical Treatises*, Biton, n. 52.

thought of. Even though definite proof is lacking, however, it is most reasonable and logical to assume that the inclusion of winch and base formed the second stage in the development of artillery.

The winch, I think, came first. With a mechanical pull-back system fitted to the rear of a *gastraphetes'* stock instead of the stomach-bruising withdrawal rest, the Greek artilleryman possessed the means to exert virtually unlimited pressure. It remained for the bowyers to manufacture bigger and better bows. At first, the operator drew the bow back by placing the front end of the stock on the ground, holding the whole machine in the vertical position, and then turning the winch. Hundreds of years later, medieval crossbowmen operated in exactly the same manner.[1]

When the bows, and, consequently, their stocks, became too heavy for easy manhandling—and this, no doubt, happened quite soon after the winch came into use—artificers were forced to design a formal base.[2] Since it was now possible to construct machines of vastly greater power than the original *gastraphetes*, they had every incentive to adapt the stock so that large non-torsion engines could hurl heavy stones. The stone-throwers employed by Onomarchus against Philip II of Macedon in 353/2 B.C. were probably of this type.[3]

From the information supplied by Biton, it is possible to form a fair idea of the size and power of the composite bows fitted in advanced non-torsion engines. The first of Zopyrus' arrow-firing machines, still called *gastraphetes* (belly-bow) although the 'gunner' fortunately did not need to use his stomach any more for pulling back, discharged two bolts at once, each being 6 feet long and 6 dactyls (about 4½ inches) in circumference.[4] The composite bow designed to achieve this feat measured 9 feet round its periphery; its girth, probably where the springs were thickest, was 15 dactyls (about 11¼ inches).[5] Thus, the thickness of the bow, that is, the maximum diameter of its cross-section, was about 3½ inches as opposed to a maximum of 2 inches for composite hand-bows of Persian, Indian, or Chinese make, and 1¼ inches for the reputedly more powerful Turkish reflex hand-bow. Again, the curving length of 9 feet shows a great increase over the 5 feet maximum for Persian, Indian, and Chinese hand-bows, and the 3 feet 10 inches of the Turkish variety.[6]

---

[1] Payne-Gallwey, *The Crossbow*, 121 ff. (especially fig. 77). Medieval cross-bows were often drawn back by other means, too.

[2] Heron, *Bel.* W 84 ff. (winch and pull-back arrangements), W 86 ff. (the base).

[3] Polyaen. ii. 38. 2; see below, p. 59.

[4] Biton W 63, and see *Technical Treatises*, Biton, n. 59; see Fig. 5 facing p. 12.

[5] Biton W 62; see *Technical Treatises*, Biton, n. 56.

[6] The measurements for the more modern composite hand-bows come from Payne-Gallwey, *The Crossbow*, app. 'The Turkish Composite Bow', 3; H. Balfour in *JAI* 19 (1890), 238.

The smaller bow of Zopyrus' second machine, the mountain *gastraphetes*, was 7 feet long and its girth 9 dactyls (6¾ inches), which means a maximum thickness of slightly more than 2 inches.[1]

Biton supplies no dimensions either for the bows or the stone-shot of the two stone-throwers with which his treatise begins. I have estimated that the bow of the first and smaller stone-thrower, that of Charon of Magnesia, had a length (peripheral) of 9 feet and a thickness of 5 dactyls (about 3½ inches) where the springs were.[2] We have calculated that the machine seems designed to take a stone shot weighing something like 5 pounds.[3] The second stone-thrower, by Isidorus of Thessalonica, really takes the breath away. For this, I estimated a bow with a length of 15 feet and maximum thickness of 1 foot, a colossal affair, and a shot weighing about 40 pounds.[4] Even if the reader considers these figures somewhat high, he can hardly reduce them by much in view of the dimensions given by Biton for other parts of the engine.

We may guess, as intelligently, we hope, as possible, that these advanced non-torsion catapults, discharging bolts or shot, could achieve a maximum effective range of about 300 yards. In addition to exceeding the range of the true *gastraphetes* by 50 yards or more, and the range of hand-bows and slings by over 100 yards, they projected missiles of greatly increased length and weight to these superior distances. Probably during this stage the term καταπάλτης (later καταπέλτης, catapult) became current to denote all machines which were capable of discharging missiles that could smash through a light shield.

Every single one of the devices which made up a developed non-torsion engine, not to mention the actual combination of all of them, excites our admiration.[5] But the bowyers have received no publicity at all, although they plainly responded well to the demand for bows of ever increasing strength. Further, one of the devices, by no means spectacular, to my mind transformed the original *gastraphetes*, which would otherwise have remained a moderately complex but relatively inefficient instrument of war,[6]

---

[1] Biton W 65–6. It shot a bolt, I estimate, with a length of 4 feet and a thickness of about 1 inch.

[2] See *Technical Treatises*, Biton, n. 12.

[3] See Fig. 6, facing p. 13, and *Technical Treatises*, Biton, n. 10.

[4] See *Technical Treatises*, Biton, n. 22.

[5] i.e. the stock with its slider moving up and down the case; the ratchets and pawls; the trigger mechanism, including the claw (χείρ), which faithfully imitates the action of the archer's fingers on the bowstring, and the trigger itself (σχαστηρία); the winch pull-back system, whether simply a matter of drum and handspike or more complex with pulleys; the base, incorporating the all-important universal-joint (καρχήσιον).

[6] The *gastraphetes* avoided the fate of the medieval cross-bow which never succeeded in demonstrating in actual war whatever advantages it was supposed to possess.

into an absolutely first-rate piece of artillery. I refer to the universal-joint (καρχήσιον), seated on the head of the main column of the base.[1]

When fitted correctly to this, the catapult proper, comprising the bow, stock, and so on, would be in that state of perfect balance which is so desirable in artillery. If properly balanced, a large arrow-firer or a gigantic apparatus like Isidorus' stone-thrower could be aimed in any conceivable direction and discharged by one man, holding the machine at the rear by the winch. Heron, introducing his description of the base in general, shows that he fully appreciated all this:

> The whole engine must be raised off the ground on a base, so that the pull-back may be easier, and must be capable of turning in whatever direction one chooses, and of being elevated so that, after the missile is in position, having aligned it on the target, we may release the bowstring. We shall aim at the target by looking down the length of the case.[2]

In point of fact, since a stone-thrower will usually operate at a fairly high angle of elevation, the Greek artilleryman would aim a heavy engine of this type in exactly the same way as lighter arrow-firing cata-pults, but would then allow the rear end to rest on the ground, or on blocks of wood or bricks, before he pulled the trigger. Otherwise he would have to crouch in a rather uncomfortable position and, possibly, have found difficulty in reaching the trigger.

§ 3. *Early Torsion Artillery*

Although these non-torsion catapults were remarkable enough, the time eventually came when artillerymen had fully exploited the poten-tialities of the composite bow. Heron reports on this critical phase as follows:

> By means of the above-mentioned engine [i.e. the *gastraphetes*], of course, a larger missile could be projected at longer range. But they wished to increase both the size of the missile and the force of projection. They sought to make the arms of the bow more powerful, but they could not realize their intention by the use of composite bows.[3]

Obviously, improved performance could be attained either by discovery of a new resilient material, or by more efficient use of one or more of the elastic materials with which the Greeks were already acquainted. In this situation, an inventive Greek engineer might possibly adopt the sort of approach which Philon later employed in his criticisms of standard

---

[1] See *Technical Treatises*, Heron, figs. 11 and 12.
[2] Heron, *Bel.* W 86.
[3] Ibid., W 81. 'By the use of composite bows' is my translation of διὰ τῶν κεράτων.

torsion catapults and in his arguments in favour of new types of artillery.[1]
Thus, artificers may have started by analysing the contribution made to
the total power of the composite bow by each of the three resilient
materials employed in it, namely sinew, wood, and horn. Perhaps, by
means of a typical blend of purely theoretical speculation and calculations based on simple experiments and observations, they may have
reached the conclusion that the sinew provided the most power, and that,
to some extent, the wood and horn were hindering the development of
greater force. Having decided to isolate the sinew, so that its superior
elasticity could be fully exploited, they will then have been compelled
to devise an entirely new method of arranging the motive power.

This is one possible way in which the Greeks arrived at the idea of
torsion artillery. On the other hand, they may have reached it by a completely different method, namely as a result of observing the resilience of
ropes of women's or animal hair, which they consequently sought to
apply to the projection of missiles. The earliest Athenian inscriptions
dealing with torsion machines mention only catapults with springs of
hair. But Athens was not in the van of progress at the time, and her
artificers may quite conceivably have employed hair because properly
prepared sinew-rope was not available. Also, Heron firmly calls the rope
used in the earliest torsion machines νευρά, sinew-rope.[2] On balance,
therefore, although the evidence cannot lead to a positive conclusion,
I think that Greek engineers most probably developed the principle of
torsion because they wished to isolate the sinew which, they believed,
contributed the major force in composite bows. Whatever in fact prompted
their experiments, artificers now proceeded to construct machines which
resembled the advanced non-torsion catapults in most respects except
that the bow was discarded.

In its place they put two wooden frames, around each of which they
wrapped strand after strand and layer after layer of sinew-cord.[3] The
two resulting bundles of sinew, each with its own frame, formed the new
springs which, like the most resilient parts of the composite bow, were
called τόνοι (or sometimes ἡμιτόνια, half-springs).[4] The frames were
fitted on each side of the fixed portion of the stock (i.e. to the front end of
the case, σῦριγξ). A certain amount of extra wooden framework was
necessary to hold the two frames rigid and at the right distance apart
from each other at top and bottom, and also to fasten the stock firmly to

---

[1] For Philon's methods of argument, see Philon, *Bel.* 57–8; 59–60; 68–9.
[2] Heron, *Bel.* W 81.
[3] Heron supplies the only account of the earliest torsion 'frames' (πλινθία), *Bel.* W 81 ff.
[4] Ibid. W 83.

them. Heron mentions the additional framework, but does not explain precisely how it was arranged.[1] If one contemplated reconstructing an early torsion engine with these 'Mark I' frames, one would have to devise an appropriate framework, obtaining assistance, of course, from Heron's later account of securing the frames in a more advanced torsion machine.[2] Philon's dimensions for the frame of his wedge-machine provide useful hints for the proportions of the earliest frames, and particularly for the cross-pieces round which the sinews are wrapped.[3]

A solid, tapering, wooden arm was inserted through the middle of each sinew-bundle.[4] They pushed the thinner end through first, and then pulled the arm until the thicker end was left just projecting slightly from the sinews. Next, they fitted a strengthened bowstring from the thin end of one arm to the thin end of the other, 'by making loops and securing these on the arms by the pins ΞO and ΠP to prevent the bowstring slipping off'.[5] Each arm 'was tightly gripped by the cords' of its spring because tension was applied in each frame by two iron tightening-levers ($\epsilon\pi\iota\zeta\upsilon\gamma\acute{\iota}\delta\epsilon\varsigma$) inserted between the layers of sinew and the cross-pieces of the frame itself. The great weakness of the whole arrangement lay in the inability of the tightening-levers to respond sufficiently to twisting. It was impossible to impart really high tension to the springs. Clearly such an engine represents the first tentative gropings with a new design and cannot have achieved any great success. It can only have been used as an arrow-firer because the power developed would be insufficient for projecting stone shot.

But a start had been made, and in a matter of months, possibly, more efficient frames were developed. The cross-pieces at the top and bottom of each frame were widened and had large holes bored into them, one for each cross-piece.[6] The iron levers for twisting the sinew were placed over these holes. The sinew-cord could now be threaded through the holes and round the iron levers, so that the complete frame looked as in Fig. 7, p. 19. We may call this the 'Mark II' frame. We can also begin to use our rendering of the Greek technical term for the cross-pieces of the frame, namely 'hole-carrier' ($\pi\epsilon\rho\acute{\iota}\tau\rho\eta\tau o\nu$). Though this translation may sound absurd, it is no more so than the Greek original which graphically portrays the main function of the cross-pieces concerned.

---

[1] Heron, *Bel.* W 82.

[2] Ibid. W 99 ff. and *Technical Treatises*, Heron, figs. 18 and 20.

[3] The cross-pieces of the earliest frames correspond to what Philon (*Bel.* 65) calls under-levers, $\kappa\alpha\tau\alpha\zeta\upsilon\gamma\acute{\iota}\delta\epsilon\varsigma$. See *Technical Treatises*, Philon, n. 84 and fig. 11.

[4] The arms ($\dot{\alpha}\gamma\kappa\tilde{\omega}\nu\epsilon\varsigma$) should be solid and should have as little resilience as possible. Ash is a suitable wood for them.

[5] See *Technical Treatises*, Heron, fig. 7.   [6] Heron, *Bel.* W 83.

'But, again,' Heron neatly reports, 'the twisting of the lever was difficult, because it could not be turned while it rested on the cross-piece [i.e. the hole-carrier], and because it touched it everywhere.' Nevertheless, before the iron levers and the hole-carrier seized up, as it were, I believe enough twisting could have been effected to impart considerable tension to the sinew-bundle. Serious trouble comes, as

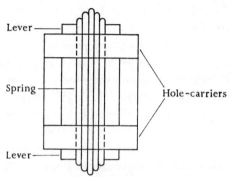

FIG. 7. Mark II frame from the front

I found with a small model built in this way, when one tries to retighten the sinews after a certain amount of shooting. The great power of the springs actually makes the iron levers dig into the wood of the hole-carriers in the course of time, so that it is virtually impossible to turn them. On the whole, however, machines with Mark II frames probably gave very promising results at first, before retightening was called for, and it is possible that efforts were now made to employ torsion artillery for hurling stone shot as well as for shooting bolts.

In due course—and certainly this development cannot have taken long either—the problem of twisting the sinew-springs satisfactorily was solved by the insertion of a (cup-)washer (χοινικίς) between each lever and the hole-carrier associated with it. Heron describes two basic types of washer, one having tenons for securing it to the hole-carrier, the other having a circular rim underneath which ran in a corresponding rebate cut round the orifice of the hole on top of the hole-carrier.[1]

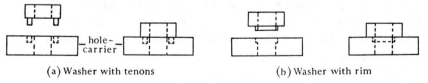

(a) Washer with tenons   (b) Washer with rim

FIG. 8. Washers

[1] Ibid. W 96 ff. See *Technical Treatises*, Heron, n. 30 and figs. 16, 17.

The washer with tenons almost certainly represents the earliest effort (Fig. 8a, p. 19). It had the advantage that it touched only a small portion of the tightening-lever's surface; but there was no provision for keeping the lever, and consequently the sinew-spring, in a central position. Therefore, when one attempted to turn the lever by means of an enormous spanner,[1] the lever would tend to become displaced and to drag the sinew-strands against the side of the hole. The rim method of fitting the washers obviated this drawback (Fig. 8b, p. 19). The arrangement of the metal washers and counterplates (ὑποθέματα), which we find in the famous Ampurias catapult, provided the most perfect system.[2]

The inclusion of washers, of which there were four altogether in each catapult, advanced the frames to the 'Mark III' stage of design. Now, at some point which Heron does not indicate, artillerymen made two important modifications to the structure of the wooden beams of the frames for holding the springs. They realized that, in the first place, it was unnecessarily laborious and expensive to construct, for each catapult, two completely separate frames which had to be solidly connected to each other and to the stock by means of a relatively complicated wooden framework. They decided to unite the two independent frames in one simple structure. The new composite frame had just two hole-carriers, each containing two spring-holes, and four vertical stanchions. No additional framework was required. The two sinew-springs were incorporated as in Fig. 9.

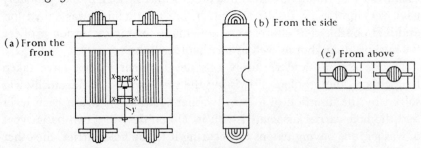

FIG. 9. Frame of Mark III arrow-shooting catapult

The small beams (marked x in Fig. 9a) and a securing pin (y in Fig. 9a) served to fasten the front end of the stock between the central stanchions. An engine equipped with this sort of composite frame

---

[1] Heron (*Bel.* W 101) indicates this instrument when he mentions turning the washers 'with the iron bar holding the ring' which must mean some sort of spanner (μοχλὸς σιδηροῦς κρίκον ἔχων); cf. Anon. Byz. *Pol.* W 254 and Wescher's fig. xcvii (MS. diagram); see Schramm, *Saalburg,* 45.

[2] See *Technical Treatises,* Heron, fig. 17.

was termed εὐθύτονος, 'having straight springs', because, looked at from above (see Fig. 9c, p. 20), the tops of the springs and the long single hole-carrier formed one straight line.

The above modification represented a distinct advance as far as simplicity of construction was concerned; but it made no difference to the thrust imparted to the missile. Artillerymen now realized that, though the washers assisted them to apply very high tension to the springs, insufficient use was being made of the tremendous power so developed. The arms, which transmitted the thrust of the springs to the missile via the bowstring, were allowed only limited movement (see Fig. 10).

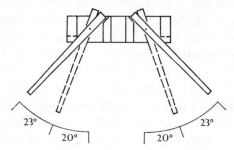

FIG. 10. Arm movement in Mark III frame

As they are being pulled back, the arms travel through an angle of 23° and, when the trigger is released, they fly forward through the same angle. Consequently, the springs can only operate on them while they are moving through this comparatively short distance. Artillerymen sought to improve this situation by a further change in the frame (see Fig. 11). They made the hole-carriers wider in the middle than at

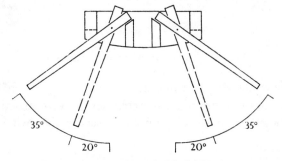

FIG. 11. Arm movement in Mark IIIA frame

the ends. This meant that the centre-stanchions (and the spring-holes) could be set slightly further back, thus allowing more room for the arm to pivot (now 35°). We propose to call catapults constructed with frames of this sort 'Mark IIIA' machines.

Well-proportioned Mark IIIA euthytone catapults proved quite admirable as long as they were employed only for shooting bolts. But there was still not enough power for the efficient projection of stone-shot.[1] Artillerymen had probably conducted experiments with a view to producing torsion stone-throwers right from the introduction of the first torsion frame; but, until the Mark III method of construction became available, they simply cannot have had enough power to achieve any worthwhile results. They probably hoped that the Mark IIIA euthytone frame would be as suitable for shot as for bolts. Disappointed in this expectation, they perceived that the springs of stone-throwers must exert pressure on the arms for an even longer time; that is, the arms had to recoil through an even greater angle than they did in the latest euthytone.

For stone-throwers, therefore, artificers eventually decided to retain the original system of construction which employed two separate frames, one for each spring. But they now made their hole-carriers in an entirely new shape, simply in order to increase the angle through which each arm could recoil.[2] We will term frames of this sort for stone-throwers 'Mark IIIB' (see Fig. 12). Here, the arms operated through an angle of

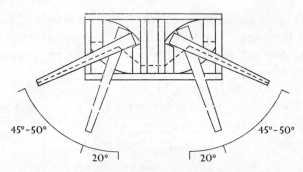

FIG. 12. Arm movement in Mark IIIB frame

45° or even as much as 50°, a marked improvement; but, of course, one had to pay for this in terms of greater complexity in construction, because of the additional framework required to secure the two independent frames.

---

[1] N.B.: Heron (*Bel.* W 74) states firmly: 'Straight-spring engines shoot arrows only.'

[2] Heron (*Bel.* W 93 ff., see *Technical Treatises*, Heron, fig. 15), Philon (*Bel.* 52, see *Technical Treatises*, Philon, nn. 14 and 18), and Vitruvius (x. 11. 4, and see *Technical Treatises*, Vitruvius, n. 22) describe three slightly different methods of designing such hole-carriers. Whichever authority one follows, the result is the same, roughly speaking.

Mark IIIB stone-throwers were called palintones (παλίντονοι) by the Greeks, probably for the following reasons. The hole-carriers point away from the operator, just as the springs of palintone composite bows point away from the archer before the bow is strung and, to some extent, even when the bowstring has been attached. A line drawn along one arm of a palintone machine, through the spring, down the hole-carrier, across to the other hole-carrier and spring, and finally along to the tip of the other arm, resembles the shape of a palintone hand-bow (see line super-imposed on Fig. 12, p. 22). As far as the Greeks were concerned, the palintone hand-bow generated more power than the short, straight (euthytone), wooden hand-bow; likewise, the palintone stone-throwing engine developed more power than the euthytone arrow-firing cata-pult.[1]

Artificers also evolved a different stock for stone-throwers and a new method of fitting the stock between the two palintone springs. They dis-carded the case (σῦριγξ) in favour of the 'ladder' (κλιμακίς), so called because of its close resemblance to an ordinary ladder. The need to reduce the total weight of stone-throwers inspired the change. A palin-tone's slider must be a little broader than a euthytone's since the former must accommodate stone shot. Therefore, the case must be broader, too. If a palintone used a case like the one employed in a euthytone of similar size, it would weigh about one-and-three-quarter times as much, because of the increase in breadth.

The best way to appreciate the change in the method of fitting the stock (i.e. the ladder) between the palintone's frames is to construct a small model. Fix the stock in position by means of the same sort of joint as one uses in a euthytone machine. This method will appear satisfactory until one starts shooting in earnest. After a few shots the joint inevitably weakens, the spring-frames begin to wobble about, and the machine becomes useless. Greek artillerymen certainly had the same experience. They solved the difficulty, as one can with one's own model, by intro-ducing the component known as the table (τράπεζα, mensa) which was placed between the two spring-frames and secured to the lower frame-work linking them together. The table also extended for some distance behind the frames and framework, so that the ladder had a lengthy and solid base to which it could be firmly attached. Further, two long struts or stays, running from the framework at the top of the spring-frames to

---

[1] It is not worth involving ourselves in discussion of the ingenious but mistaken explana-tion of the difference between euthytones and palintones offered by E. P. Barker, "Παλίντονον and Εὐθύτονον", in CQ 14 (1920), 82 ff.

the rear end of the ladder, contributed greatly to the stability of the whole engine (see Fig. 13).[1]

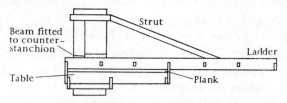

Side - elevation of stone-thrower.
Near frame, slider, washer etc., and winch omitted

FIG. 13. Side-elevation of stone-thrower

The development of Mark III frames led, after due experimentation, to two specialized derivatives, the Mark IIIA euthytone (straight-spring), arrow-firing catapult and the Mark IIIB palintone (V-spring) stone-thrower. Of course, some experiments in the direction of these specialized types may have already taken place while the basic design of the frames was still in the Mark II stage; but I do not think that much could or would be done until the inclusion of the washers enabled artillerymen to extract maximum power from the sinew-springs. With the advent of Mark IIIA and IIIB machines a highly paid and fully experienced artificer, urged on by an ambitious master who was prepared to authorize unlimited expenditure, could build catapults just as successful as any produced later, at any rate until the latter half of the second century B.C. But even the expert could not guarantee a completely efficient machine every time, and an inexperienced mechanic had little chance of producing an efficient one at all.

§ 4. *Standard Torsion Artillery and the Formulae for Calibration*

It was simply a question now of discovering, by a long series of practical experiments, the most suitable dimensions for all component parts of a given catapult, but for the sinew-springs above all. We may regard the springs as cylinders; Greek artificers certainly did so. Which gives the best performance: a squat, thick cylinder of sinew or a tall, thin one? How can one decide what size of cylinder performs most efficiently with a given length or weight of missile? These were the vital questions which occupied the attention of leading artillerymen after the development of the Mark IIIA euthytone and the Mark IIIB palintone. Until they were

[1] The struts are mentioned only by Heron (*Bel.* W 101); Vitruvius (x. 11. 9) describes stays of a different sort, but see *Technical Treatises*, Vitruvius, n. 37.

satisfactorily solved the construction of any machine could only be, at the best, a hit-or-miss affair.

Philon provides an interesting account of the great period of experiment with dimensions,[1] concluding as follows: 'Later engineers drew conclusions from former mistakes, looked exclusively for a standard factor with subsequent experiments as a guide, and introduced the basic principle of construction, namely the diameter of the circle that holds the spring.'[2] By the phrase 'diameter of the circle that holds the spring' Philon and other Greek engineers meant, in effect, the diameter of the spring-cylinder. Philon, and Heron for that matter, seems to suggest that engineers were looking for, and found, one 'basic principle' only. But Greek artillerymen were actually seeking solutions to several distinct, though closely related, problems. First, they determined the best relationship between the diameters and heights of the sinew-springs. Secondly, they discovered how to decide the optimum size for the springs of a machine shooting an arrow of given length or a shot of given weight. Thirdly, they demonstrated that all measurements of a given machine could be conveniently regarded as depending upon the diameter of the spring (or, to be more precise, of the hole in the frame through which the spring passed). The results of all their investigations were summarized in two calibrating formulae, one applying to euthytone arrow-firers and the other to palintone stone-throwers, and two corresponding lists of dimensions.

The size of spring for a euthytone catapult was given by this equation: $D = L/9$ where D represents the diameter, in dactyls, of any one of the holes in the frame through which the springs pass (i.e., effectively, the diameter of the springs), and L is the length, also in dactyls, of the missile which the machine is intended to shoot.[3] For example, if the bolt is to be 3 spans (τρισπίθαμον) long, the diameter of the springs, or their holes in the frame, will be one-ninth of 36 dactyls, which is four dactyls.

The formula for stone-throwing palintones is slightly more complicated:

$$D = 1 \cdot 1 \sqrt[3]{(100\ M)}$$

D again means the diameter of the spring-hole in dactyls; M represents the weight of the proposed shot in Attic minas.[4] Hence, if an engine is intended to hurl a shot weighing 80 minas, the diameter of the spring-hole will be 22 dactyls.[5]

---

[1] Philon, *Bel.* 49–51; cf. 58 and Heron, *Bel.* W 112–13.   [2] Philon, *Bel.* 50.
[3] Heron, *Bel.* W 114 and see *Technical Treatises*, Heron, n. 43; Philon, *Bel.* 54–5; Vitruvius, x. 10. 1.   [4] Heron, *Bel.* W 113–14; Philon, *Bel.* 51.
[5] $D = 1 \cdot 1 \sqrt[3]{(100\ M)} = 1 \cdot 1 \sqrt[3]{(8,000)} = 1 \cdot 1 \times 20 = 22$ dactyls.

There is no magic about the formulae. Though indispensable, they are utterly useless by themselves. To be of any value, to assist the artillery-man to construct a catapult, each formula must be accompanied by the appropriate list of dimensions. Thus, we would have very little hope of re-creating any catapult accurately if we had to rely on Heron's *Belopoeica* alone. Though this treatise describes the formulae, it does not include the dimensions, possibly because the concluding paragraphs have been lost. Fortunately, Philon and Vitruvius remedy the deficiency,[1] each source offering two lists of dimensions, one for euthytones and the other for palintones. Both lists supply measurements in terms of the diameter of the spring's hole so that, when used in association with the corresponding formula, each list is automatically valid whatever the size of the machine which one intends to build. At the end of this chapter I include two tables of dimensions which are based on all the information supplied by Philon and Vitruvius. It will be observed that the two sources differ very little indeed in their recommendations, though, as we shall see later, one or two of the differences probably have considerable significance.

As an example of the procedure to be adopted, and which the Greeks themselves adopted, in constructing a catapult, let us go through the initial stages in building a machine to shoot a bolt 3 cubits long. We must first apply the formula for straight-spring (euthytone) arrow-firers and discover the diameter of the spring's hole (N.B. 3 cubits = 72 dactyls). $D = L/9$; therefore, $D = 72/9$; and $D = 8$ dactyls. The result (8 dactyls) will be not only the diameter of the holes in the frame through which the springs pass, but will also form the basic unit of measure for all the machine's components. One first draws a diagram of the frame ($\pi\lambda\iota\nu\theta\acute{\iota}o\nu$), following the instructions given by Heron. It sometimes happens that one can supplement the excellent descriptions provided in Heron's *Belopoeica* by reference to one or more of the other sources. Anyone constructing a trigger mechanism, for instance, would be well advised to study the relevant section of Heron's *Cheiroballistra*.[2] When making the frame of a straight-spring engine, however, it is not so much a question of finding additional information as of deciding whether one wants to give the catapult the stamp of a machine of the third century or of the first century B.C.

If the former is required, we will stick to Heron's account in the *Belopoeica* and refer to Philon for measurements.[3] Since Philon is rather

---

[1] Philon, *Bel.* 54, and Vitr. x. 10 for arrow-firers; Philon, *Bel.* 53–4, and Vitr. x. 11 for stone-throwers.   [2] Heron, *Cheiroballistra*, W 125–8; cf. Vitr. x. 10. 4.

[3] Heron, *Bel.* W 91 ff. (stanchions), W 104 ff. (frame in general); Philon, *Bel.* 54 (measurements).

sparing with his measurements, we shall be forced to employ Vitruvius to fill the gaps.[1] If we desire the latter type of catapult we must use Vitruvius primarily, but glance at Heron's *Belopoeica* for supplementary explanations. For the present purpose let us plan an engine of the third century B.C.

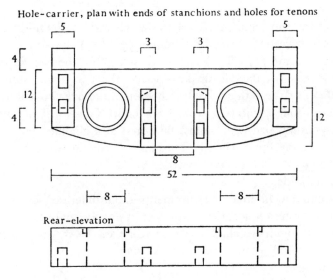

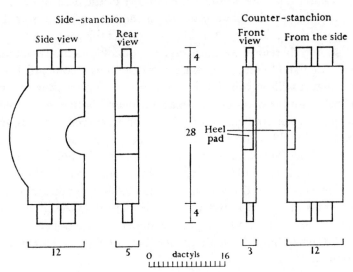

Fig. 14. Details of frame of a euthytone, arrow-shooting catapult

[1] Vitr. x. 10. 2–3.

Having drawn diagrams, we take our list of dimensions and note that the hole-carriers (περίτρητα) of a euthytone frame should be $6\frac{1}{2}$ diameters long by 1 diameter thick; their breadth must be $1\frac{1}{2}$ diameters at the ends and 2 diameters in the middle. Since we have worked out our diameter and found that it is 8 dactyls, each of the two hole-carriers will be $(6\frac{1}{2} \times 8 =)$ 52 dactyls long, $(1 \times 8 =)$ 8 dactyls thick, $(1\frac{1}{2} \times 8 =)$ 12 dactyls wide at the ends, and $(2 \times 8 =)$ 16 dactyls wide in the middle.

The four vertical stanchions are all $(3\frac{1}{2} \times 8 =)$ 28 dactyls high excluding tenons, and $(1\frac{1}{2} \times 8 =)$ 12 dactyls wide; but the two side-stanchions are $(\frac{5}{8} \times 8 =)$ 5 dactyls thick, whereas the two centre-stanchions are $(\frac{3}{8} \times 8 =)$ 3 dactyls thick. Each stanchion must have two tenons $(\frac{1}{2} \times 8 =)$ 4 dactyls long projecting from each end.[1] These will fit into holes of corresponding size which must be bored and chiselled out of the hole-carriers at appropriate points. The gap between the two centre-stanchions will be $(1 \times 8 =)$ 8 dactyls in order to take the case (σῦριγξ) which is 1 diameter wide.

We can now fill in all measurements in our diagram (see Fig. 14, p. 27) and determine the location of the centres of the main holes in the hole-carriers through which the springs will pass. Next, one selects suitable pieces of wood, planes them, marks them out very carefully, and cuts them to size.

Extreme care must be exercised when we mark out the hole-carriers and it is essential to draw on them the outlines of the ends of each stanchion and of the mortise-holes into which the tenons of the stanchions will fit. Incidentally, no ancient mechanic supplies the width and breadth of these tenons; therefore, we must make reasonable estimates for them. Feeling a little like Philon in one of his more pompous moments, I would point out that it will be your lot, in the course of constructing any catapult, to find a number of omissions regarding details both of measurement and design; but the application of a little common sense enables one to arrive at a thoroughly satisfactory, and probably very accurate, solution to all minor difficulties of this sort. When preparing the hole-carriers, one has sixteen tenon-holes and four spring-holes to bore and chisel out. Even a modern power-drill and razor-sharp chisel cannot significantly reduce the tediousness of this task. But if one does not allow the monotony to blunt one's enthusiasm and care, the complete frame appears so satisfyingly solid, when finally glued together, that all efforts seem more than amply repaid.

Before fastening the stanchions and hole-carriers together, one cuts

---

[1] Or, possibly, the tenons should each be $(\frac{3}{8} \times 8 =)$ $5\frac{1}{4}$ dactyls long.

circular rebates round the lips of the spring-holes, in which the circular rim (τριβεύς) on the underside of each washer can run. If the washers are to be metal ones, a metal counter-plate (ὑπόθεμα) should be inserted in each rebate.[1] Also, a metal heel-pad (ὑποπτερνίς) must be let in to the side of each centre-stanchion where the heel (πτέρνα) of the arm will crash against it on recoil.[2] One can now insert the stanchions' tenons in the corresponding holes in the hole-carriers, applying glue to them, and see the result of one's first labours before forging the four washers (χοινικίδες) and tightening-levers (ἐπιζυγίδες) to the correct dimensions.

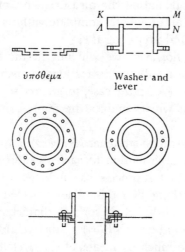

ὑπόθεμα   Washer and
                    lever

Fig. 15. Washer according to the Ampurias catapult

Round metal washers will be most suitable for a comparatively small catapult like our three-cubit machine, and one cannot do better than base the design on the washers of the Ampurias catapult.[3] To ensure that the springs cannot relax once they have been tightened up, one bores holes in the washer and the counter-plate through which retaining pins can be pushed. The arrangement of these holes in the Ampurias catapult is a masterpiece of ingenuity. Each counter-plate possesses sixteen holes, so that there is an angle of $22\frac{1}{2}°$ between the holes. The washer has two groups, diametrically opposed, of three holes each; these holes are 15° apart. Consequently, one need only turn the washer through an angle of $7\frac{1}{2}°$ before being able to slip the two retaining pins in

[1] Heron, Bel. W 97.   [2] Ibid. W 93.
[3] For what follows see Fig. 15. But use Vitr. x. 11. 5 as well (the washer of a euthytone was probably quite similar to that of a palintone), and see Technical Treatises, Vitruvius, fig. 8. Cf. Schramm, Saalburg, 43 ff.

once again. This is a tremendous advantage when one wishes to add a vital extra bit of tension to springs that are already very tight.

The levers (ἐπιζυγίδες) of the Ampurias catapult were forged round where they fitted into the notches of the washers, but oval where the springs passed round them. If one makes levers which are basically rectangular, it is essential to file them down in the centre until they are virtually oval, otherwise they will chafe and break the adjacent spring-cords.

When the frame and its accoutrements are ready, we adopt exactly the same procedure in calculating the measurements of the stock, with its various components, and the base, complete with its universal-joint, and in planing, cutting, and preparing them.

For the moment, however, we will not fit the stock to the frame, though we can make all the necessary arrangements, and we will not bore the hole in the stock (in the case, to be precise) for the pin or roller in the universal-joint which enables the main part of the catapult to elevate and depress.

We must now construct a stretcher (ἐντόνιον), a machine which assists us to impart considerable tension to each strand of each spring as we thread it through.[1] The full process, as conducted by Greek and Roman engineers, was something like this. They selected sinew-rope with a diameter of one-sixth of the whole spring's diameter; in our three-cubit catapult, the rope would be ($\frac{1}{6} \times 8 =$) $1\frac{1}{3}$ dactyls thick. But they aimed to tighten the rope so much by means of the stretcher that its diameter would be reduced by one-third, that is, to eight-ninths of a dactyl. Therefore, having set a pair of callipers to an aperture of eight-ninths of a dactyl, and having wedged the frame in the most satisfactory position between the beams of the stretcher, they fastened one end of the sinew-rope firmly to the lower tightening-lever, threaded the other end through the washers and hole-carriers, past the upper tightening-lever, and attached it to the near-by windlass on the stretcher. They turned the windlass with handspikes until tests with the callipers showed that the cord had been subjected to the correct tension. At this point a clip (Heron's περιστομίς, Philon's ἀπόληψις) was pushed over the cord and the upper lever so that the highly tensed strand could not relax again. They then untied the cord from the windlass, threaded it back through the spring-holes in the opposite direction, wrapped it round the stretcher's

---

[1] See Heron, Bel. W 107 ff. and Vitr. x. 12; cf. Philon, Bel. 57, for criticism of the stretcher. Unless you want really superlative performance, there is no need to build one. You can simply thread the spring-cord by hand and rely on the tension obtained by twisting the tightening-levers; this provides quite satisfying power.

lower windlass, and stretched the second strand, 'gradually releasing the clip's grasp'. Once more there was the testing with the callipers and the application of a clip.

This operation was repeated again and again until no more cord could possibly be inserted even if Heron's stringent recommendations were followed to the letter. Although the first two strands were tested for tension by means of the callipers, one could simply pluck each subsequent strand and compare the musical note with the one emitted by the first or second strand. The musical method would probably give a sounder result, so to speak, because different parts of the spring-cord (whether it was made of sinew or hair) might vary significantly in thickness. Certainly, it would be extremely useful when one sought to 'line up' the second spring of the catapult with the first. A non-musical artilleryman, however, must stick to callipers.[1] They pushed and pulled the last bit of cord through the middle of the whole bundle and pressed it against one of the levers; in this position the other strands held it absolutely firm.

When the first spring was complete, they released the frame from the stretcher and wedged it in again in a different position so that the stretcher could cope with the second spring. This was threaded through and tightened in exactly the same way as the first. The two springs had to be tightened to precisely the same degree; in other words, they had to be perfectly balanced, so that the missile would fly straight and true. They achieved balance, as we have already explained, either by the musical method or by using callipers with the same aperture, the former system being preferable.

Finally, one fits the stock between the frame's centre-stanchions, pushes the arms through the centres of the springs, and attaches the bow-string. It remains to bore a hole in the stock for the universal-joint's roller, and one must bore this more or less at the point of balance of the single unit which the stock and frame now form. Since the frame is very heavy, we shall find that the fulcrum lies at a point in the stock only a few dactyls behind its junction with the frame. It is best to push the slider out to the front as far as it normally travels and then to insert the roller in such a position that the winch at the rear of the stock can slightly

[1] But Vitruvius thought an artilleryman should definitely be musical (i. 1. 8): 'Musicen autem sciat oportet, uti canonicam rationem et mathematicam notam habeat: praeterea ballistarum, catapultarum, scorpionum temperaturas possit recte facere. In capitulis enim dextra ac sinistra sunt foramina hemitoniorum, per quae tenduntur ergatis aut suculis et vectibus e nervo torti funes, qui non praecluduntur nec praeligantur, nisi sonitus ad artificis aures certos et aequales fecerint. Bracchia enim, quae in eas tensiones includuntur, cum extenduntur, aequaliter et pariter utraque plagam emittere debent. Quod si non homotona fuerint, impedient directam telorum missionem.'

outweigh the frame at the front. In this way one avoids the embarrassment of seeing the frame taking control and the winch ascending into
the air just when one is trying to wind it. At the same time, when all is
ready for shooting, the slight pressure of one hand under the rear of
the stock suffices to direct it while one is taking aim.

Philon's remarks on the subject of running in his wedge-machine seem
worth following, and probably were followed by the Greeks, when the
time comes to build up the power of a conventional euthytone.[1] Take
a few practice shots without missiles and without drawing the bowstring
back too far. This gives the strands of the springs a chance to settle down,
and there will probably be a slight general relaxation of each spring,
unless one has operated the stretcher with incredible efficiency. We can
tighten the springs again by twisting the levers, all four by exactly the
same amount. Then we shoot bolts in earnest, drawing the bowstring
gradually further and further back each time, until consistently good
range is attained. At this stage, if not long before, we begin to realize what
a remarkably fine instrument the catapult is. It may be clumsy to manhandle from place to place; but, once set up in position on its base, it
exhibits excellent characteristics.

They built stone-throwing palintones by exactly the same method,
using the other formula and list of dimensions. One can readily appreciate, however, that stone-throwers were rather more complicated and
required greater attention to detail.[2] In the first place, they tended to be
much larger. We have calculated, for example, that the stanchions of
a three-cubit arrow-firer (by no means the smallest of its breed) should be
28 dactyls high (1 foot 9 inches). But the stanchions of even a small ten-
mina (about 9-pound shot) stone-thrower must be $60\frac{1}{2}$ dactyls high (about
3 feet 9 inches). All other components will also be larger in proportion.

Secondly, the construction and fitting of the framework, which must
hold the stone-thrower's two independent and curiously shaped spring-
frames with absolute firmness, require much time and trouble. The
ladder and the table, which does not figure in a euthytone engine, involve
more labour, too. The trigger mechanism alone is simpler, because the
claw needs one prong only instead of two. On the other hand, the bowstring (νευρά) must be in the form of a band, at least in the centre where
it will contact the shot, and it must have a ring plaited carefully into it
behind its central point. The single prong of the claw engages in this
ring and then releases it, and consequently the bowstring, when one
squeezes the trigger. It would probably be convenient to incorporate

---

[1] Philon, *Bel.* 66.   [2] Heron, *Bel.* W 91–104; Vitr. x. 11.

a system for pulling the slider forward, in view of its size, as well as the normal, essential one for pulling back.

We may term arrow-shooting euthytones and stone-throwing palintones constructed with the help of the formulae 'Mark IVa' and 'Mark IVb' machines respectively.[1] Such catapults can be regarded as the standard artillery of the Mediterranean world from about the middle of the third century B.C. to the end of the first century A.D. at least. However, certain quite important modifications of detail, introduced between the time of Philon and that of Vitruvius,[2] and reflected in the artillery writings of the latter, justify us in distinguishing improved versions of the standard engines, 'Mark Va' and 'Mark Vb', from roughly the middle of the first century B.C. onwards.

§ 5. *Further Observations on the Calibrating Formulae*

After the discovery of the formulae and the lists of dimensions, any reasonably competent worker in wood and metal could construct a successful piece of torsion artillery at the first, and every other, attempt if he followed the instructions closely. The relationship between the diameter and height of each spring-cylinder was the most important point. Though the appropriate formula supplies the diameter of the springs, one may think that the measurement of their height has been ignored. But this is not so, because, if we build the frame, washers, and levers in strict accordance with the list of dimensions, the springs which fit in the frame will automatically turn out to be of precisely the right height in relation to their diameter.

The other proportions recommended in the lists of dimensions represent the results of long years of research into the optimum sizes for almost every single component of these engines. Greek artificers determined, in the case of each separate part, the minimum measurements which would allow it to stand up to the strains imposed. Thus, every section of a catapult is fully capable of performing its allotted task, yet it is no more bulky than absolutely necessary.

One can envisage numerous circumstances in which Greek artillerymen would not apply the formulae as we ourselves have done in the previous section. Probably they were sometimes asked to construct a machine to fit a given space (on a city-wall or in the chamber of a tower, for example) rather than to plan an engine for a specific length or weight of missile. Alternatively, they may have been instructed to ensure that the

---

[1] See Figs. 16 and 17 (pp. 34 and 35). [2] Discussed below, pp. 42 f.

machine could be transported, when dismantled, in a certain size of cart over difficult paths. Suppose, for instance, that an order was placed for a stone-thrower to go in the chamber of a tower where the available floor-area measured 24 feet by 12 feet.

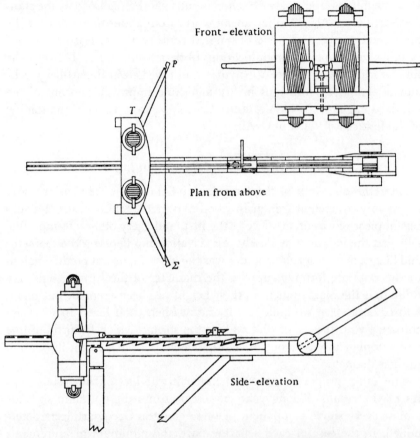

Front-elevation

Plan from above

Side-elevation

FIG. 16. Mark IVa straight-spring arrow-shooting catapult

The complete length of a stone-thrower, including the maximum projection of the handspikes behind the stock and small allowances for clearance at front and rear, comes to 30 diameters of the spring-hole (see Fig. 18, p. 36). There will generally be no need to allow for the projection of the slider (χελώνιον) at the front when it is pushed forward, because it will be able to run out through a loop-hole in the tower.[1] The

[1] If the requirement was a stone-thrower to shoot always at an angle of elevation of 45°, then the complete length taken up would only be 22 diameters. On the whole, though, it is more probable that they would want to shoot at all angles of elevation from the horizontal to 45°.

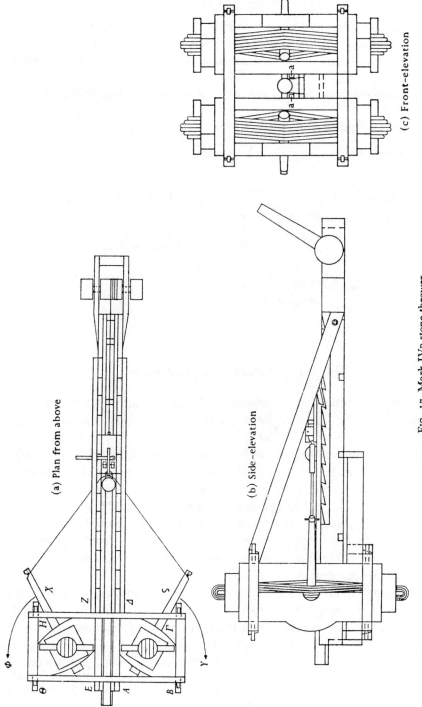

(a) Plan from above

(b) Side-elevation

(c) Front-elevation

FIG. 17. Mark IVв stone-thrower

maximum width of the engine, with slight clearance allowed for, amounts to 15 diameters of the spring-hole. Since the artilleryman had to fit 30 diameters into 24 feet (or 15 diameters into 12 feet), the greatest possible diameter for the spring of the stone-thrower would be $\frac{24}{30}$ or $\frac{4}{5}$ ft., that is, approximately $12\frac{3}{4}$ dactyls. He then applied the formula in reverse:

$$D = 1\cdot1 \sqrt[3]{(100\ M)}; \text{ therefore, } 12\frac{3}{4} = 1\cdot1 \sqrt[3]{(100\ M)}; \frac{(12\frac{3}{4})^3}{(1\cdot1)^3} = 100\ M;$$

therefore, $100\ M = 1{,}558$, and $M \doteq 15\frac{1}{2}$ minas.

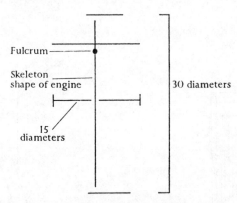

FIG. 18. Skeleton shape of stone-thrower

Having made the above calculations, though not in the same way as we have done, the Greek artificer would probably decide to construct a stone-thrower with a spring-diameter of $12\frac{3}{4}$ dactyls, shooting stones weighing about 15 minas, to make the best use of the space available. The average artilleryman might not have conducted these calculations at all. Instead he would have referred to a list, like the one given by Philon in his *Belopoeica*,[1] matching a number of standard weights of shot against corresponding diameters already calculated by an expert. Looking there for a suitable diameter, he would note that a spring-hole of $12\frac{3}{4}$ dactyls is correct for a fifteen-mina stone-thrower. Thus, he obtained the basic information accurately and quickly.

We have so far ascertained that the formulae and lists of dimensions have two meanings. First, strict and careful use of them means that, whatever size of machine we construct, the optimum relationship between the diameter and height of each spring is readily obtained. Therefore, the springs produce the maximum possible power from a given hank of

[1] Philon, *Bel.* 51, and see *Technical Treatises*, Philon, n. 11; for a Roman list, see Vitr. x. 11. 3 and *Technical Treatises*, Vitruvius, n. 21.

sinew-rope. Secondly, they mean that all components of the machine are just right, from every point of view, for the jobs they are required to do. But they have a third meaning, too, which we have not yet discussed. Heron, Philon, and Vitruvius seem to imply that a stone shot of given weight or a bolt of given length can only be hurled to the greatest possible range by machines whose springs have exactly the right volume. Use of the formulae and lists of dimensions, of course, naturally leads to the production of springs of the correct volume in each case.

Now one can readily understand that springs of insufficient volume— that is, springs which are simply too small—cannot hurl a given missile to a satisfactory distance. But what happens if the springs (and, consequently, the whole machine) are larger than the formulae provide for? If, for the sake of argument, we make a one-talent (sixty-mina) stone-thrower, and if we then use it to hurl a shot weighing only 30 minas, will the engine fail to achieve the normal range which it attains with a shot of 60 minas? More important, will a thirty-mina stone-thrower achieve longer range with a thirty-mina shot than a one-talent engine can attain with a thirty-mina shot? One must, I believe, give a negative answer to both these questions.[1] What on earth, then, do the formulae mean in this connection?

Any product, ancient or modern, is inevitably subject to limiting factors. Considerations of time, money, labour, space, transport facilities, availability of materials, and so on, restricted the designs of Greek artillerymen. Theoretically, they could always have built the largest possible engine, whatever size of missile they intended to shoot. But, even if we ignore the financial aspect, these colossal machines would often have caused great embarrassment to a city which had no walls or towers large enough to accommodate them; to a besieger who could not transport them to the beleaguered town; to an admiral whose ships they capsized. Moreover, it is not true that a one-talent engine could hurl a thirty-mina shot twice as far as its normal one-talent stone, or twice as far as a thirty-mina machine could throw it.

Greek experiments, in the years before the formulae, yielded the following results. They found that unduly small springs gave a poor performance with a given size of missile. When they gradually increased the size of the machine and the springs, they discovered that, up to a point, substantially better performance resulted on each occasion. But they

[1] Although it has not been practicable to compare the performances of large engines with missiles of different sizes, experience with a full-scale reproduction of a small, three-span arrow-firer demonstrates the point adequately.

eventually reached a stage where each increase in the size of machine and springs gave less and less improvement in range and force on impact with the same missile.

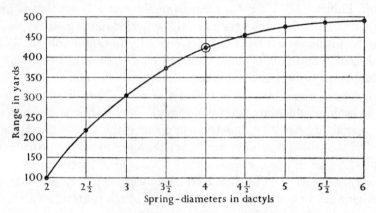

FIG. 19. Graph illustrating experiments

One can best demonstrate by a rough graph (Fig. 19) the picture which emerged after many experiments by Greek engineers.[1] This demonstration attempts to show the performance achieved by machines of different sizes shooting a bolt 3 spans (i.e. 36 dactyls, about 27 inches) long. Maximum effective range attained has been plotted against the diameter of the springs in the catapult that achieved it.[2] Until the diameter was raised to 4 dactyls, each increase in the diameter of the springs (and, therefore, in their total volume) produced a significant increase in range. But further enlargements of the springs, in spite of the added expense and labour involved in constructing a much larger catapult, did not result in a marked improvement in range. Thus, from every point of view, the most efficient machine for shooting a three-span bolt was obviously one designed to employ springs with a diameter of 4 dactyls.

Having made similar discoveries with regard to bolts of other sizes, the Greek artificers realized that they could express the results of all their experiments with arrow-firing engines in terms of a very simple formula. From experiments on the same lines with stone-throwers they deduced

[1] This graph is not based on actual experiments, and the figures used are simply estimates. But, though the details may not be accurate, I think it does illustrate in a general way what really would happen.

[2] Once the Greeks had discovered the best relationship between the diameter and the height of the spring-cylinder, it was only necessary to quote the diameter of the spring in order to indicate its volume.

the corresponding formula for palintones. The third meaning of the formulae, then, is that they facilitate the construction of the most efficient machine, taken all round, for a given missile. On occasions when they needed a little extra range, they could always employ smaller missiles than usual.

But why was it necessary to make the whole catapult larger in each case? Why did they not simply enlarge the frame and the springs, leaving the stock quite small? In the first place, this would have led only to a very slight economy, because the frame and its subsidiary parts are the most difficult and costly to produce. Greek engineers did try, however, to enlarge the springs without increasing the size of the frame, as Philon reports in a most illuminating passage:

> The man who wants to shoot far must try to put on as much spring-cord as possible. . . . But, since the spring passes through the holes in the hole-carrier, he who intends to put in more spring-cord must make the holes in the hole-carrier larger (otherwise they will not take more), so that the surrounding edges are left extremely thin and are naturally weak. It is impossible to make the hole-carrier broader, for it will then exceed the dimensional scale.[1]

Broader hole-carriers would make the frame heavier. Therefore, the stock would not balance the frame. Of course, they could enlarge the stock, too; but, then, they would be building a bigger machine altogether. Thus, as Philon says, they were confined to increasing the size of the holes and trying to hold the hole-carriers together with liberal amounts of iron plating. It was essential to preserve the balance, without which precise aiming would have been difficult if not impossible.

Machines constructed accurately in accordance with the lists of dimensions only balance satisfactorily at a point in the stock just behind the frame. Therefore, the universal-joint at the head of the base lies almost flush against the centre-stanchions of the frame when the stock is in the horizontal position. For this reason one cannot lay either a euthytone or palintone at an angle of depression. This characteristic becomes important when fortifications are designed to incorporate batteries of artillery, as we shall see later.[2]

§ 6. *The Theorem of the Two Mean Proportionals*

There was obviously no difficulty at all in working out the formula for straight-spring arrow-firers; but, having developed their interesting formula for stone-throwers, Greek artificers presumably experienced

---

[1] Philon, *Bel.* 56.   [2] See below, p. 118.

some little trouble in using it because of the cube root. If the result of multiplying the weight of the shot in minas by 100 turned out to be a convenient figure, either 1,000 (the cube of ten) or 8,000 (the cube of twenty), all was straightforward, of course. Most weights of shot, however, did not lend themselves to easy calculation. Since they possessed no logarithmic tables, many artillerymen had to resort to the rough estimates recommended by Philon.[1]

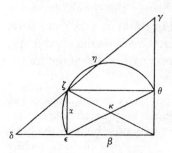

FIG. 20. Geometric application of the theorem of the two mean proportionals

But if the artificer knew his geometry, he could seek assistance from the famous theorem of two mean proportionals (sometimes called the doubling of the cube), which enabled him to discover all the relevant cube roots with a considerably greater degree of accuracy by geometrical construction. For instance, knowing that ten is the cube root of 1,000, he made the line α in the above figure (Fig. 20) 10 units long. He drew the line β twice as long—20 units (which, incidentally, is the cube root of 8,000). When he had completed the construction either in the manner described by Heron or in accordance with Philon's method,[2] the measurement of δε gave him the cube root of 2,000, and θγ represented the cube root of 4,000. He then multiplied each of the two measurements by one-and-one-tenth and obtained the spring-diameters, in dactyls, for a twenty-mina and a forty-mina stone-thrower respectively.

If he proceeded to draw the line α 10 units long as before, but made β 30 units long (the cube root of 27,000), and repeated the construction once more, the measurement of δε supplied him with the cube root of 3,000, that of θγ provided the cube root of 9,000.[3] By adding the extra tenth in each case in accordance with the formula, the artilleryman completed his calculations for the spring-diameters, in dactyls, of the thirty-mina and the ninety-mina stone-throwers. Furthermore, using the same construction several times with different measurements for the lines α and β, he could eventually work out the spring-diameters for all required sizes of shot. Most mechanics doubtless preferred to consult a

[1] Philon, *Bel.* 51. We owe the discovery and initial development of logarithms to John Napier, who published his *Mirifici Logarithmorum Canonis Descriptio* in 1614, and to his friend Henry Briggs.

[2] Heron, *Bel.* W 117 f.; Philon, *Bel.* 51.

[3] See Heron, *Bel.* W 114–16. Strictly speaking, one ought to call this trebling the cube. If we confine ourselves solely to doubling the cube, we shall not get very far. It is clear from Heron that ancient mathematicians developed the κύβου διπλασιασμόν in a variety of ways.

table of spring-diameters and weights of shot that had already been calculated by an expert.[1] Even at the best, the geometric construction left a loop-hole for human error, but it was the most accurate method available for finding the cube root of an unsympathetic number.

Heron and Philon give the theorem of the two mean proportionals considerable prominence, and Vitruvius reveals his acquaintance with it, though he does not go into details.[2] Thus, the employment of the theorem for determining the basic measurement of a stone-thrower seems to have been one of its most important practical applications, and this is confirmed by Eratosthenes.[3] The latter devised a geometric construction which differs greatly from those described by Heron and Philon, and which he succeeded in applying rather cleverly by means of a small contraption like the most primitive of primitive slide-rules.[4] Eratosthenes' method appears to have been the simplest and least susceptible to error of all those available in the ancient world.

§ 7. Modifications introduced between the Discovery of the Calibrating Formulae and the Time of Vitruvius (c. 25 B.C.)

Although the discovery of the formulae for calibration and the associated lists of dimensions would seem to have brought the constructional development of torsion euthytone arrow-firers and palintone stone-throwers virtually to perfection, ancient engineers still stubbornly persisted in the search for even greater power. At first, some of them tended to seek a radical solution. Ctesibius, about the middle of the third century B.C., conducted serious experiments with new resilient materials. In his small stone-thrower fitted with air springs, he arranged for the heels of the two arms, when the slider was winched back, to press bronze pistons further and further into bronze cylinders. The idea was that, on the release of the trigger, the air thus compressed in the cylinders would exert a tremendous thrust behind the shot through the arms and the banded bowstring.[5] His so-called bronze-spring engine, basically a euthytone arrow-firer, worked in a similar way. The heels of the arms pressed against metal springs as the bowstring was pulled back. These springs

---

[1] As given by Philon (Bel. 51) and Vitruvius (x. 11. 3).

[2] Vitr. x. 11. 1-2.

[3] Ap. Eutocius, Comm. on Archimedes, de sph. et cyl., in Archimedes, iii (ed. J. L. Heiberg, Leipzig, 1881), 19 ff., 106.

[4] Eutocius in Archimedes, iii. 102 ff. Eutocius (op. cit. 66 ff.) reviews numerous methods of making the geometric construction, including those of Heron and Philon.

[5] Philon, Bel. 77-8.

were supposed to reassert themselves violently when the operator pulled the trigger.[1]

Towards the end of the third century Philon played a large part in designing an arrow-shooting catapult which employed conventional spring materials, sinew or hair, but which had a revolutionary type of spring-frame. The most important change lay in the fact that Philon's frame embodied within itself the means of creating high tension in the springs. It did not need the services of an additional machine, the stretcher (ἐντόνιον), nor did it require washers and tightening-levers, components sharply criticized for their deleterious effect on the spring-cord. Philon formed the two springs by wrapping spring-cord round his special frame, then supplied initial tension by driving in wedges, two for each spring. When the tension eventually relaxed after constant shooting, he drove the wedges in further to restore the power. It seems most probable that this novel spring-frame could accommodate somewhat larger springs than the frame of a standard catapult of the same size.[2]

There is no sign, however, that any of these machines actually proved itself in practice, though each one incorporated far-reaching and ingenious innovations. In spite of certain weaknesses and disadvantages the standard Mark IVa and Mark IVb catapults survived the challenge, and, between the time of Philon and that of Vitruvius, other artificers succeeded in rendering standard engines more powerful by a series of smaller, more subtle, but highly effective modifications.[3] In the course of the second century B.C. artillerymen began to fit arrow-shooting euthytones with curved arms which meant that the springs could be, as it were, more fully wound up. Then, probably during the earlier half of the first century B.C. and possibly as a result of the work of that eminent artilleryman Agesistratus, the spring-frames and their related components were cleverly modified. Palintones, and very probably euthytones also, were equipped with washers of a new type, oval instead of round. This simple change in shape enabled artificers to insert a significantly larger quantity of cord in each spring. But larger springs were heavier as well as more powerful and tended to upset the delicate balance between frame and stock. Thus, partly for this reason, consequential adjustments had to be made to some of the components of the frames. That is why Vitruvius' lists of dimensions differ in some respects from those supplied by Philon. For convenience we may call catapults and *ballistae* embodying all the

---

[1] Philon, *Bel.* 67–73. [2] Ibid. 56–67.
[3] For more detailed discussion of the modifications which are mentioned or implied by Vitr. x. 10 and 11 see Appendix 1 (arrow-shooting engines) and Appendix 2 (*ballistae*).

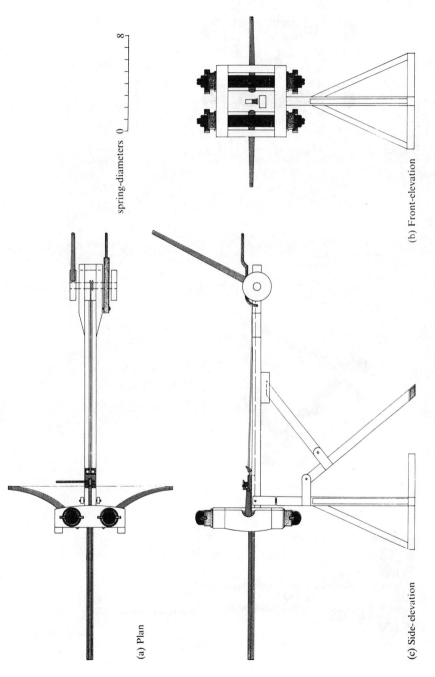

spring-diameters 0　　　　　　　8

(a) Plan

(b) Front-elevation

(c) Side-elevation

FIG. 1.21. Mark Va Catapult (Vitruvius)

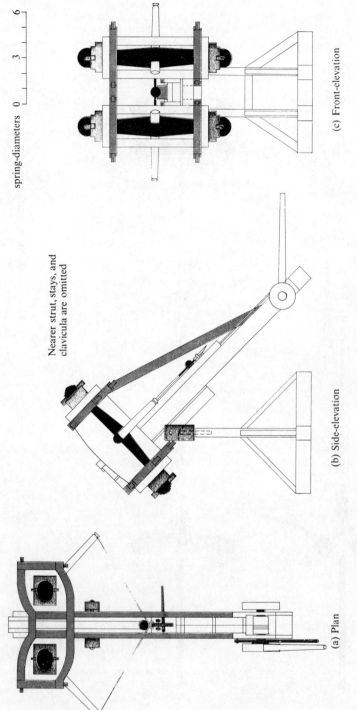

spring-diameters

0   3   6

(c) Front-elevation

Nearer strut, stays, and
clavicula are omitted

(b) Side-elevation

Fig. 1.22. Mark Vb *ballistra* (Vitruvius)

(a) Plan

modifications reflected in Vitruvius Mark VA and Mark VB machines. The extremely effective and efficient Mark V engines became the normal artillery of the Early Roman Empire and remained standard, as far as we can see, until about A.D. 100. Subsequent changes will be discussed when the time comes to examine Roman Imperial Artillery (Chapter 8, below).

TABLE ILLUSTRATING CONSTRUCTIONAL DEVELOPMENT OF
TWO-ARMED CATAPULTS

Type of Engine	Main improvement	Authorities	Date of introduction
NON-TORSION CATAPULTS			
Arrow-shooting *gastraphetes*		Heron	399
Arrow-shooting *gastraphetes* (advanced)	Winch and base	Biton	399–360
Stone-throwing *gastraphetes* (advanced)		Biton	Before 353
TORSION CATAPULTS			
Mark I, arrow-shooting	Pair of simple spring-frames	Heron	*c.* 350
Mark II, arrow-shooting	Spring-frames with holes	Heron	Before 340
Mark III, arrow-shooting	Washers	Heron	After 340
Mark IIIA, arrow-shooting	Euthytone frame	Philon	Before 334
Mark IIIB, stone-throwing	Palintone frames	Philon	334–331
Mark IVA, arrow-shooting	Built acc. to formula for euthytones	Heron and Philon	*c.* 270
Mark IVB, stone-throwing	Built acc. to formula for palintones	Heron and Philon	*c.* 270
Modified Mark IVA	Curved arms	Pergamum Relief, Vitruvius	*c.* 150
Mark VA, arrow-shooting	Improved washers	(Agesistratus), Vitruvius	*c.* 60
Mark VB, stone-throwing	Improved washers	(Agesistratus), Vitruvius	*c.* 60
Special *ballista*, arrow-shooting	All-metal frames	*Cheiroballistra*, Trajan's Column	*c.* A.D. 100

All dates are B.C. unless otherwise indicated

LIST OF DIMENSIONS FOR EUTHYTONE, ARROW-SHOOTING CATAPULTS

All figures given below are in diameters of the spring-hole (*διάμετροι, foramina*). For any particular catapult this diameter will be one-ninth of the length of the bolt which the machine is designed to shoot, i.e. $D = \frac{1}{9} L$. Figures in round brackets indicate dimensions which are not specifically provided by the ancient sources, but which can readily be calculated from available measurements. Figures in square brackets represent estimates for dimensions which are not supplied and which cannot be calculated so easily. This list is not exhaustive, and further estimates will be required in matters of detail by anyone attempting to reconstruct a catapult accurately; but all the vital measurements are fully covered.

Component	Translation	Height		Length		Width		Thickness		Breadth		Diameter or curvature	
		Ph.	V.	Ph.	V.	Ph.	V.	Ph.	V.	Ph.	V.	Ph.	V.
διάμετρος, τρῆμα, foramen	spring-hole											1	1
πλινθίον, capitulum	frame	(5½)	(6)	(6½)	(6)								
περίτρητον, tabula, peritretus	hole-carrier			6½	(6)	1½ 2 1½	1½ 1¾ 1½	1	1				
παραστάτης, parastatica	side-stanchion	3½	4			1½	(1½)	⅝	⅝				
τόρμοι, cardines	tenons		½										
ἀντιστάτης, μεσοστάτης	centre-stanchion (one of two)	3½				1½		⅜					
parastas media	centre-stanchion (single)		(4)				1		1¾				
intervallum	aperture		[1¼]				¼						
χοινικίς, modiolus	washer	[¾]	[¾]									1¼	1¼
σῦριγξ, canaliculus	case		1	16	19				1				
regulae	side-pieces of case		[⅓]		19				[⅓]				
suculae regulae	side-pieces of windlass				3				(1)		½		
buccula, scamillum, loculamentum	back-piece		½		(2)						1		
ἄξων, sucula	windlass				4								$\frac{5}{12}$
χείρ, epitoxis	claw				¾				¼		¼		
χελώνιον, chelonium	block								¼				
σχαστηρία, manucla	trigger				3				¼		¼		
δίωστρα, χελώνιον, canalis fundus	slider		¾		16				¼				

		Ph.	Ph.	V.	V.	V.
βάσις, columellae basis	ground-base	12	8			
στυλίσκος, columella	main column of base					$\frac{3}{4}$ $\frac{3}{4}$
ἀκέλη, capreoli	supporting legs		9 $1\frac{1}{2}$	$\frac{1}{8}$	$\frac{5}{8}$ $\frac{3}{8}$ $\frac{7}{16}$	
τόρμος, columellae cardo	tenon					
καρχήσιον, caput columellae antefixum	universal-joint	2				
ἀντίβασις, ἀναπαυστηρία, minor columna	cross-piece, rest		$\frac{3}{4}$ 8	$\frac{3}{4}$	1 $\frac{5}{8}$	
ἀντηρείδιον, subiectio	stay		12	$\frac{3}{4}$ $\frac{3}{4}$	$\frac{5}{8}$	
κώλυμα, chelonium, pulvinus	stop	$1\frac{1}{2}$	$2\frac{1}{2}$		$\frac{1}{2}$	$2\frac{1}{4}$
carchesium scutularum	handspike drum					
σκυτάλη, scutula	handspike		10	[$\frac{1}{8}$]	[$\frac{1}{2}$]	
ἀγκών, bracchium	arm	7	7	[$\frac{1}{8}$]	$\frac{9}{16} - \frac{7}{16}$	8

The columns headed Ph. give the measurements provided by Philon (*Bel.* 55 ff.); the columns headed V. supply Vitruvius' dimensions (x. 10)

LIST OF DIMENSIONS FOR PALINTONE, STONE-THROWING ENGINES

All the measurements supplied below are in diameters of the spring-hole (*διάμετροι, foramina*). For any stone-thrower the diameter of the spring, in dactyls, is one-and-one-tenth times the cube-root of the weight in drachmae which that stone-thrower is meant to hurl. Figures in round brackets represent dimensions which are not directly given by the ancient sources, but can be easily deduced from them. Figures in square brackets are estimates of measurements for which the sources supply little guidance.

Component	Translation	Height		Length		Width		Thickness		Breadth		Diameter or curvature	
		Ph.	V.	Ph.	V.	Ph.	V.	Ph.	V.	Ph.	V.	Ph.	V.
διάμετρος, τρῆμα, foramen	spring-hole											1	1
περίτρητον, scutula	hole-carrier	1	1	$2\frac{3}{4}$	$2\frac{3}{4}$					[$2\frac{1}{2}$]	$2\frac{1}{2}$		
ὑπόθεμα	counter-plate	$\frac{1}{4}$											
χοινικίς, modiolus	washer	$\frac{3}{4}$	$\frac{3}{4}$	2	2					[$2\frac{1}{2}$]	$1\frac{5}{12}$		
τριβεύς	rim or flange							$\frac{1}{5}$					
ἐπιζυγίς, epizygis	lever				[3]	$\frac{2}{5}$		$\frac{1}{5}$					
παραστάτης, parastata	side-stanchion	$5\frac{1}{2}$	$5\frac{3}{16}$			$1\frac{7}{12}$	[$1\frac{7}{12}$]	$\frac{29}{48}$	$\frac{11}{18}$				
ἀντιστάτης	counter-stanchion	$5\frac{1}{2}$	($5\frac{3}{16}$)			$1\frac{7}{12}$	[$1\frac{7}{12}$]	$\frac{29}{48}$	($\frac{11}{18}$)				
regulae	little beams		$\frac{1}{4}$						$\frac{1}{5}$?		$\frac{1}{5}$		
κανών, regula exterior	outer framework beam				suitable			$\frac{4}{9}$	$\frac{1}{2}$	$\frac{5}{9}$	$\frac{1}{2}$		
κανών, regula in mensa	framework beam joined to table				8			$\frac{4}{9}$	$\frac{1}{2}$	$\frac{5}{9}$	$\frac{1}{2}$		$\frac{3}{4}$
cardines	framework tenons				2				$\frac{1}{4}$				
τράπεζα, mensa	table			9	(9)	($1\frac{7}{10}$)							
ἐπιπήγματα τῆς τραπέζης	long joists of the table	1		(9)		$\frac{1}{4}$							
transversarii mensae	cross-pieces of the table						$\frac{1}{4}$		$\frac{1}{4}$				
σανίς	table-board							$\frac{1}{8}$					
ἱστὸς τῆς κλιμακίδος, scapus climacidos	side-pole of the ladder	1 +	$1\frac{1}{8}$	19	19			$\frac{1}{4}$	$\frac{1}{4}$				
πλάτος τὸ ἐντός, intervallum	gap between side-poles of the ladder					$1\frac{1}{5}$	$1\frac{1}{4}$						
πτερύγιον, pterygoma	ridge-pole			19	(19)	$\frac{1}{4}$	$\frac{1}{4}$	$\frac{1}{18}$					
διαπήγματα, interiores regulae	'rungs' of the ladder							$\frac{1}{6}$	$\frac{3}{16}$	$\frac{1}{3}$	$\frac{5}{16}$		
quadratum	square								$\frac{1}{4}$				

anterides	stays	suit-able	$3\frac{1}{4}$			$\frac{3}{16}$	$\frac{3}{4}$
χελώνιον, chelonium	slider		$11\frac{1}{2}$	$1\frac{1}{4}$	$1\frac{3}{16}$	$\frac{3}{4}$	$\frac{1}{2}$
extantia chelonii	projection of slider	$\frac{1}{2}$					
chelonii replum	lid of slider				$\frac{1}{4}$	$\frac{1}{12}$	$\frac{7}{16}$
ἄξων, axon, axis	winch		3				
basis, eschara	long ground-joist of base		8			1	1
antibasis	short ground-joist of base		4			1	1
columnae	columns of base	suit-able	6		$\frac{1}{2}$	$\frac{1}{2}$	$\frac{1}{2}$
ἀγκών, bracchium	arm	6	6	$\frac{1}{2}$	$\frac{3}{8}$		$\frac{1}{4}$
νευρά	sling	$2\cdot1 \times 6$		$\frac{1}{2}$	$\frac{3}{8}$–$\frac{5}{8}$		$\frac{1}{2}$

N.B. Philon is responsible for the measurements in the columns headed Ph.; Vitruvius' dimensions are recorded in the columns headed V

II

THE INVENTION OF THE CATAPULT

DURING the year 399 B.C., the entire city of Syracuse became one great arsenal.[1] By offering handsome rates of pay, Dionysius I gathered there a remarkable assembly of expert craftsmen because he intended to manufacture vast quantities of arms of many existing types and also, almost certainly, to conduct researches into new forms of armament.[2] Artificers arrived from other Sicilian cities under the tyrant's control, from Italy, from old Greece, and from the dominions of Carthage.[3] They set up their workshops in every available space whether publicly or privately owned, taking over the entrance halls and rear chambers of temples, the *gymnasia*, the colonnades in the main square, and even the most splendid private houses.[4]

Dionysius appointed notable Syracusans, obviously chosen from the ranks of his most loyal supporters, to supervise the work, one for each little factory.[5] The great Sicilian historian Philistus, a close friend of the tyrant who had assisted him to establish his power,[6] was very probably one of these supervisors; certainly he witnessed personally the extraordinary activity in his city at that time. Later on, in spite of his friendship with the tyrant and in spite of his high regard for tyranny as a form of government,[7] Philistus was exiled by his master (386 B.C.); but, being subsequently recalled, he served as an admiral under Dionysius II. He wrote his histories while in exile, the events of 399 B.C. in Syracuse being included in the second series, in four volumes, of his *History of Sicily* ($\Sigma\iota\kappa\epsilon\lambda\iota\kappa\acute{a}$), which began immediately after the taking of Acragas by the Carthaginians in 406 B.C.[8] As a historian Philistus was rated highly. Cicero considered him a major (*capitalis*) historical writer and *paene pusillus Thucydides*.[9] Quintilian designated him *imitator Thucydidis*.[10] This

---

[1] D.S. xiv. 41. 6: ἔγεμε πᾶς τόπος τῶν ἐργαζομένων . . .

[2] Ibid. 41. 3. He certainly planned that some technicians should design and construct *quinqueremes* (ναῦς πεντήρεις), warships of a size not previously attempted.

[3] Ibid. There is nothing to suggest that these craftsmen, even those who came from τῆς Καρχηδονίων ἐπικρατείας, were not Greeks. There may have been a handful of foreigners among them, but that is all.

[4] Ibid. 41. 6.   [5] Ibid. 41. 4.   [6] Ibid. xiii. 91. 4.

[7] Nep. *Dion*, 3. 2; Plut. *Dion*, 11; Cic. *De Or*. ii. 57.

[8] D.S. xiii. 103. 3.   [9] *Ad Q. Fr.* ii. 11. 4.   [10] *Inst. Orat*. x. 1. 74.

reliable eye-witness, worthy of mention in the same breath with Thucydides, was the ultimate source for Diodorus Siculus' detailed account of the year 399 B.C. in Syracuse, which Philistus had recorded 'in a marvellous piece of descriptive writing'.[1]

In one of those many workshops which filled Syracuse at the time, and in which the artificers were inspired not only by generous basic wages but also by additional incentives for outstanding craftsmanship,[2] catapult-artillery was invented. Diodorus puts it like this: 'Artillery was discovered at that time in Syracuse, a natural consequence of the assembly in one place of the most skilful craftsmen from all over the world.'[3] Such a definite pronouncement must refer to one of the three major developments in the history of catapult construction, these being the invention of the *gastraphetes*,[4] the introduction of torsion springs,[5] and the discovery of the formulae for calibration.[6] We can immediately rule out the third development, because the formulae may reasonably be attributed to the reign of Ptolemy II in Egypt (285–246 B.C.).[7] Furthermore, the whole tenor of Diodorus' statement, which reflects, of course, the account of the contemporary Philistus, suggests that we have to do with the very first appearance of any form of artillery whatsoever. Therefore, it was the *gastraphetes*, non-torsion artillery, that was invented in 399 B.C.

But many modern scholars seem to assume, with little or no hesitation, that Diodorus here records the invention of torsion catapults, powered by springs of sinew or hair.[8] It is surely incumbent upon those who take this view to produce at least a particle of evidence demonstrating the existence prior to 399 B.C. of the non-torsion engines which undoubtedly preceded the torsion variety probably by a considerable length of time.[9] In reality, however, no Greek writer mentions the employment of any type of artillery at all before 399 B.C.

It is inconceivable, for instance, that non-torsion engines would have escaped the notice of Thucydides, if they had been in existence at the time of the Peloponnesian War. He presents his account of the siege of Plataea as a real show-piece, an example of the best modern methods of

---

[1] F. Jacoby, *FGH* iii b (Text), 584: 'in einer bewunderten ekphrasis'.
[2] D.S. xiv. 41. 4; 42. 1.
[3] Ibid.: καὶ γὰρ τὸ καταπελτικὸν εὑρέθη κατὰ τοῦτον τὸν καιρὸν ἐν Συρακούσαις, ὡς ἂν τῶν κρατίστων τεχνιτῶν πανταχόθεν εἰς ἕνα τόπον συνηγμένων. Cf. Aelian, *V.H.* vi. 12.
[4] See above, pp. 5 ff.   [5] See above, pp. 16 ff.
[6] See above, pp. 24 ff.   [7] See below, pp. 62 f.
[8] e.g. Schramm, *Saalburg*, 18; *Poliorketik*, 216; R. Schneider in *RE* s.v. 'Geschütze', col. 1303; M. Pöhlmann, *Untersuchungen*, 7. But G. T. Griffith in *OCD*, s.v. 'Artillery', and Tarn, *HMND*, 104, briefly subscribe to the view that torsion came in later.
[9] Heron, *Bel.* W 75.

attack and defence, technical details receiving full and sympathetic treatment.[1] In such circumstances, the presence of even the most primitive *gastraphetes* could not have passed undetected or unrecorded by the historian. Nor is there any hint of artillery in Thucydides' reports on the great Athenian siege of Syracuse.[2] But, from the point of view of military machinery, the name of Nicias, one of the Athenian commanders outside Syracuse, has some interesting associations.

Whatever other reasons prompted the choice of this man as a commander for the Sicilian expedition, his reputation as an engineer no doubt did something to influence the Athenian assembly. In the *Birds*, performed in 414 B.C., Aristophanes makes Euelpides say jokingly to Peisthetairos: 'You are already out-shooting Nicias with your machines' (ὑπερακοντίζεις σύ γ᾽ ἤδη Νικίαν ταῖς μηχαναῖς).[3] At first sight, the remark seems suggestive of artillery; but it transpires that ὑπερακοντίζειν, according to Aristophanic usage,[4] means no more than 'out-do'. In any case, even if we attach more importance to the technical background of the word, the phrase need not imply any more than out-shooting Nicias by building higher siege-towers to give javelin-men and, perhaps, archers and slingers greater range. In the absence of further details it is impossible to base a claim for the existence of the catapult on this humorous remark. Thucydides' account of the same Nicias' attack on Minoa (427 B.C.) is equally unhelpful. There Nicias' first move was to take two projecting towers by assaulting them with machines from the seaward side (ἑλὼν οὖν ἀπὸ τῆς Νισαίας πρῶτον δύο πύργω προύχοντε μηχαναῖς ἐκ θαλάσσης . . .).[5] The unqualified term 'machines' is entirely indefinite. They were almost certainly either light wooden towers mounted on ships, possibly fitted with drawbridges,[6] or small rams or even simple scaling-ladders.[7]

---

[1] The technical material comes in Thuc. ii. 75–8 (429 B.C.); iii. 20–3 (428 B.C.).

[2] Id. vi. 96–vii. 18.

[3] *Birds*, 363; cf. Phrynichus, Μονότροπος (also 414 B.C.) *ap.* Suidas s.v. ὑπερακοντίζεις:

ἀλλ᾽ ὑπερβέβληκε πολὺ τὸν Νικίαν
στρατηγίᾳ πλήθει τε τῶν εὑρημάτων.

[4] Cf. *Knights*, 659; *Plutus*, 666.
Thuc. iii. 51. 3.

[6] I suggest a very primitive, ship-mounted tower basically similar to the one designed by Poseidonius for Alexander the Great; see Biton, W 52 ff.

[7] A. W. Gomme, *A Historical Commentary on Thucydides*, ii (1956), 334, proposes scaling-ladders on the ground that anything larger would have been too heavy for Nicias' ships. There is no sign of artillery at the Periclean siege of Samos (441/0 B.C.): D.S. xii. 28. 3; Plut. *Per.* 27. 3. The tradition that a certain Artemon was Pericles' engineer on that occasion and that he invented two machines, a tortoise (*testudo*, χελώνη) and a ram (*aries*, κριός), is not altogether above suspicion; Servius, *ad* Verg. *Aen.* ix. 503. See Gomme, op. cit. i (1945), 354 f. Even if the tradition is true, Artemon's machines have nothing to do with catapults.

Thucydides also applied the word 'machine' (μηχανή) to two unusual fire-producing engines, one employed by the Thebans against Delium,[1] the other by Brasidas at Lecythus.[2] In each case the engine is a crude flame-thrower and not a piece of artillery for shooting fire-balls or flaming bolts.[3] The Thebans' machine was really a gigantic bellows which blew flames against Delium's wooden palisades. Similarly, Brasidas' engine was designed to blow flames at wooden breastworks at Lecythus, and the word ἐνήσειν used for this 'blowing' must be carefully distinguished from ἀφιέναι, the usual term for discharging a missile from the hand or from a catapult. We can at least draw one significant conclusion from the descriptions of these machines: Thucydides was interested in, and quite prepared to describe, even relatively unimportant military engines; it is hard to believe that he would have omitted to mention the *gastraphetes* or have found no occasion to do so, had it existed in his time.

Likewise, there is no sign of any sort of artillery in the detailed accounts given by Diodorus of the impressive Carthaginian sieges in Sicily towards the end of the fifth century B.C.,[4] which probably exerted considerable influence on the development of Greek siege-technique during the next two or three decades. At Selinus in 409 B.C., the Carthaginians had six large wooden siege-towers superior in height to the walls of the town,[5] six iron-plated rams,[6] and numerous archers and slingers to keep the defenders' heads down.[7] The Selinuntines resisted only on their walls and in the breaches, while their women and children passed them food and ammunition.[8] When the city was on the verge of capture, fierce fighting raged in the streets, the women and children now hurling brickbats and tiles from the roof-tops until they ran out of missiles.[9]

There was one offensive and one defensive variation during the ensuing siege of Himera. Having undermined the walls, the Carthaginians set the pit-props in the mine or mines on fire and thus brought down a stretch of wall.[10] On the other hand, the defenders of Himera organized a sally on a large scale in the belief that the failure to adopt an aggressive

---

[1] Thuc. iv. 100.   [2] Ibid. 115. 2–3.

[3] For catapults shooting flaming bolts, see particularly D.S. xx. 96. 7.

[4] Selinus and Himera, 409 B.C.; Acragas, 406 B.C.

[5] D.S. xiii 54. 7: ἐξ μὲν γὰρ πύργους ὑπερβάλλοντας τοῖς μεγέθεσιν . . .; 55. 7: . . . τῶν ξυλίνων πύργων πολὺ τοῖς ὕψεσιν ὑπερεχόντων.

[6] Ibid. 54. 7: τοὺς ἴσους δὲ κριοὺς κατασεσιδηρωμένους . . .

[7] Ibid. . . . τοῖς τοξόταις καὶ σφενδονήταις πολλοῖς χρώμενος (Hannibal) ἀνέστελλε τοὺς ἐπὶ τῶν ἐπάλξεων μαχομένους. Ibid. 55. 6: . . . τῷ δ' ὕψει τῶν πύργων οἱ μαχόμενοι πολλοὺς τῶν Σελινουντίων ἀνῄρουν.

[8] Ibid. 55. 4: . . . τάς τε τροφὰς καὶ βέλη . . . παρεκόμιζον . . . For a definition of βέλος see Heron, *Bel.* W 75.

[9] D.S. xiii. 56. 8: . . . ἐνέλιπε τὰ βέλη.   [10] Ibid. 59. 8.

type of defence at Selinus had led to the fall of that city. The only addition to the Carthaginian repertoire at Acragas in 406 B.C. was the employment of siege-mounds to span a stream and facilitate the approach of their siege-towers and rams.[1] Diodorus mentions no other machines or devices in connection with this group of sieges.

Finally, before abandoning the search for artillery in Greek and Carthaginian operations towards the end of the fifth century B.C., we should note the employment of cranes, κεραῖαι and κεραῖαι λιθοφόροι, in siege-warfare for dropping heavy objects on hostile personnel and machines. The Plataeans, in 429 B.C., used a pair of cranes to drop large beams on one of the Peloponnesian rams and thus snapped its head off.[2] In 407 B.C., the Athenian admiral Conon, having been defeated by the Spartan Callicratidas off the Ἑκατοννήσοι, took refuge in Mytilene where he prepared to ward off further Spartan attacks which he expected to come from both land and sea. He blocked the harbour entrance partly, where it was shallow, by scuttling barges filled with ballast and partly, where it was deep, by mooring big merchant ships designed for carrying stone.[3] The crews of the latter used their cranes to drop stones on the Spartan ships, the effect on the Spartan sailors and marines being quite impressive.[4]

There were clearly, then, very many occasions in the final third of the fifth century B.C. on which non-torsion engines could have been employed. It is also clear that Thucydides and the source, almost certainly Philistus, for Diodorus' account of the sieges in Sicily had considerable interest in military engines and siege-technique. Therefore, the complete absence of any reference to gastraphetae in the period before 399 B.C. can only be explained on the ground that the Greeks possessed no artillery of any type before that date.

But there are, at first sight, a few indications that some form of artillery may have previously existed elsewhere, outside the Greek world. In the Bible, in the second book of Chronicles, the writer relates: 'Uzziah made in Jerusalem accurately designed machines to be on the towers and breastworks, to hurl missiles and large stones.'[5] The fame of Uzziah's engines was apparently widespread. Uzziah lived about 780–750 B.C.,[6]

---

[1] D.S. xiii. 86, 1 and 3.   [2] Thuc. ii. 76. 4–5.
[3] D.S. xiii. 78. 4: . . . ὁλκάδας . . . οὔσας λιθοφόρους.
[4] Ibid. 78. 7: οἱ δ' ἐπὶ τῶν μεγάλων πλοίων ἐφεστῶτες ἐπέρριψαν ταῖς τῶν πολεμίων ναυσὶ τοὺς ἀπὸ τῶν κεραιῶν λίθους. Ibid. 79. 3: πλεῖστοι δ' ὑπὸ τῶν λιθοφόρων κεραιῶν ἔπιπτον, ὡς ἂν ἐξ ὑπερδεξίων τόπων βαλλόντων λίθους ὑπερμεγέθεις τῶν Ἀθηναίων.
[5] Chron. ii. 26. 15.
[6] For Uzziah's date, and that of Ezekiel, see S. A. Cook, *The Old Testament, a Reinterpretation* (London, 1936), Appendix.

but the chronicler wrote about 250 B.C.[1] Nothing could be more natural than that he should commit an anachronism, particularly as siege-technique was at a high peak of efficiency when he was writing. This sort of objection cannot, however, be raised against an artillery term used by Ezekiel, because he both lived and wrote about 580 B.C.[2] The word in question is βελοστάσεις which occurs twice in the Greek version of his prophetic description of the dreadful siege which Jerusalem was shortly to undergo. Βελόστασις, corresponding to the Latin *ballistarium*, means a platform for artillery. The Hebrew text, however, gives *karim* which means battering-rams, so that the person who translated Ezekiel's work into Greek, at a time when artillery was very common, was led into making a simple, but understandable, mistake. Incidentally, those responsible for the Authorized and Revised Versions of the English Bible avoided the error. Thus, the evidence for early artillery in Biblical texts is misleading and due to human failings in their composition and transmission.

Since Ezekiel's prophecies concern the forthcoming siege of Jerusalem by the Chaldaean Nebuchadnezzar, we are drawn to look for artillery in the great eastern armaments which certainly, above all the Assyrian, possessed formidable siege-trains. Rawlinson saw, in an Assyrian relief, what he thought was a representation of two one-armed stone-throwing engines (μοναγκῶνες, *onagri*).[3] On the right of the relief, it appears that two long, thin beams rise almost vertically with a wall in the background; on the left, some irregularly shaped stones or bricks, which Rawlinson takes to be the missiles, are seemingly falling to the ground. The long beams, if that is what they are, could be parts of any very simple appliance, such as crude rams or grappling hooks; but, in the complete absence of even the slightest additional evidence, it is unjustifiable to transform the straightforward, innocent beams into the arms of *onagri* and, solely by vivid imagination, to surround them with all the essential major and minor components which make up these relatively complicated machines.

In a lengthy list of inventions and inventors, the elder Pliny remarks: 'They say that Pisaeus invented hunting-spears and, among pieces of artillery, the scorpion; the Cretans invented the catapult, the Syrophoenicians the *ballista* and sling.'[4] The compilation of lists, sometimes on

---

[1] For discussion of this date see H. P. Smith, *Old Testament History* (Edinburgh, 1903), 419, note.   [2] Ezek. 4. 2; 21. 22.
[3] G. Rawlinson, *Five Great Monarchies of the Eastern World*, i² (London, 1871), 472.
[4] Pliny, *NH* vii. 201: '... invenisse dicunt ... Pisaeum venabula et in tormentis scorpionem, Cretas catapultam, Syrophoenicas ballistam et fundam ...'

curious subjects, became a fairly popular practice in the Hellenistic period,[1] and Pliny must have used such a list, or a whole series of them. There is, of course, no chance of discovering the ultimate source of information. It is very probable that the above artillery items, if they are not products of the moderately fertile imagination of some ill-informed Greek,[2] resulted from misunderstanding of vague and anachronistic references to machines like the passages in the Bible which we have just discussed. Pöhlmann pointed out that the Phoenicians were very unlikely to have invented any piece of artillery because they were more adept at taking over than discovering things.[3] Also, catapult (καταπέλτης) is a good Greek word. If the Phoenicians had invented it the catapult would have had a less Greek-sounding name.[4]

On the one hand, then, we are faced with a number of indications that some form of artillery may have existed outside the Greek world before 399 B.C. There is also a brief suggestion that the catapult was not invented in Syracuse. But not one piece of this evidence is to any degree certain, and much of it is palpably erroneous. On the other hand, Diodorus, following a good contemporary source, states straightforwardly and in an account full of circumstantial detail that the first artillery was invented at Syracuse in 399 B.C. After the occasion mentioned by him there is a gradually increasing volume of evidence about catapults in Greek and Roman literature and inscriptions.

However, before abandoning altogether the theory that non-torsion engines existed earlier than 399 B.C., we should consider one final point that may be advanced in its favour. Talking about the siege-towers and rams which Dionysius I produced at the siege of Motya in 397 B.C., Tarn stressed the fact that some of Dionysius' technicians came from the Carthaginian sphere and suggested that 'the knowledge which came to him had travelled along a line Assyria—Phoenicia—Carthage—Sicily'.[5] We might then argue that knowledge of artillery arrived by the same route and that the statements of Pliny and Diodorus can be reconciled with each other to some extent.

Yet the use of artillery in Dionysius' operations round Motya came as a complete shock to the Carthaginian forces. The tyrant's navy was caught by Himilco, the Carthaginian admiral, in a harbour opposite

---

[1] W. W. Tarn and G. T. Griffith, *Hellenistic Civilisation*[3] (London, 1952), 293.

[2] I say 'moderately fertile' because the inventions of catapult and *ballista* were attributed to peoples rather than individuals or even cities. This is another indication of the unreliability of Pliny's information.

[3] Pöhlmann, *Untersuchungen*, 28.

[4] Ibid. 30.   [5] Tarn, *HMND*, 102 f.

Motya; but he had it dragged overland to the open sea where it engaged the Carthaginians; simultaneously, 'from the land, the Syracusans employed arrow-shooting catapults and destroyed numbers of the enemy; this weapon created great consternation because it was first invented at that time.'[1] The surprise, it seems, was as valuable a result of its employment as the actual damage inflicted. If the Carthaginians had had the slightest inkling of the existence of such artillery, surprise would have been out of the question. Further, if we suppose that Dionysius' engines were torsion catapults of the Mark I or Mark II type and that the Carthaginians were already familiar with gastraphetae of various sorts,[2] we must then proceed to make the impossible assumption that the first, relatively primitive, torsion machines were so markedly superior to the advanced non-torsion artillery as to produce a really startling impression. Thus, there can be very little doubt that the pieces of artillery invented at Syracuse in 399 B.C. were gastraphetae, early non-torsion engines, and that no artillery had existed anywhere in the world before that time.

Shortly after his reference to the invention of artillery, Diodorus remarks, 'catapult-bolts of all kinds were prepared, and a large number of other missiles' (κατεσκευάσθησαν δὲ καὶ καταπέλται παντοῖοι καὶ τῶν ἄλλων βελῶν πολύς τις ἀριθμός; in view of the context, καταπέλται παντοῖοι would seem to mean 'catapult-bolts of all kinds' rather than 'catapults of all kinds').[3] It can be argued that more types of artillery are implied than just the true gastraphetes.[4] For one thing, gastraphetae obviously cannot have varied significantly in size. Consequently, we would expect the missiles for Dionysius' machines to be more or less uniform and not 'of all kinds'. But the characteristics of the early pieces of artillery would at first be largely unknown. It would not be easy, especially before catapults had been fired in anger, to determine the most efficient design for the bolts. For instance, how long were these bolts to be? What was the best relationship between the length of the bolt and the diameter of its cross-section? What was the most satisfactory weight for the metal head to fit a wooden shaft of given size? How were the flights to be rearranged so that they would not hinder the discharge of the missile along the groove in the gastraphetes' stock, but would still keep the bolt on its course?

[1] D.S. xiv. 50. 4: ἀπὸ δὲ τῆς γῆς τοῖς ὀξυβελέσι καταπέλταις οἱ Συρακόσιοι χρώμενοι συχνοὺς τῶν πολεμίων ἀνῄρουν· καὶ γὰρ κατάπληξιν εἶχε μεγάλην τοῦτο τὸ βέλος διὰ τὸ πρώτως εὑρεθῆναι κατ' ἐκεῖνον τὸν καιρόν.
[2] On early torsion artillery see Heron, Bel. W 81; and see above, pp. 16 ff.
[3] D.S. xiv. 43. 3.
[4] On the true gastraphetes see above, pp. 5 ff.; and Heron, Bel. 75.

The artisans at Syracuse would have been very fortunate if they had discovered solutions to all these problems in a short period of time. Probably, in the early stages, they selected a number of designs for the bolts which seemed to give promising results in terms of range and penetrative power and then manufactured a batch of bolts in accordance with each specification.

It may be, of course, that we should not attach too much technical significance to Diodorus' 'catapult-bolts of all kinds', because we could take it as a stock phrase meaning little more than 'large numbers of catapult-bolts'. However, it is just possible that it does possess some technical implication and that it suggests rather more than the explanation offered in the preceding paragraph. There seems to be no reason why the artisans at Syracuse should not have developed more advanced non-torsion engines later in the year 399 B.C., substituting a winch-mechanism for the stomach-rest and, possibly, designing a base. In that case Dionysius set off for Motya with some true *gastraphetae* and some more advanced non-torsion artillery, the machines varying in size between narrow limits and hence justifying the statement that all kinds of bolts were prepared. But it is certain, I think, that all Dionysius' pieces of artillery were small and designed solely for shooting bolts.

The principal limiting factor would be the composite bow. We have no information about the development of this type of bow for artillery purposes, but the master bowyers would only be able to produce larger and more powerful bows gradually. We may reasonably estimate that a period of thirty years or more elapsed between the making of the first composite bow for the first *gastraphetes* and the production of enormous bows like the one for the big non-torsion stone-thrower designed by Isidorus of Abydus.[1]

An attempt must now be made to discover when torsion artillery was invented. The earliest indisputable evidence for catapults with springs of sinew or hair occurs in an inscription relating to military and other stores deposited in the Chalcotheca, the treasure-house and arsenal on the Acropolis at Athens. The relevant lines run as follows:

. . . . : κα[ταπάλτ]	. . . catapults,
ας διπήχεις τριχο[τόνους ἐ]	two-cubit, with hair springs,
50 ντελεῖ(ς) : ΙΙΙ: κατα[πάλτας]	complete : 3 ; catapults,
διπήχεις τριχοτό[νους οὐχ]	two-cubit, with hair springs, not in
ὑγιεῖς οὐδ' ἐντελε[ῖς : ΙΙΙ :]	good order and not complete : 3 ;
ἑτέρους δύο κατα[πάλτας τρ]	two other catapults, three-

[1] Biton, W 48 ff. For discussion of the size of the bow for Isidorus' machine see *Technical Treatises*, Biton, n. 22, and above, p. 15.

[ι]πήχεις τριχοτό[νους οὐχ ὑ]
55 [γιεῖ]s οὐδ' ἐντελεῖς: [ἑτέρους]?
[καταπάλτας] τρ[ιχ]οτό[νους?][1]

cubit, with hair springs, not in
good order and not complete; other
catapults with hair springs . . .

All the catapults listed here, whether complete and in good repair or not, and whether designed for shooting bolts with a length of 2 cubits or 3 cubits, possess springs made of hair. There is nothing to show that the hair was supplied by women rather than horses; we may guess that it was horse-hair. The form of the lettering in the inscription apparently belongs to the Lycurgean period, 338–326 B.C. Therefore, torsion artillery definitely existed by the latter date, 326 B.C.

But another Attic inscription, which can definitely be attributed to the year 330/29 B.C., also indicates the existence of torsion engines though the springs themselves are not specifically mentioned.[2] It is mainly an inventory of naval equipment, but includes some articles found 'in the large building by the gates' of the Peiraeus. Among these articles were:

πλαίσια καταπαλτῶν
τῶν ἐξ Ἐρετρίας : ΔΙ·
330 σωλῆνες καταπαλτῶν
ΔΙΙΙΙ: βάσεις καταπαλ-
τῶν : ΓΙΙ : τόξα ἐσκυτω-
μένα : ΙΙ : σκορπίων
σωλῆνες : ΓΙ : ἐπιστύ-
335 λια : Γ : τρόχιλοι : ΙΙΙ :
ἀπὸ τοῦ μηχανώματος·
βέλη καταπαλτῶν ἀνη-
κίδωτα καὶ ἀπτέρωτα
ΗΗΗΗΓΓ: καὶ ἠκιδωμένα
340 ΓΙ: σχίζαι (εἰς) βέλη καταπαλτῶν: ΔΔΔ ΓΙ[Ι]·

Frames of the catapults
from Eretria: 11 ;
Stocks for catapults: 14;
Bases for catapults: 7;
Bows cased in leather: 2 ;
Stocks for scorpions: 6;
Cross-beams (?): 5;
Pulley-wheels: 3 (from
the machine);
Bolts for catapults, without
heads and without flights:
455; Bolts with heads: 51 ;
Unprepared shafts for catapult-
bolts: 47.

For our present purpose the interesting item occurs in the first two lines quoted above—'eleven πλαίσια belonging to the catapults from Eretria'. The term πλαίσιον does not appear in the works of the technical writers on artillery-construction, but their standard word for the wooden frame which holds the spring of a torsion catapult is πλινθίον. There is clearly a very close connection between πλαίσιον and πλινθίον;[3] in fact, πλαίσιον seems to be the Attic equivalent of πλινθίον.[4] Thus the inscription offers very strong evidence for the existence of eleven frames for torsion catapults in the Peiraeus in 330/29 B.C.

As a result of the fortunate inclusion of these catapults' place of origin, Eretria, we have a chance of tracing with some degree of probability the

[1] IG² ii. 1467, B, col. ii, ll. 48–56.
[2] IG² ii. 1627, B, 328–41. The significant items reappear in later inventories of the Athenian curatores navales: IG² ii. 1628, D, 510 ff. (326/5 B.C.); 1629, E, 985 ff. (325/4 B.C.); 1631, B, 220 ff. (323/2 B.C.).
[3] LS⁹ s.v. πλαίσιον.   [4] Suidas, s.v. πλινθωτόν; cf. Xen. An. iii. 4. 19.

history of the engines. The most probable occasion for their transfer to Athens was in the summer of 340 B.C. An Athenian expedition under Phocion assisted the Eretrian democrats to expel from their city the tyrant Cleitarchus, installed there by Philip II of Macedon as part of his attempt to build up a pro-Macedonian stronghold in Euboea.[1] If Phocion brought back the Eretrian catapults after this successful operation, it is most likely that they were Macedonian in origin, sent to Eretria to help Cleitarchus maintain his position. It is far more probable that they represented part of the Athenian share of the booty seized from the tyrant than that the Eretrians gave the Athenians some of their own catapults as a reward for services rendered. Few cities could afford much artillery at this time. Even wealthy Byzantium found herself without any, or at least with an inadequate number, when she had sent to Perinthus engines which she could not really spare.[2]

The only people who may have had a surplus of artillery in the first two-thirds of the fourth century B.C. were Dionysius I of Syracuse, the Phocians who robbed the Delphic treasury to buy arms and hire mercenaries, and Philip II himself. There is thus some probability that the first torsion engines of which we have certain knowledge can be linked with Macedon. Indeed, though definite information simply does not exist, a good deal of circumstantial evidence suggests that the principle of torsion was first discovered in Macedon under the auspices of Philip II.

The founder of the new Macedonia possessed a good corps of engineers under the famous Thessalian Polyidus; he had the foresight and the money to finance the research work of his technical experts; he was a man with ambitions, and their fulfilment required, from the military point of view, that he should not only create a formidable field-army, but also a powerful siege-train that could take even the strongest city. Athenaeus Mechanicus makes the following rather general, but relevant and perhaps important, comment on technical progress during the fourth century B.C.:

All this sort of machine-construction developed in the tyranny of Dionysius the Sicilian, and in the reign of Philip, son of Amyntas, when Philip was besieging Byzantium. Particularly successful in this craft was Polyidus the Thessalian, whose pupils, Diades and Charias, went on campaign with Alexander.[3]

It is reasonable to suppose that the two rulers, who undoubtedly made

[1] Plut. *Phocion*, 12 f.; D.S. xvi. 74. 1; K. J. Beloch, *Griechische Geschichte*, iii. 1 (Berlin, 1922), 552 f.
[2] D.S. xvi. 76. 4.   [3] Ath. Mech. W 10, 5 ff.

the largest contribution in that period to the general development of siege-equipment, were also responsible for vital stages in the development of the catapult, one of the most noteworthy machines in the armoury of the besieger. It is significant, too, that Dionysius is definitely associated with the crucial first stage of artillery-construction.

We do not know, of course, whether the Macedonian arsenal contained any artillery of any sort when Philip II succeeded to the throne. Fairly early in his reign, however, he underwent a chastening experience, in which artillery played a decisive part, and which must have convinced him of its value, if he did not already appreciate it. Probably in 354 B.C.,[1] when he was beginning to become involved in the affairs of Thessaly, Philip came into conflict in that area with Onomarchus the Phocian.

On one occasion Onomarchus chose a very favourable battlefield in front of a semicircular range of hills.[2] Concealing infantry and stone-throwing engines on the heights, he led other units down to the partially enclosed plain beneath. When Philip attacked, Onomarchus' men pretended to flee into the semicircular recess and the Macedonians naturally followed eagerly. The Phocian artillerymen then used the stone-throwers (πετροβόλους μηχανάς) to pour a devastating hail of shot upon the Macedonians from the hills round the killing ground. Thereupon, Onomarchus rallied his soldiers, charged the disorganized Macedonian phalanx, and forced Philip to draw off. The latter is reported to have said afterwards: 'I did not fly, I retreated as rams do that I might make a more vigorous attack later.'

Onomarchus' stone-throwers were very probably small non-torsion engines like the one designed by Charon of Magnesia and described by Biton,[3] which was not altogether too cumbersome for use in the field and hurled a shot weighing about 5 pounds.[4] Philip's discomfiture under the fire of these machines may well have persuaded a man of his character to promote the production of artillery and to encourage his artificers to seek improvements in catapult-design. Macedonian preoccupation with catapults among other things was a subject for jest about 345 B.C. At least, that seems a plausible interpretation of a phrase in a fragment of Mnesimachus' comedy entitled *Philip*.[5] But Philip II's siege-train and

---

[1] H. D. Westlake, *Thessaly in the Fourth Century B.C.* (London, 1935), 173 f.
[2] Polyaen. ii. 38. 2, is the source for the following account.
[3] Biton, W 45 ff. See above, p. 15; Fig. 6, facing p. 13.
[4] See *Technical Treatises*, Biton, n. 10.
[5] J. M. Edmonds, *The Fragments of Attic Comedy*, ii (Leiden, 1959), 366 ff., frg. 7, line 10: καταπέλταισι δ' ἐστεφανώμεθα. He would date the *Philip* in 345 B.C. (op. cit. 368–9, note a).

artillery did not create a really striking impression until he assaulted Perinthus in 340 B.C.[1] As Niebuhr remarked long ago, 'Es ist die Belagerung, bei der die Mechanik sich aus den Windeln hob'.[2] But the records of the siege of Perinthus mention no other pieces of artillery except arrow-shooting catapults (ὀξυβελεῖς).[3] Macedonian stone-throwers do not appear until Alexander's attack on Halicarnassus some years later (334 B.C.).[4]

It is now time to attempt a reconstruction of the early history of torsion engines, though we must emphasize once again the tenuous nature of the evidence. The principle of torsion was probably discovered by artificers working in Macedonia under Philip II and Polyidus between 353 and 341 B.C. There exists no hint of torsion catapults before Philip's reign. At the sieges of Perinthus and Byzantium (340 B.C.) Philip deployed torsion arrow-shooting catapults, while the machines used by the defenders were still presumably of the non-torsion variety. Since the reasonably detailed account of the sieges given by Diodorus contains no trace of the employment of stone-throwers, we may estimate that Philip's catapults had spring-frames (πλινθία) no more advanced than the Mark II stage.[5]

The catapults which we suggested above came to Athens ultimately from the hands of Philip's engineers, via Eretria, would be of the same Mark II type. Let us look more closely at the relevant inscription.[6] After the eleven catapult-frames (πλαίσια) that we have already discussed, fourteen σωλῆνες of catapults are recorded. The word σωλήν is not exactly a technical term for a part of a catapult; but Heron uses σωλῆνα πελεκινοειδῆ to denote the dove-tailed groove which runs along the top of the fixed portion of a catapult stock, the case (σῦριγξ),[7] and Biton employs the diminutives σωληνίδια and σωλήνια for the similar dove-tails in the stock of his first stone-thrower.[8] Therefore, σωλήν is an early or Attic equivalent of σῦριγξ, the fixed stock; it may even mean the whole stock, including both case (σῦριγξ) and slider (διώστρα).[9]

The next item, seven bases (βάσεις) for catapults,[10] is straightforward enough and requires no comment. Then we find two bows cased in

---

[1] N.B.: D.S. xvi. 74; Ath. Mech. W 10, 5 ff; cf. Vitr. x. 13. 3.
[2] Quoted by Wüst, *Philipp II*, 130 n. 3.
[3] For ὀξυβελεῖς, see D.S. xvi. 74. 4; 75. 3.
[4] Arr. *Anab.* i. 22. 2.
[5] On Mark I and Mark II stages of development, see above, pp. 17 ff.
[6] *IG²* ii. 1627, B, 328–41, quoted above, p. 57.
[7] Heron, *Bel.* W 75: . . . ἔχων ἐν τῇ ἐπάνω ἐπιφανείᾳ σωλῆνα πελεκινοειδῆ τὸν ΚΛ.
[8] Biton, W 46: ἐν σωληνιδίοις; W 46: τῶν σωληνίων.
[9] The complete stock of a euthytone catapult is illustrated in Fig. 16 (p. 34), though the frames shown there are of a more advanced type than the πλαίσια in the present inscription.
[10] For illustration of a typical base for any sort of catapult see Fig. 21, facing p. 42.

leather (τόξα ἐσκυτωμένα). Since these occur in the middle of a list of artillery components, they must be powerful bows to be fitted to non-torsion catapults. Hence, as we would expect at Athens in this period of transition, torsion and non-torsion machines existed side by side. Later, the slender evidence supplied by the available inscriptions from the end of the fourth century suggests that the Athenians soon began to concentrate on torsion artillery.[1]

The list continues with six stocks (σωλῆνες) belonging to scorpions, that is, to small torsion or non-torsion catapults. Then come five ἐπιστύλια. It is very difficult to identify these components because the only other use of the term in an artillery-context seems to be Philon's application of it to the protective boxes which cover the top and bottom of the frame of his novel wedge-engine.[2] I would propose that ἐπιστύλια may be the early or Attic version of περίτρητα, hole-carriers. In that case they indicate five spare hole-carriers—in other words, spare horizontal cross-pieces for torsion frames. On the other hand, they may mean protective covers, which were certainly not employed for the top and bottom of Mark III or Mark IV frames, but which would have been appropriate for Mark I and Mark II frames, especially for the former, because Philon's wedge-engine resembled this quite closely in some respects.[3]

The relevant section of this inscription ends with three pulleys, sheaves, or rollers, presumably belonging to the pullback system of a particularly large catapult, and considerable numbers of catapult-bolts in various states of readiness. On the whole the inscription supports the view that, about 340 B.C., when the catapults were probably brought to Athens from Eretria, torsion engines were still in an early stage of development.

The appearance of really powerful stone-throwers will provide the surest indication that artificers have added the washers to the frames and have thus begun the Mark III stage of construction.[4] At Tyre in 332 B.C. Alexander actually employed stone-throwers (πετροβόλους κατα-πέλτας) with some effect against the walls.[5] These engines were almost certainly torsion stone-throwers, because I doubt whether even the most powerful non-torsion machines would have been worth using for this

---

[1] Cf. IG² ii. 1467, B, col. ii, ll. 48–56 (the Lycurgean inscr.); ibid. 1475, B, ll. 30–5 (c. 318/17 B.C.); ibid. 1487, B, ll. 84–90 (306/5 B.C.). There is no hint of non-torsion artillery in any of these.

[2] Philon, Bel. 62: ... ἀντὶ δὲ τοῦ περιτρήτου παρ' ἡμῖν ἐπικεῖσθαί τι καθάπερ ἐπιστύλιον ...

[3] See above, p. 42.

[4] On Mark III catapults see above, pp. 19 ff.

[5] D.S. xvii. 42. 7; 45. 2: ὁ δ' Ἀλέξανδρος ἐπιστήσας ἐπὶ τοὺς ἁρμόζοντας τόπους τοὺς πετροβόλους καταπέλτας καὶ λίθους μεγάλους ἀφιεὶς ἐσάλευε τὰ τείχη ...

purpose. Alexander already possessed stone-throwers at Halicarnassus (334 B.C.),[1] but they figured there solely against personnel when the Macedonians were repulsing a sally, so that they may have been non-torsion engines. It is more probable, however, that they would be small experimental Mark III stone-throwers, the lessons derived from which enabled the Macedonian mechanics to develop the powerful stone-throwers at Tyre just two years later.

We may reasonably conclude that Mark III frames were first produced between 340 and 332 B.C. There then followed a lengthy period of experiment during which the Mark IIIA arrow-shooting catapults and the Mark IIIB stone-throwers were evolved, and the most suitable measurements for every component of a given engine were determined.[2] This gradual process reached its climax with the discovery of the formulae for calibration and the introduction of the corresponding lists of standard dimensions.[3] Referring to the discovery of the formulae, Philon states: 'Alexandrian craftsmen achieved this first, being heavily subsidized because they had ambitious kings who fostered craftsmanship.'[4] The kings mentioned must have been the Ptolemies, because Egypt had ceased to be an independent kingdom long before the Macedonian conquest and there is no evidence for artillery there before Alexander. Since Philon employs the plural 'kings', we may presume, in the absence of other evidence, that the formulae were not discovered under Ptolemy I, and that the reign of Ptolemy II (283/2–246 B.C.) is the earliest possible period for their introduction.

Ctesibius, probably the most famous of all engineers in antiquity, almost certainly reached professional maturity soon after 270 B.C. under Ptolemy II.[5] Yet no evidence suggests that he played any part in the discovery of the calibrating formulae. In fact, the character of his work on artillery, his attempts to employ new resilient materials, shows that the formulae were already in existence, that conventional torsion artillery had reached an advanced stage of development, and that he was thus more or less compelled to direct his researches in this field along highly original lines. A fair amount of circumstantial evidence, therefore, points to an early portion of Ptolemy II's reign as the most probable time within which the formulae were invented.

In 276/5 B.C., Ptolemy II married his full sister Arsinoe, a person of considerable ability, who proceeded to put the Egyptian war machine on

---

[1] Arr. *Anab.* i. 22. 2.

[2] On the experimental period see above, p. 25. For Mark IIIA and Mark IIIB artillery see pp. 21 ff.

[3] See above, pp. 24 ff.   [4] Philon, *Bel.* 50.   [5] Cf. Ath. xi. 497d.

a sound footing, so that the First Syrian War ended in Egypt's favour in 273/2 B.C. There is a strong possibility that the formulae and lists of dimensions were developed during Arsinoe's energetic preparations for the final campaigns of this war, that is to say, between 275 and 273 B.C.

Advanced non-torsion artillery remained in use for quite a long time after the invention of torsion. As late as 240 B.C. Biton devoted the artillery sections of his constructional treatise exclusively to non-torsion engines. Of course, he may have been something of a crank like the Chevalier de Folard, who, in A.D. 1727, recommended a return from gunpowder- to catapult-artillery.[1] But in the early days of torsion at least, the composite bows probably offered one or two advantages over sinew- or hair-springs. Though the former provided a relatively moderate performance, the constructor of a given machine could depend on obtaining the results which he expected from it. The builder of a torsion catapult did not quite know what was going to happen; the performance might turn out to be most gratifying, on the other hand it could be altogether disappointing. Again, composite bows were probably less affected by, and certainly easier to protect from, changes in the dampness of the atmosphere. Further, once produced by the bowyer, the composite bow would give satisfactory service with little or no attention right to the end of its working life. Torsion springs, however, required fairly regular and expert maintenance if they were to remain at peak efficiency.

Understandably, therefore, some artificers and some city-authorities might well consider that the greater simplicity and reliability of non-torsion catapults outweighed the prospect of the higher performance that torsion-engines could sometimes, but by no means always, provide. A decision must have been taken on these lines at Thessalonica after 315 B.C. when the city was founded by Cassander, because Biton describes an enormous non-torsion stone-thrower designed there by Isidorus of Abydos.[2] The discovery of the formulae and the establishment of standard dimensions, which facilitated the consistent production of torsion machines with high performance, ultimately brought interest in non-torsion artillery to an end. Biton seems to be the last of a line of engineers and technical writers who confined their attentions to machines of the older type.

After his time there is no definite trace of non-torsion catapults until we reach the fourth century A.D., when the *arcuballista*, presumably a lineal descendant of the *gastraphetes*, appears on the scene. In the course of the half-century after 275 B.C., torsion engines constructed in

---

[1] Payne-Gallwey, *The Crossbow*, 273.   [2] Biton, W 49.

accordance with the formulae, that is, the Mark IVA arrow-firers and Mark IVB stone-throwers, became the standard artillery throughout the Mediterranean area. They remained standard, though with one or two important modifications which are reflected in Vitruvius' descriptions, until at least A.D. 100.[1]

[1] See above, pp. 41 ff. and below, pp. 199 ff.

III

THE DIFFUSION OF ARTILLERY

§ 1. *Early Spread of Non-torsion Artillery*

KNOWLEDGE of early artillery, invented in 399 B.C., took some time to reach other parts of the Mediterranean world. We do not know whether Dionysius I originally tried to retain a monopoly of the new weapon, but he certainly seems to have been concerned, about 370 B.C., with the introduction of catapults into Greece proper, to Sparta and Athens, to be precise. Plutarch provides evidence for Spartan contact with artillery in his collection of royal Laconian pronouncements: 'Archidamus, son of Agesilaus, on seeing a piece of catapult artillery then brought over from Sicily for the first time, cried, "Heracles, man's martial valour is of no avail any more."'[1] The phrase for 'a piece of catapult artillery' is κατα-πελτικὸν βέλος, which Tarn takes to mean 'a catapult arrow'.[2] But, though βέλος generally means 'missile', it sometimes indicates the machine that hurls the missile,[3] and catapult bolts by themselves would be neither particularly impressive nor particularly useful. Archidamus' emphatic exclamation can only have been caused, surely, by his witnessing a demonstration of actual shooting by a non-torsion catapult. It is interesting to have a record of the spontaneous reaction of a competent officer to his first experience of an early piece of artillery. This Sicilian machinery most probably arrived in the Peloponnese along with the troops under Cissidas, sent by Dionysius I in 368 or 367 B.C., who assisted Archidamus to win his 'tearless' victory over the Arcadians and Argives.[4]

A fragmentary inscription from Athens,[5] listing items stored on the Acropolis in 371/0 B.C., probably in the Parthenon, includes the following points of interest:

$$[\sigma\acute{\omega}\rho\alpha\kappa o\iota\ \tau o\xi \epsilon\upsilon\mu]\acute{\alpha}\tau\omega\nu\ [\delta]\acute{\upsilon}[o]$$
$$[\sigma\acute{\omega}\rho\alpha\kappa o\iota\ \kappa\alpha\tau\alpha\pi]\alpha\lambda\tau\hat{\omega}\nu\ \delta\acute{\upsilon}[o]$$

The restorations are supported by two further inscriptions that include the same items, which were apparently later stored in the Chalcotheca.[6]

---

[1] Plut. *Mor.* 191E. [2] *HMND* 105 [3] e.g. Philon, *Pol.* 82. 8; 97. 10.
[4] Xen. *HG* vii. 1. 28–32; D.S. xv. 72. 3–4. [5] *IG*² ii. 1422, ll. 8 f.
[6] Ibid. 120, ll. 36 f. (362/1 B.C.): σώ]ρακοι τοξευμάτω[ν . .]/[σ]ώρακοι καταπαλτῶν ‖. Ibid. 1440, l. 48 (350 B.C.): σώρακοι τοξευμάτων :‖: σώρακοι καταπαλτῶν :‖:.

In view of the context, it seems certain that we have to do here with 'two boxes of arrows' and 'two boxes of catapult bolts'. From this we can infer that Athens possessed catapults about 370 B.C., since bolts without artillery would be ridiculous. Athens was on rather good terms with Dionysius I about this period and very probably he supplied the artillery. In 367 B.C. the Athenians made an alliance with him and his descendants.[1] One year earlier they had passed a decree honouring Dionysius I and his sons, in which mention was made of a crown previously voted to the tyrant.[2] It has been suggested that the crown was awarded 'perhaps in recognition of the help rendered to the cause of Sparta and Athens' in 369 B.C.[3] I propose that the Athenians were prompted to bestow the crown and other honours by rather more tangible benefits closer to home, including a gift of non-torsion catapults and boxes of bolts. At the end of the fourth century they certainly honoured the metic Euxenides of Phaselis with a crown because, among other things, he supplied Athens with sinew for torsion catapults in the course of the Four Years War (307–304 B.C.).[4]

The Phocians could have derived their engines,[5] or knowledge of how to build them, either from Sparta or from Athens, for they enjoyed the support of both powers at the beginning of the Sacred War.[6] We have noted above that a reverse at the hands of the Phocians possibly inspired Philip II of Macedon to take an interest in artillery.[7] Byzantium possessed catapults (non-torsion) by 340 B.C.,[8] probably as a result of her connection with Athens. The defenders of Halicarnassus employed arrow-firers, presumably non-torsion engines, against Alexander (334 B.C.).[9] When the latter arrived at Tyre (332 B.C.), that city already boasted a lavish store of catapults. Although Tyrian technicians constructed numerous additional machines at the start of the siege,[10] all their artillery was probably of the non-torsion type.

In most of the above examples it has been possible to show at least a thin line of formal contact going back to Syracuse, the place of invention. But the spread of artillery could just as easily have occurred in a more unofficial way. Dionysius' concourse of engineers no doubt broke up eventually. Those who had been concerned directly with the production of *gastraphetae* took their specialist knowledge with them when they sought

[1] Tod, no. 136.
[2] Tod, no. 133.
[3] By Tod, *ad* no. 133.
[4] *IG*² ii. 554.
[5] Polyaen. ii. 38. 2, discussed above, p. 59.
[6] Beloch, *Griechische Geschichte*, iii. 1 (Berlin, 1922), 247 f.
[7] See above, p. 59.
[8] D.S. xvi. 74. 4; the catapults sent to assist Perinthus.
[9] Ibid. xvii. 24. 6.
[10] Ibid. 41. 3.

employment elsewhere. Another generation of expert constructors of artillery would be trained by these men. By haphazard channels of this sort appreciation of artillery and of its significance may have penetrated to the designers of the fortifications at Messene. An attempt will be made later to show that the earliest period of fortification here, immediately after its foundation by Epaminondas in 369 B.C., allowed for the inclusion of catapults in the defences.[1]

§ 2. *Athenian Artillery*

Athens had non-torsion catapults by 370 B.C. Some twenty or thirty years later a gravestone was set up at the Peiraeus bearing the following inscription:

'Hρα[κ]λείδας

Μυσός

καταπαλταφέτας[2]

The apparent pride, reflected here, of Heracleidas the Mysian in his profession of artilleryman will be particularly gratifying to modern gunners. However, in fact, many tombstones of the same sort readily commemorate far less romantic professions; we find a tailoress and a hotel-proprietress, for example. Naturally, we cannot say for certain that Heracleidas was employed as an artilleryman in Attica.[3] But, since he died in the Peiraeus, it is likely that he was serving the Athenian government in that capacity. Non-torsion and torsion catapults were certainly stored in the Peiraeus in 330/29 B.C. and had probably been there since 340 B.C. Therefore, artillery formed part of the port defences, and at least a nucleus of professionals would be needed to operate the machines. I offer the following hypothetical reconstruction of Heracleidas' career. He was originally employed by Hermias of Atarneus, who is known to have built up a small, but powerful, military force in the middle of the fourth century B.C.[4] The treacherous capture of Hermias by the Persians (*c.* 342/1 B.C.) caused Heracleidas to remove to Athens and seek employment there.

We ought, in passing, to consider what duties the ancient artilleryman (καταπαλταφέτας) performed. There is no direct evidence on the subject. Clearly, his primary function was to shoot catapults at targets and hit them. This cannot have been easy for the inexperienced because

---

[1] See below, pp. 126 ff.   [2] *Syll.*[3] iii. 1249; *IG*[2] ii. 9979.
[3] Launey, 830.
[4] For a summary of Hermias' career and references, see Tod, *ad* no. 165.

catapults have no precise sighting arrangements. In particular, great skill and long practice were required before a man could estimate correctly the angle of elevation at which to lay a catapult in order to achieve exactly the right range. The artilleryman must also have been capable of maintaining catapults in first-rate working order. In torsion engines this included, above all, the tuning of the springs, and I suppose that the καταπαλταφέτας could operate the stretcher (ἐντόνιον), by means of which new sinew-cord could be inserted at the correct tension and old springs could be retightened after being loosened off in a period of idleness.[1]

No doubt he carried out minor repairs, too. But I do not think that he could have been expected to possess the knowledge of carpentry, metalwork, artillery dimensions, and the manufacture of spring-cord necessary to enable him to build a catapult from scratch. The latter task belonged to the expert artificer (μηχανοποιός, ὀργανοποιός). Finally, some professional artillerymen were required to give instruction in the operation of catapults, but this aspect of their duties will be discussed a little later.

A small group of inscriptions reflects the first major Athenian effort to produce a quantity of defensive artillery during the period (338–326 B.C.) when Lycurgus and his party were striving to put the city in a strong position.[2] The earliest of these, from the Lycurgean period itself, has already been examined.[3] The second inscription, dated 321/0 B.C., includes the following items:

72 ...7...ται βαρ[β]αρικ[α]ὶ κα[τα]πα-
[λτῶν προ]σκεκρουμέναι ...7...

77 [ι χαλκοθ]ήκηι βέλη καταπαλτῶν π-
....9.... ἄνευ σωράκων, τὰ μὲν ὑ-
[γιῆ τὰ δ' οὐ]χ ὑγιῆ: Χ Π HHH.[4]

The former seem to be damaged catapult components, perhaps [παρα-στά]ται βαρβαρικαί, that is side-stanchions of foreign design or with foreign designs on their iron plating.[5] The second item records a fairly impressive number (1,800) of unboxed catapult bolts, some serviceable, others not. Finally, another brief record of catapults kept on the Acropolis in 318/17 B.C. contains:

---

[1] On the stretcher and stringing see Heron, *Bel.* W 107 ff.; Vitr. x. 12; and *Technica Treatises*, Heron, n. 36 and fig. 23; Vitruvius, n. 66.

[2] W. S. Ferguson, *Hellenistic Athens* (London, 1911), 8 ff.; Beloch, op. cit. 610 f.

[3] Above, pp. 56 f.

[4] *IG*² ii. 1469, B, col. i, ll. 72–3 and 77–80. The catapult parts were stored probably, the missiles certainly, in the Chalcotheca.

[5] [μεσοστά]ται and [ἀντιστά]ται are also possible. The decoration of both woodwork and plating appears to have been usual. Cf. Philon, *Bel.* 61; 66. N.B., too, the tombstone of Vedennius, Plate 1 at the end.

30	[. . ; καταπάλ]τας διπ[ήχεις]	Catapults, two-cubit,
	[νευροτόνους;] ΔΓΙ; [βέλη.]	with springs of sinew (?) : 16; Bolts.
	[σώρακοι κατα]πα[λ]τῶν; Δ [. .]	Boxes of catapult bolts: 10 (+);
	[ἕτερον καταπάλ]την δίπ[ηχ]-	Another catapult, two-cubit,
	[υν νευρότονον ;Ι]; καταπ[ά]-	with springs of sinew (?) : 1;
35	[λτην δίπηχυν τρ]ιχότονον.¹	Catapult, two-cubit, with springs of hair.

Since the Lycurgean inscription (above, pp. 56 f.) mentions springs of hair only, it might be preferable to restore τριχοτόνους and τριχότονον respectively in lines 31 and 34 here, to agree with the definite record of a hair-spring engine in line 35. Though Heron seemingly implies that sinew was used for the springs of the earliest torsion catapults,² it may be that he is mistaken and that horse-hair was the original material. But a sentence in Plutarch relating to Alexander's siege of Gaza (332 B.C.) strongly suggests that the Macedonians employed sinew for catapult springs at that date.³

Therefore, I suspect that the Athenians were unable to manufacture sinew-cord in the time of Lycurgus and had to be content with horse-hair. In the present inscription and in the one ascribed to the Lycurgean period the catapults appear as two-cubit or three-cubit machines according to the length of the bolt which they were designed to shoot. This does not mean that discovery of the formulae was just round the corner. Even in the early stages of torsion it would be clear that the size of a particular machine depended to some extent on the length of bolt for which it was intended. The Athenian and other artificers of this period were probably the people Philon had in mind when, in an interesting and important passage, he referred to 'engineers in the old days' and 'the old engineers'.⁴ There may be some significance in the absence of stone-throwers in this group of inscriptions, and the Macedonians may have had a monopoly of torsion stone-throwing catapults at least until the death of Alexander.

The Athenians made their next intensive effort with regard to fortifications and armament, including artillery, at the beginning of the Four Years War (307–4 B.C.).⁵ The rapid success of Demetrius Poliorcetes against Cassander's garrison in the Peiraeus (307 B.C.) no doubt warned the Athenians of the inadequacy of their defences against a powerful siege-train well equipped with artillery.⁶ Urged on by Demochares, who forcefully advocated wall-building and the preparation of missiles and machines,⁷

---

¹ IG² ii. 1475, B, ll. 30–5.
² Heron, Bel. W 81.
³ Plut. Alex. 25. 4.
⁴ Philon, Bel. 50.
⁵ Ferguson, op. cit. 112 ff.; Launey, 831.
⁶ D.S. xx. 45.
⁷ [Plut.] Vit. X Or. 851 D: (Δημοχάρει) . . . οἰκοδομὴν τειχῶν, καὶ παρασκευὴν ὅπλων καὶ βελῶν καὶ μηχανημάτων, καὶ ὀχυρωσαμένῳ τὴν πόλιν ἐπὶ τοῦ τετραετοῦς πολέμου . . .

the latter obviously including catapults, they set about putting things in order, and the most important evidence for the provision of artillery is supplied by an inscription listing the following items which were stored (306/5 B.C.) in the Erechtheium or Chalcotheca:

κα[ὶ - - - - κατα]-
85 [πά]λτην πετροβόλον καὶ ὀξ[υβελῆ - -]
[τ]ετράπηχυν ἐντελῆ, Βρομίο[υ ἔργον?]·
[ἕ]τερον καταπάλτην τρίπηχυν π - - -
[ἐ]ντελῆ· ἕτερον καταπάλτην τρί[πηχυν
νευρ]-
[ό]τονον θυριδωτὸν ἐντελῆ· ἕτερον [καταπά]-
90 [λ]την τρισπίθαμον νευρότονον [ἐντελῆ].¹

And a stone-throwing and arrow-shooting catapult, four-cubit, complete, the work of Bromios; another catapult, three-cubit, complete; another catapult, ´three-cubit, with sinew-springs, fitted with an aperture, complete; another catapult, three-span, with sinew-springs, complete.

The first catapult, apparently constructed by a μηχανοποιός called Bromius, was designed for shooting both stone shot and bolts. It probably had Mark IIIB frames (see above, p. 22) and two sliders, one for each type of missile. As an arrow-firer it was rated a four-cubit engine. It is the earliest double-purpose machine known, and its bolts were the same length as those of the similar, but obviously far more sophisticated palintone catapult with which, probably over two centuries later, Agesistratus achieved a most impressive range.² The final line of the inscription mentions a three-span engine—a popular size,³ and it provides definite proof of the employment of sinew-springs at Athens; the decree honouring the metic Euxenides because he supplied the city with sinew for catapults in this war confirms the fact.⁴

¹ IG² ii. 1487. B, ll. 84–90. In l. 85, I think it is better to restore ὀξ[υβόλον - -] in view of IG² ii. 468, l. 5 (c. 306 B.C.). The description θυριδωτόν (l. 89), 'equipped with a window', is tantalizing because it presumably indicates an important and perhaps novel feature of this particular three-cubit catapult. The implied θυρίς, 'window' or 'aperture', seems to correspond to what Philon (Bel. 64. 9; 76. 48) calls the διόπτρα in Mark IVA arrow-firing euthytones, i.e. the gap between the two centre-stanchions which is also enclosed, at top and bottom, by the upper hole-carrier and the stock respectively. The διόπτρα gave assistance in aiming (implied by Heron, Bel. W 86: διὰ γὰρ τοῦ μήκους τῆς σύριγγος διοπτεύοντες ἐπιτευξόμεθα τοῦ σκοποῦ. Cf. Heron, Dioptra, 4). All torsion catapults, whether arrow-firers or stone-throwers, can be regarded to some extent as having an aperture of this sort. But it clearly became a most prominent feature and a real help in aiming when ancient engineers produced the first proper euthytones with one single frame holding both springs, prototypes of the stage which we designated Mark IIIA (see above, pp. 20 f., and Figs. 9 and 10, pp. 20 and 21). Hence, we suggest that the catapult in question was one of the first single-frame machines constructed at Athens.

On the other hand, θυριδωτόν need imply no more than the presence of a small aperture in the metal shield covering the front of the frame, a gap just large enough to allow for the operation of the slider and the projection of the missile (see Vedennius' catapult, Plate 1 at the end). Of course, any theory based on one isolated term must be purely speculative.

² Ath. Mech. W 8, 8–9: . . . τετράπηχυς, παλίντονος ὤν . . .

³ Cf. D.S. xx. 49. 4. Demetrius Poliorcetes used three-span catapults at the sea-battle off Cyprian Salamis in 307 B.C. The present Athenian artillery preparations may owe something to Demetrius and his father; see Launey, 831.

⁴ IG² ii. 554, ll. 15–16: καὶ νῦν εἰς τοὺς καταπάλτας ν[ε]-/[υ]ράς ἐπέδωκεν . . .

Another contemporary inscription, though fragmentary, demonstrates the existence of Athenian stone-throwers (πετροβόλους) side by side with arrow-firers (ὀξυβόλους).[1] We have also various pieces of equally fragmentary evidence for the provision of missiles.[2] Ferguson made the reasonable suggestion that the Athenians stored catapults and missiles on the Acropolis during a temporary easing of the situation between Cassander's invasion in the late summer of 306 B.C. and his formidable siege of the city in 304 B.C.,[3] from which, incidentally, Athens was saved by the arrival of Demetrius straight from his gloriously unsuccessful siege of Rhodes. The defensive preparations at least preserved the city until relief came.

Thus, the Athenians paid considerable attention to artillery in the last third of the fourth century and, unless the scanty information which chance has preserved for us is entirely misleading, they made efforts to keep abreast with the gradually improving methods of construction. They certainly appreciated the importance of torsion at a fairly early stage. A brief example given by Aristotle may be taken to illustrate the general familiarity of Athenians with artillery. In the *Nicomachean Ethics*, one instance of a person acting involuntarily through ignorance (ὃ δὲ πράττει ἀγνοήσειεν ἄν τις) is the accidental firing of a shot by a man who only intended to point something out, 'as the fellow did with the catapult'.[4]

Aristotle also provides the earliest evidence for the organized instruction of Athenian ephebes in shooting with catapults. As part of their plan to restore the city's military power after Chaeronea (338 B.C.), the Athenians instituted a thorough reorganization of the training of their young men about 335 B.C. Since the state intended to maintain substantial batteries of artillery, it had to produce men to work them. Therefore catapult shooting was introduced into the ephebic training programme, and one of the ephebes' official instructors was henceforth a professional artilleryman (καταπαλταφέτης).[5] From a number of decrees relating to ephebic training which have survived from the period between the early

---

[1] Ibid. 468, ll. 1 and 5.

[2] Ibid. 1487, B, ll. 102-4 (305 B.C.); 468, l. 8: βέλη ξυστά, 'trimmed bolts'; 1488, l. 1.

[3] Ferguson, op. cit., 115, n. 2; 117: 'The catapults and missiles had not been idle on the Acropolis for more than a year.'

[4] Arist. 1111ª6: . . . ἢ δεῖξαι βουλόμενος ἀφεῖναι, ὡς ὁ τὸν καταπέλτην. [Arist.] περὶ ἀκουστῶν, 800ᵇ13 refers briefly to catapults, but this is not relevant here because the treatise was probably written later by Straton (Ross, *Aristotle*, 12).

[5] Arist. *Ath.* 42. 3: χειροτονεῖ δὲ [sc. ὁ δῆμος] . . . διδασκάλους, οἵτινες ὁπλομαχεῖν καὶ τοξεύειν καὶ ἀκοντίζειν καὶ καταπάλτην ἀφιέναι διδάσκουσιν. On the date (328–324 B.C.) and authorship of this treatise I accept the views of K. von Fritz and E. Kapp, *Aristotle's Constitution of Athens* (New York, 1961), 5. In what follows about ephebes I am much indebted to Launey, 831 f., 1103.

third century and the beginning of the first century we can compile the following list of artillery instructors at Athens:

Decree	Date	Instructor
*IG*² ii. 665, ll. 27, 66–70	283/2	Mnesitheos, son of Mnesitheos, of Coprus (Μνησίθεος Μνησιθέου Κόπρειος)
Hesperia, 2 (1933), 159	c. 232/1	Pedieus of Oea (Πεδιεὺς ᾽Οῆθεν)
Hesperia, 30 (1961), 12, l. 11	c. 186/5	Pedieus, son of Neandros, from Ceramicus (Πεδιεὺς Νεάνδρου ἐκ Κεραμέων)
Hesperia, 15 (1946), 198 ff., no. 40, ll. 124–6	172/1	Neandros, son of Pedieus, from Ceramicus (Νέανδρος Πεδιέως ἐκ Κεραμέων)
*IG*² ii. 944b, ll. 20–5	c. 158¹	
Hesperia, 24 (1955), 231, l. 138; 232, ll. 292–4	128/7	Pedieus from Ceramicus (Πεδιεὺς ἐκ Κεραμέων)
*IG*² ii. 1006, l. 46	123/2	Calchedon, son of Calchedon, of Perithoidae (Καλχήδων Καλχήδονος Περιθοίδης)
*IG*² ii. 1008, ll. 39–40, 131–3	119/18	
*IG*² ii. 1009, ll. 22–3	117/16	
*IG*² ii. 1011, ll. 28, 60, 120–2	107/6	Callias of Aegilia (Καλλίας Αἰγιλιεύς)
*IG*² ii. 1028, ll. 53, 154–9	101/0	

It appears that the artillery instructor was always an Athenian citizen, that he generally held office for a considerable time, and that the same family might produce a line of expert artillerymen. In fact, the ancestors of the Pedieus who was catapult instructor in 128/7 plainly passed on their specialist knowledge from uncle to nephew and from father to son, and this family produced prominent artillerymen at Athens for over a century. A family tree has been reconstructed as follows:[2]

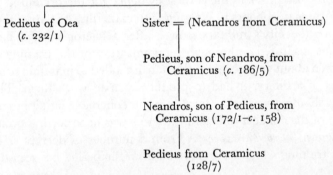

Pedieus of Oea   Sister ═ (Neandros from Ceramicus)
(*c*. 232/1)

Pedieus, son of Neandros, from
Ceramicus (*c*. 186/5)

Neandros, son of Pedieus, from
Ceramicus (172/1–*c*. 158)

Pedieus from Ceramicus
(128/7)

It is possible that the last Pedieus owed his appointment to his family connections rather than to his skill with catapults, and it seems that he gave instruction only in the operation of arrow-shooting machines. Although the slight, but perhaps significant, change in ephebic artillery

[1] I accept the date for this inscription which was suggested by B. D. Meritt in *Hesperia*, 11 (1942), 300 f.

[2] By B. D. Meritt, op. cit. 301, on whose table 1 the above pedigree is based. The dates in brackets under the names represent the years in or around which the various members of the family definitely held the appointment of artillery instructor. In fact, each person most probably held the post for several years.

policy in 123/2 B.C. probably indicates a temporary and exceptional reversal of the general trend, it is just conceivable that the new instructor, Calchedon, brought greater knowledge and energy to his task.[1]

At any rate, in 123/2 B.C. there was great excitement. The *cosmetes*, Dionysius, encouraged practice with catapults,[2] and the ephebes, inspired by him apparently,[3] repaired an old stone-thrower and renewed training with this type of artillery after a lapse of many years.[4] The incident suggests that, as we should expect, interest in artillery declined at Athens in the second half of the second century and that, for some time past, Athens probably had not had a single stone-thrower in working order. Only the enthusiasm of Dionysius led to a temporary and limited return to the old tradition.

§ 3. *Artillery in the Hellenistic World Excluding Athens*

Although other powers and cities besides Macedon, Athens, Byzantium, Halicarnassus, and Tyre may have obtained catapults of one sort or another before Alexander commenced his conquest of Persia, the most widespread diffusion of artillery began after his death. His immediate successors, many of whom personally witnessed the martial feats to which catapults sometimes made a by no means insignificant contribution, could not afford to be without numerous powerful pieces of artillery.[5] Their descendants took the same view. City authorities felt compelled to incorporate catapults in their defences. In many cases, no doubt, cities acquired artillery or artificers or technical advice from one of the great monarchies. But, wherever they got their machines from, they had to devise a means of training men to operate them.

The records of a number of cities show that instruction, practice in shooting, and regular competitions in marksmanship were instituted in

---

[1] Although it is Dionysius the *cosmetes* who took all the credit for the extra artillery practice and the repair of the stone-thrower, as we shall see in the next paragraph, Dionysius' enthusiasm would have been useless without the expert support of Calchedon.

[2] *IG*² ii. 1006, l. 65.   [3] Ibid., ll. 81–3.

[4] Ibid., ll. 34 ff.: . . . καταπάλτην λιθοβόλον ἕνα τῶν ἀρ[χαίων ἐ]κ τῶν ἰδίων ἐθερά[πευσαν καὶ τὰ ἐλλείπον]τα προσκατασκευάσαντες ἀνενεώσαντο διὰ πλειόνων ἐτ[ῶν] τήν τε χρῆσιν τοῦ ὀργάνο[υ καὶ μάθησιν] . . .

[5] In 323 B.C. Antipater prepared catapults for the defence of Lamia (D.S. xviii. 12. 4: παρασκευάς . . . καταπελτῶν . . . ποιούμενος). Two years later Ptolemy I equipped many Egyptian strongpoints with all kinds of artillery (D.S. xviii. 33. 3: βέλεσι παντοδαποῖς) to resist Perdiccas' attack. In 319 B.C. Arrhidaeus besieged Cyzicus with arrow-shooting and stone-throwing catapults (ibid. 51. 1: καταπέλτας ὀξυβελεῖς τε καὶ πετροβόλους); the defenders borrowed artillery from Byzantium (ibid. 51. 6: βέλη). For other examples of artillery used by the *Diadochi* see the accounts of the sieges of Megalopolis (318 B.C.), Salamis, and Rhodes, below, pp. 104 f., 105 ff.

connection with the *gymnasia*.[1] By the end of the fourth century the authorities of the *gymnasium* at Samos had already included a contest in shooting with arrow-firing catapults as the first event in the monthly sports. An inscription from that period preserves the name of a winner from one age-group of competitors (the young men, *νέοι*).[2] In the second century the Samians added a contest with the stone-thrower at the end of the programme of events in each age-group. The winners on one sports day are recorded as follows:

6 λιθοβόλωι· Μέντωρ Ζωίλου παλλήκων.	For the stone-thrower: Mentor, son of Zoilus, of the youths.
καταπάλτηι· Ἀστερίσκος Ἀστερίσκου	For the catapult: Asteriscus, son of Asteriscus.
19 λιθοβόλωι· Θεόκριτος Θεοκρίτου.[3]	For the stone-thrower: Theocritus, son of Theocritus.

Mentor won the last event on the programme for those under eighteen years of age (*πάλληκες*)—shooting with the stone-thrower—and Asteriscus was successful in the first event for ephebes, the contest with the arrow-firing catapult. Theocritus was victorious with the stone-thrower among the ephebes. Launey draws our attention to the early age at which Mentor and his rivals commenced artillery lessons. If these boys continued to practise regularly as they grew older, their city would have very little need to employ professional artillerymen.

An inscription from the island of Ceos records the regulations for a festival contained in an early third-century law of Coresus near Iulis.[4] The gymnasiarch was required to 'take out [the young men] for practice in javelin throwing, archery, and shooting with the arrow-firing catapult (*καταπαλταφεσία*) three times per month',[5] apparently in preparation for the competitions to be held at the festival. Any young man (*τῶν νεωτέρων* probably indicates ephebes and *νέοι*) who did not turn out for this, though fit enough to do so (*δυνατὸς ὤν*), was liable to a fine not exceeding one drachma. The law stated that the standing committee of the city-council should make a catapult and 300 bolts available for the practice sessions and the contest.[6] The first prize for artillery shooting was to be a helmet, a pike (*κοντός*), and 8 drachmae, the second prize a pike and 2 drachmae.[7] Since the law makes separate mention of contests for children under

---

[1] The following account owes much to Launey, 832 ff.

[2] *BCH* (1881), 481 f., no. 4, l. 5: [Ἀπ]ολλώνιος Ἀπολλωνίου καταπά[λτηι]. Cf. *AM* 24 (1903), 357 f., 366. There is also another long list covering a period of eight months (Michel, 899).

[3] Syll.³ iii. 1061, ll. 6–8, 19 (Michel, 900). The word *παλλήκων* applies, of course, to all names on the list up to and including Mentor.

[4] Syll.³ iii. 958.   [5] Ibid., ll. 24 f.   [6] Ibid., ll. 37 f.

[7] Ibid., ll. 31 f. Alternatively—though this seems far less likely—the figures in drachmae may indicate the value of the prize, e.g. 'a helmet and a pike worth eight drachmae'.

eighteen, and since their competitions do not include shooting with artillery, it appears that catapult instruction at Coresus did not commence before the ephebate.

There is also some evidence for catapult competitions at Cyaneae in Lycia,[1] and Launey would link the stone-shot found at Babylon with *gymnasium* contests there (109/8 B.C.) under the philhellene Arsaces Epiphanes.[2] It seems, however, that *gymnasia* in some cities did not include artillery in their training programmes or competitions at all.[3] It may be that these relied exclusively on professional artillerymen, either natives of their own city or men imported from outside. Although we do not possess anything like a complete picture of the situation, the Rhodians, who could boast a substantial force of artillery as early as the end of the fourth century, appear to have depended on hired engineers and artillerymen to a significant extent.

Charon of Magnesia designed a small stone-thrower (non-torsion) at Rhodes, most probably in the period before the Macedonian occupation (which began in 332 B.C.).[4] The repeating catapult which Philon examined there was constructed by Dionysius of Alexandria.[5] The chief artillery officer in a Rhodian expeditionary force sent against the pirates of Aigila towards the end of the third century B.C. was a certain Πολέμαρ- χος Κασαρεύς who, like most of his colleagues, came from the Rhodian Peraea.[6] Rhodes constantly maintained her strength on the production side. Only a few years after the devastating earthquake which brought down the Colossus she was able to send 300 talents of prepared hair (about 8 tons) and 100 talents of prepared sinew (over two tons) for catapult springs to help Sinope in a crisis (*c.* 220 B.C.). At the same time, Rhodian aid to that city included four stone-throwers and expert artil- lerymen to operate them—ἔτι δὲ λιθοφόρους (= λιθοβόλους) τέτταρας καὶ τοὺς ἀφέτας τούτοις.[7]

Rhodes herself received considerable assistance of the same sort after the earthquake disaster of 227 B.C. Those who desired to see Rhodes retain her position in the Aegean gave artillery a fairly high priority among

---

[1] Launey, 833, approves the restoration proposed by Robert, *Ét. Anat.* 399 ff., l. 10, in a 'gymnastic' inscription from the town—ἀκοντιστῶν καὶ τοξοτῶν καὶ [ἀφ]ε[τῶν]. I regard the case for competitions at Eleusis in the second century B.C. as too indefinite to merit consideration (Launey, 825; *AM* 62 (1937), 3 ff.).

[2] Launey, 873. On the shot found at Babylon see R. Koldewey, *The Excavations at Babylon* (London, 1915), 50.

[3] Launey, 833, instances Tralles, Erythrae, Teos, and Sestos, in this category.

[4] Biton, W 45.   [5] Philon, *Bel.* 73.

[6] Launey, 457, n. 7; cf. *ClRh* ii. 169, no. 1.

[7] Plb. iv. 56. 3. Cf. Walbank, *Polybius*, 512 f. There is no real evidence for the assumption made by Tarn (*HMND* 114 f.) that all this hair was supplied by women.

their various donations. Hieron II of Syracuse sent fifty three-cubit catapults (καταπέλτας τριπήχεις),[1] and Seleucus II Callinicus provided 1,000 talents of hair for catapult springs and the same quantity of resin.[2] Rhodes kept thoroughly up to date in catapult construction probably because she maintained close contact with developments in the Alexandrian workshops. Though there were undoubtedly differences in detailed technique between the two engineering establishments, Philon claimed to have based his accounts of the formulae and lists of dimensions for standard Mark IVA and Mark IVB catapults on information collected during long associations with the artificers in each city.[3] He could not have done this if their methods had not been approximately similar.

At the end of the fourth century Antigonus and his son Demetrius Poliorcetes controlled certainly the most spectacular, and perhaps the most formidable, artillery among the successors of Alexander; but in the third century the Ptolemies may have gained a slight superiority in this arm over the other Hellenistic monarchs. Certainly, the workshops in Alexandria became prominent in this period, discovered the formulae for calibration, and produced that notable artificer Ctesibius. The Ptolemaic dynasty sometimes deployed its catapults to help its friends and possessions abroad. A marble tablet from the island of Samothrace, for example, records a decree of the people in praise of Hippomedon, Ptolemy III's general in the Hellespont and Thrace during some period between 240 and 221 B.C.[4] It appears that he had shown the Samothracians suitable respect, enjoyed initiation into the local mysteries, left a garrison to protect their mainland possessions, and last, but perhaps not least, supplied 'missiles, catapults, and men to work them' (καὶ βέλη καὶ καταπάλτας καὶ τοὺς χρησομένους τούτοις).[5] Another Samothracian inscription, probably closely related to the one concerning Hippomedon, records a decree honouring the citizen Epinicus. Appointed governor of Maronea by Ptolemy III, he assisted his city against barbarian attacks by sending, among other things, 'catapults, missiles, and men to work them' (καὶ καταπάλτας καὶ βέλη καὶ τοὺς χρησομένου[ς] τούτοις).[6] The artillery of both

---

[1] Plb. v. 88. 8.

[2] Ibid. 89. 9: . . . ῥητίνης καὶ τριχός . . . ταλάντων χιλιάδας. Resin may have been used in the preparation of hair-rope for catapult springs. As far as I know, resin is not mentioned elsewhere in this connection, but Philon (Bel. 61 : ἔλαιον; and 67) recommends letting the spring-cord (sinew, in his case) lie in an oil-bath to 'nourish' it. Since oil and resin both repel water, they would protect the spring from dampness. Perhaps resin was particularly used for springs of hair.

[3] Philon, Bel. 51.

[4] For detailed discussion of the date see Bengtson, Strategie, iii. 178 ff.

[5] Syll.³ i. 502, l. 10.   [6] In AJPh 60 (1939), 452 ff., ll. 21 f.

Hippomedon and Epinicus originated with Ptolemy III, who either sent the catapults direct from his workshops in Alexandria or detached artificers from Egypt to build them on the spot in Samothrace. Whichever course was adopted, the machines would belong, at that time, to the Mark IVA type.

Towards the end of the third century Philip V of Macedon employed artillery frequently and on a fairly large scale. During the winter campaign, 219/18 B.C., he advanced on Psophis in Elis collecting catapults or, at least, the missiles for them from the cities through which he passed.[1] Psophis fell to Philip mainly because the defenders ran out of bolts and shot.[2] In 218 Philip set up arrow-firers and stone-throwers at suitable points round Palus in Cephallenia to prevent the defence interfering with his assault works.[3] The following year Philip laid siege to the Aetolians in Phthiotic Thebes, having prepared the necessary equipment at Larissa during the previous winter. His apparatus included 150 arrow-firing catapults (Mark IVA) and twenty-five stone-throwers (Mark IVB).[4] His employment of artillery at Echinus in 210 B.C. will be discussed later in an examination of that notable siege.[5]

Enough evidence has been presented to show how knowledge of artillery spread throughout the Aegean and eastern Mediterranean areas after the death of Alexander the Great, and how common catapults became not only in the arsenals of the great monarchs but even in relatively unimportant cities.[6] Though the evidence for artillery in the western Mediterranean area is not so extensive or precise, the same state of affairs clearly existed in that region.

§ 4. The Spread of Artillery in the West

Though catapults are not specifically mentioned in connection with Dionysius' series of sieges during the early eighties of the fourth century, he presumably employed non-torsion arrow-firers as he had done previously at Motya (397 B.C.).[7] Recognizing their potential usefulness, city

[1] Plb. iv. 70. 2.   [2] Ibid. 71.
[3] Ibid. v. 4. 6: τὰ βέλη καὶ τοὺς πετροβόλους. In this context βέλη appears to mean arrow-shooting catapults.
[4] Ibid. 99. 7: καταπελτῶν μὲν ἑκατὸν πεντήκοντα πετροβολικῶν δ' ὀργάνων πέντε καὶ εἴκοσι... Walbank, Polybius, 627, draws attention to the proportion between arrow-firers and stone-throwers, 6 : 1, and notes the similar proportion between the two types at New Carthage (Livy, xxvi. 47. 5–6).
[5] See below, p. 109.
[6] In many of the latter cases, as in Samothrace, the artillery may have been provided originally by one of the great monarchs.
[7] D.S. xiv. 103. 3 (Caulonia, 389); 107. 2 (Hipponium, 388); 108. 3 (Rhegium, 388/7). On Motya see below, p. 99.

authorities in Sicily and south Italy would look round for craftsmen to build machines for them. There is at least one example of this procedure. Probably about the middle of the fourth century the artificer Zopyrus of Tarentum designed a mountain-*gastraphetes* (an advanced non-torsion engine) for the city of Cumae in Italy.[1] There is no evidence, of course, as to when, or by what means, the idea of using torsion springs to provide the propulsive force penetrated to the West. However, Agathocles brought down a very large building, obviously a tower, with the aid of a stone-thrower and mining or boring operations during his attack on Croton (*c*. 295 B.C.).[2] His approximately contemporary success at Hipponium (*c*. 294 B.C.) was attributed largely to his stone-throwers.[3] The effectiveness of these pieces of artillery strongly suggests that they were Mark IIIB torsion stone-throwers, so that torsion arrived in Sicily by about 300 B.C.

After they had experienced the first siege ever supported by artillery at Motya in 397 B.C., the Carthaginians no doubt took steps to secure non-torsion catapults. It is not improbable that the Tyrians derived their knowledge of non-torsion machines from their friends in Carthage. At any rate, Tyre possessed a fair number of arrow-shooting engines by 332 B.C. Conversely, after the exploits of Alexander the Great, the Tyrians may have passed back information about torsion artillery to the Carthaginians. The latter certainly owned considerable numbers of catapults early in the third century. When Pyrrhus approached Lilybaeum offensively in 277 B.C., they collected such a tremendous quantity of arrow-shooting catapults and stone-throwers that there was no room for them all on the fortifications.[4] Likewise, they had many engines in the Second Punic War, for Scipio Africanus found in New Carthage in 209 B.C.:

120	catapults	of the larger sort;
281	,,	of the lesser sort;
23	*ballistae*	of the larger sort;
52	,,	of the lesser sort.[5]

---

[1] Biton, W 65. On the date of Zopyrus, see *Technical Treatises*, Biton, n. 52. Expert artificers would seem to have travelled widely in search of employment, for this same Zopyrus built another non-torsion catapult at Miletus (Biton, W 61–2).

[2] D.S. xxi. 4. 1: . . . καὶ διὰ πετροβόλου καὶ διορυχῆς τὸν μέγιστον οἶκον (πύργον, Reiske) καταρράξας . . .

[3] Ibid. 8. 1: ὁ δὲ Ἀγαθοκλῆς πολιορκήσας τῶν Ἱππωνιατῶν πόλιν . . . καὶ διὰ μηχανῶν πετροβόλων τῆς πόλεως ἐκυρίευσαν (-ε ?) καὶ ταύτην εἶλον (-εν ?).

[4] D.S. xxii. 10. 7: τοσοῦτον γὰρ πλῆθος καταπελτῶν ὀξυβελῶν τε καὶ πετροβόλων ἤθροιστο παρὰ Καρχηδονίων ὥστε τὸ τεῖχος μὴ χωρεῖν τὸ πλῆθος τῆς παρασκευῆς.

[5] Livy, xxvi. 47. 5–6. I suggest that the larger catapults were three-cubit, the lesser two-cubit, engines. The larger and smaller *ballistae* may have been one-talent and thirty-mina machines respectively.

He also captured an immense number of large and small scorpions.[1] This is not a bad haul even for what was plainly the main Carthaginian arsenal in Spain.[2] At Carthage itself, somewhat later, they kept an even more impressive store of artillery. Scipio Nasica and Cornelius Hispanus, sent in 149 B.C. to take over the war material which the Carthaginians had agreed to surrender in the hope of preserving peace, received 'about 2,000 arrow-shooting and stone-throwing catapults'.[3] The Carthaginian commissioners who negotiated the hand-over were appalled on reflecting 'that the city was unarmed, destitute, without a ship, without a catapult, without a round of ammunition'.[4]

In fact, numerous stone shot have been found in and around the site of Carthage, 5,600 in all,[5] which, as I understand it, are Punic shot belonging to the period up to the destruction of the city by the Romans in 146 B.C. Analysis of these strikingly reveals the problems that beset the ancient artilleryman. Although the shot can be divided into groups according to their weight and size, the former being by far the more important factor, there is still a significant variation in the weights of shot between the limits chosen for each group. For example, among the stones found at Bardo which Rathgen studied in more detail, 184 belonged to an apparently natural group between $6\frac{1}{2}$ and $7\frac{1}{2}$ kilograms, that is, roughly between 15 and 17 minae.[6] A catapult detachment using a pile of ammunition like this might easily shoot first with a seventeen-mina stone and then proceed to hurl a fifteen-mina shot at the same target. We begin to wonder what effect this had on the accuracy of the shooting. The difficulty was present, of course, wherever stone-throwers were employed.

Ancient artillerymen discovered by experience, I think, what variation in the weight of shot was allowable for a given size of stone-throwing catapult. Provided all their shot belonged within the predetermined weight limits, they could expect to achieve a high percentage of hits on a given

[1] Large scorpions were probably three-span, lesser scorpions one-cubit, arrow-firers.
[2] Plb. x. 8. 3; Livy, xxvi. 43. In this same war the Carthaginian garrison of Capua covered the return of a sallying party successfully with *ballistae* and scorpions (Livy, xxvi. 6. 3–4, 211 B.C.).
[3] App. *Pun.* 80: . . . καὶ καταπέλτας ὀξυβελεῖς τε καὶ λιθοβόλους ἐς δισχιλίους.
[4] Ibid. 82: . . . ὡς ἡ μὲν πόλις ἐστὶν ἄνοπλος, ἔρημος, οὐ ναῦν, οὐ καταπέλτην, οὐ βέλος . . . ἔχουσα. It seems that the Carthaginians only surrendered their catapult bolts. The stone-shot would have been much more difficult to dispose of.
[5] For the evidence and discussion see B. Rathgen, 'Die Punischen Geschosse des Arsenals von Karthago und die Geschosse von Lambaesis', in *Zeitschrift für historische Waffenkunde*, v (Dresden, 1909–11), 236–44; E. von Röder, 'Die Kaliber der antiken Geschütze', ibid. 311 ff.
[6] See the table given by Rathgen, op. cit., 240.

target even if they laid the machine at the same angle of elevation every time and pulled it back by the same amount. In general, stone-throwers engaged large targets—siege-engines, hostile artillery, weak points in fortifications, and groups of soldiers. Also, they operated over relatively modest ranges, up to 400 yards, let us say. It is even possible that an extremely skilful and experienced detachment of artillerymen might learn to appreciate very small differences in the weights of the shot they handled and to make suitable adjustments to their catapult's angle of projection in order to compensate for these differences. Before we attempt to use the shot found at Carthage in order to establish what sizes of stone-throwers were common there in the third and second centuries, we must examine the theories of von Röder and Rathgen on the subject.

The former believed the reconstruction of a table of standard Carthaginian calibres to be impossible, because there was such a tremendous variety in size and weight among the Punic shot. Also, he attached considerable importance to the fact that the stones were not perfectly round, but had a small flattened portion. He concluded that the shot were intended for one-armed stone-throwers (μοναγκῶνες, onagri).[1] For all we know, von Röder could be right. But there is little evidence for the employment of onagri before the fourth century A.D.[2] On the other hand, the terminology used in the references to artillery both at Carthage and at New Carthage, which have been discussed above, does not give the slightest hint that the Carthaginians possessed anything but the standard two-armed arrow-firers and stone-throwers. Further, although the onager can certainly cope with irregularly shaped shot much more easily than ballistae, round stones are still the most suitable and effective.[3] The flat section which appears on all the Carthaginian shot seems to me to have one function only—it stops the stones rolling away from the stock-pile of ammunition at inconvenient moments. It certainly would not help the stones to fit better into the sling of the one-armed engine.

Rathgen starts from the assumption that high-trajectory stone-throwing engines altered range by using heavier or lighter shot.[4] There is, however, no evidence for this procedure, and it seems to be a most inefficient method except in unusual circumstances.[5] Nevertheless, he concludes that

---

[1] Von Röder, op. cit. 311 f. [2] See *Technical Treatises*, The Onager, § 1.

[3] As a matter of fact, Philon (*Pol.* 95. 36–9) specifically recommends hurling irregular (μὴ στρογγύλους) shot from defensive stone-throwers (πετροβόλων, presumably two-armed engines) on to pathways being prepared by besiegers for the approach of mobile siege-machines. Therefore, two-armed stone-throwers were definitely not confined to hurling round shot. [4] Rathgen, op. cit., 240 f.

[5] E.g. an artilleryman might choose a somewhat lighter shot than usual if he wanted to engage a target just beyond the normal maximum range of his machine.

Punic artillery can be divided into three calibres on the basis of the existing shot. Engines of the smallest category hurled stones weighing up to 3·5 kilograms. The machines which Rathgen designates lighter artillery operated with shot varying between 4 and 14 kilograms. Heavier machines used shot weighing from 16 to 40·5 kilograms. This interpretation has very little in common with what we know of the formula for stone-throwers and of their calibres from Philon and Vitruvius.[1] The crux of the matter is this. Rathgen believed that ancient artillerymen altered the range of a stone-thrower entirely by varying the weight of the shot. I believe that they obtained the correct range primarily by elevating or depressing the stock, and only used other methods in exceptional circumstances.

In point of fact, the Carthaginian shot correspond fairly closely in their variations of weight, and in the sizes of machine which they imply, to the balls found at Pergamum.[2] Pergamene shot seem rather more regular and had no flat portion. They generally weighed somewhat lighter than the theoretical calibre for which they were clearly intended, and this characteristic was particularly noticeable with the heavier calibres. It was suggested that the shot were sprinkled with water by the artillerymen to maintain the correct weight for shooting.

At Carthage, at Dr. Petit's house, 50 balls were found weighing between 35 and 40·5 kg. These clearly formed an ammunition dump for a $1\frac{1}{2}$-talent stone-thrower (90 minae = 39·3 kg.); they correspond to the group of 57 shot at Pergamum ranging from 38·7 to 40·0 kg. and attributed to the same calibre. A substantial number of Carthaginian balls (81 from Bardo alone) weighed between 20·0 and 26·0 kg. and belonged to the 1-talent (26·2 kg.) calibre. Pergamene shot numbering 353, from 22·8 to 25·8 kg., were judged to belong to this size of stone-thrower. The excavators at Pergamum ascribed 188 balls, from 16·2 to 20·1 kg., to 3 groups, of which the lightest was intended, they thought, for a presumed $37\frac{1}{2}$-mina stone-thrower. The heaviest group naturally belonged to the standard 40-mina calibre, and the intermediate group was to be divided between the two others. I propose that all these balls were meant for 40-mina stone-throwers, and that the small number of Carthaginian shot weighing from 16·0 to 18·5 kg. also served as ammunition for this calibre (40 minae = 17·5 kg.).

The 30-mina engine was fairly popular at Pergamum (118 balls

---

[1] Philon, *Bel.* 51; Vitr. x. 11. 2–3. See above, pp. 24 ff.

[2] *Alt. Perg.* x. 50–1 (table). The Pergamene calibres are: 10 M (?); 13 M (?); 15 M; 18 M (?); 20 M; 30 M; 37½ M (?); 40 M; 1 T; 65 M (?); 90 M; 105 M; 2 T; 3 T.

between 12·35 and 13·5 kg., the theoretical calibre being 13·1 kg.), and there is some evidence for it at Carthage (shot from 11·5 to 14 kg.). The smallest calibre for which any significant evidence exists at Pergamum is the 20-mina machine (67 balls plus 20 more rather smaller which the excavators attribute, with hesitation, to a presumed 18-mina calibre). At Carthage, however, no fewer than 3,500 balls weighed from 5·0 to 7·5 kg. (11·5–17·1 minae). It is quite possible, I think, that all these shot were intended for machines of 15-mina calibre. Alternatively, it may be that local conditions, the width of the rampart walk, the size of the chambers in the towers, caused the Carthaginians to employ slightly unusual small calibres in order to make the best use of their defences. If so, it is probable that they had one group of 13-mina machines and another of 16-mina engines. One further significant batch of Carthaginian shot, from 4·0 to 4·5 kg., clearly belonged to the 10-mina calibre (4·4 kg.). We can say for certain, therefore, that the Carthaginians regarded stone-throwers of calibres between 10 and 20 minae as the most useful for the defence of their city. At Pergamum heavier calibres were more popular, most probably because the arsenal there concentrated on powerful offensive equipment.[1]

While the Pergamene shot were more carefully worked and more regular than those found at Carthage, 353 stones discovered outside the ancient circuit of Rhodes showed, it has been claimed, even greater refinement.[2] Certainly these Rhodian shot of blue crystalline limestone were carefully inscribed with letters indicating their weight, most of which still show traces of the red paint applied to the incisions to make the weight-marks readily visible.[3] It is most important to note that these

[1] *Alt. Perg.* x. 52 mentions stone-shot found elsewhere; e.g. the largest ball in the Scipionic camp at Numantia belonged to the 10-mina calibre.

At the Musée Borelly, Marseilles, I saw a number of shot, some found in the area of the Gare St. Charles where Caesar's besieging forces had their main camp in 49 B.C., others from Entremont near Aix-en-Provence. I had an average stone of basalt weighed at the local butcher's; it was exactly 7·650 kg., i.e. 17·8 minae. It was probably meant for a 20-mina engine. R. Koldewey, *The Excavations at Babylon* (London, 1915), 50, divides the Greek or Parthian shot found there into three groups, though he provides no numbers. The first of these (20·2 to 20·25 kg.) roughly suits the 50-mina calibre; the second group (7·0 to 7·75 kg.), though somewhat on the light side, suggests 20-mina stone-throwers; finally, balls between 4·0 and 4·5 kg. were intended for 10-mina engines.

[2] A convenient summary of information about the Rhodian shot is supplied by L. Laurenzi, 'Perchè Annibale non assediò Roma', in *Studi Annibalici*, Atti del Convegno svoltosi a Cortona —Tuoro sul Trasimeno—Perugia, Ottobre, 1961 (Cortona, 1964), 141–51.

[3] See *Studi Annibalici*, Tav. 36, figs. 7 and 8. In a short and rather uninformative note (in *BCH*, 1888, 346) H. Lechat recorded a dozen shot found mainly in a big square tower at the Peiraeus. Most of them were no bigger than two fists, as he puts it; but some, if not all, will have been artillery balls. One example had two Δ's inscribed upon it, presumably indicating that it weighed 20 minae. Now the spring-diameter of a 20-mina stone-thrower is 14¾

balls were prepared in accordance with the Attic system of weights (1 mina = 0·436 kg.). Laurenzi points out that there was some irregularity in weight, as we would expect even in the best regulated circles, particularly with the heavy-calibre shot.[1] Also, he rightly observes that the shot of larger calibres were not intended for use with artillery, but simply for dropping on hostile machinery close under the city wall by means of wooden channels.[2] On the basis of the shot found, the most popular calibres at Rhodes appear to have been those of 25 minae (85 shot) and 30 minae (83 shot). There were only seven one-talent balls.

§ 5. *Early Roman Artillery*

An aetiological myth, for which the earliest evidence comes about the middle of the third century A.D., explained that the worship of *Venus Calva* was instituted at Rome after the attack on the city by the Gauls, *c.* 390 B.C. On that occasion Roman matrons were supposed to have contributed their hair for the manufacture, in emergency, of catapult-springs.[3] This story can have no foundation in fact, and probably arose because it was known that, very much later, in a similarly critical situation (148–146 B.C.), the Carthaginian women sacrificed their hair, and that women in other cities had done the same.[4] Livy records that, in 386 B.C., Camillus intended to besiege Antium, but he realized the need for artillery and other machinery and returned to Rome to persuade the senate to support his plan for a methodical assault.[5] It is just conceivable that the Romans had non-torsion artillery at this time;[6] but it would be somewhat surprising in view of the apparent slowness with which catapults spread from Syracuse to more prominent places.

dactyls. Since the diameter of the shot for a given stone-thrower is roughly three-quarters of the spring-diameter, the diameter of a 20-mina shot will be about 11 dactyls, i.e. 8 inches. The diameter of two human fists is 5 to 6 inches so that, if the double delta symbol is on the largest of Lechat's balls, the weight will have been correctly indicated. One other example at the Peiraeus exhibited the symbol Σ. Could this really be *M*, i.e. 1 mina?

[1] The following calibres are represented at Rhodes: 5 M; 10 M; 15 M; 20 M; 25 M; 30 M; 40 M; 50 M; 1 T; 1 T 10 M; 1 T 20 M; 1 T 30 M; 100 M (i.e. 1 T 40 M); 2 T 30 M; 3 T; 3 T 30 M; 4 T 30 M; 6 T; 7 T; 10 T.

[2] Laurenzi (*Studi Annibalici*, 149) regards shot weighing 3 talents and upwards as not meant for artillery. I am inclined to disagree with the inclusion of the 3-talent shot in this non-artillery category, because there is a little evidence for the existence of this artillery calibre (e.g. Archimedes' enormous engine on the great ship 'Syracosia'; see below, p. 91 n. 5) and Rhodian artificers could have constructed such engines if anyone could.

On rolling large balls down wooden runways on to besieging engines see Schramm, *Poliorketik*, 237, and Taf. 24, Abb. 79.

[3] Cypr. *Idol. Van.* ii. 10; Lact. *Div. Inst.* i. 20. 27; Serv. *ad* Verg. *A.* i. 720; Veg. *Mil.* iv. 9.

[4] e.g. at Salonae, Caes. *BC* iii. 9. 3.   [5] Livy, vi. 9. 2.

[6] Livy's word for artillery here (*tormentis*) really indicates torsion engines, but one need not suppose that he was concerned with technical details.

The Romans were certainly familiar with artillery by the time of the first Punic War.[1] At one point a small Roman fleet was proceeding along the southern coast of Sicily; when threatened by a superior Carthaginian squadron, it put in to a bay and beached under cover of the catapults of a small town.[2] In 256 B.C. Regulus took artillery with him on his expedition to Africa, primarily intended, no doubt, for employment in sieges—above all, the attack on Carthage itself. When encamped beside the River Bagradas, his army was plagued by an enormous snake, 120 feet long, which was eventually slain by catapults and *ballistae*. Its jaws and skin were sent back to Rome where they were displayed in a temple at least until 133 B.C. There are many versions of this incident, which created a great impression.[3] It would seem, then, that the Romans began to understand the importance of artillery early in the third century, probably during the war with Pyrrhus and their subsequent close contact with the Greek cities in south Italy. Its use was so general in the Second Punic War that Plautus could make numerous jokes involving artillery and, presumably, could be sure that his audience would appreciate them. For instance, a character in the *Captivi* belligerently observes: 'Meus est ballista pugnus, cubitus catapulta est mihi.'[4]

---

[1] Note a Roman experience in 282 B.C., Frontin. *Strat*. i. 4. 1.

[2] Plb. i. 53. 11. See Walbank, *Polybius*, 117 f.

[3] Gell. vii. 3 (the best account, based on Tubero); Val. Max. i. 8. 19 (taken from Livy); Plin. *NH* viii. 37; Sil. vi. 211 ff. (the most elaborate and bloodthirsty version); also reflected in Sen. *Clem*. i. 25. 4.

The ancients tended to exaggerate the size and capacity of African reptiles. Lucan (ix. 727 ff.), for instance, credited them with the ability to crush and consume not only oxen but even elephants! Other tales are rather less far-fetched. Diodorus tells how a python 20 cubits long was captured in Egypt and transported to Alexandria. Suetonius (*Aug*. 43) mentions a serpent 50 cubits long which Augustus put on show outside the *comitium*. Some modern writers claim to have seen snakes of incredible length; but, on the basis of properly authenticated evidence, zoologists nowadays seem to regard about 30 feet as the maximum length of pythons and related reptiles. While the experts may just be able to concede the existence of snakes 45 or even 75 feet long, almost everyone views with extreme suspicion the 120 feet of the Regulus serpent, even bearing in mind the fact that a snake-skin may expand by as much as a third in length when removed from the body.

The original authority or authorities for the story, who will have seen the serpent's skin in the temple at Rome before 133 B.C., may have written XXX or LXX for the figure CXX which the extant sources give. In any case, we certainly need not disbelieve the presence of artillery in Regulus' expeditionary force or the fact that a large python was killed by Roman artillery in North Africa in 256 B.C., just because the reptile in question has enjoyed posthumous literary elongation.

[4] Plaut. *Capt*. 796. Of course Plautus may well have taken over his references to artillery direct from Greek New Comedy, and we have already noted (see above, p. 59 n. 5) a light-hearted mention of catapults in Mnesimachus' *Philip* (Middle Comedy), so that such jokes may have been common in later Greek Comedy. These things suggest that Athenian audiences were accustomed to, and appreciated, witticisms of this sort in the latter part of the fourth century when, as we have seen (above, pp. 68 ff.), Athens was very interested in producing artillery for defence and in training artillerymen. But the Roman public from the

Second Punic War onwards most probably understood and enjoyed artillery jokes too, for Plautus could easily have omitted them if he thought his audience would find them meaningless.

For Plautine usage with regard to artillery terminology see P. Langen, *Beiträge zur Kritik und Erklärung des Plautus* (Leipzig, 1880), 275. Langen's conclusion, that *catapulta* and *ballista* in Plautus always mean the missiles rather than the machines, is undoubtedly sound. It is also very probable that Plautus means a piece of artillery by the word *ballistarium*, which normally indicates the platform on which machines were mounted. Other references to artillery in Plautus: *Bacch.* 709 f.; *Curc.* 394, 398, 689; *Pers.* 28; *Poen.* 200–2; *Pseud.* 564 f.; *Trin.* 668.

IV

RANGE AND EFFECTS

No satisfactory results have ever been obtained by those who have tried to calculate the ranges of catapults theoretically.[1] The only way to secure reliable figures for range would be to build a full-scale reproduction of a catapult with the greatest care and in accordance with ancient instructions, and then to tune it to the highest pitch. In fact, because Greek and Roman artillery varied in performance according to its size, type, and the stage of construction to which it belonged, it would be necessary, ideally, to construct a whole range of engines. Even then, with the help of modern resources, we should find difficulty in obtaining from our machines the full propulsive power which an ancient technician, steeped in the long practical tradition of artillery craftsmanship, could develop. Schramm made the most important and successful experiments of this kind with a few full-scale models early in the present century. At Heller, near Dresden, his artillery achieved the following ranges:

Machine	Range
Two-cubit arrow-shooting catapult	370 metres
Three-span arrow-shooting catapult (based on the remains found at Ampurias)	305 metres
Small stone-thrower (with $1\frac{1}{2}$-mina stone)	184 metres
Small stone-thrower (with 1-lb. lead shot)	over 300 metres
Smaller *onager*	over 200 metres
Larger *onager*	over 300 metres[2]

In addition, at an unspecified shorter range, a bolt from the two-cubit catapult penetrated an iron-plated shield, 3 centimetres thick, to half its length—far enough, as Diels remarked, to put the man holding the shield out of action. Having constructed a few models myself, and having experienced the practical problems involved in securing high performance,[3] I acknowledge with admiration Schramm's notable achievements. I am certain, however, that it is possible to improve upon his ranges substantially for the following reasons.

[1] These are discussed and criticized by Schramm, *Saalburg*, 27 ff.
[2] Ibid. 29 f.; Diels, *Antike Technik*, 103.
[3] My three-span catapult (see Plate 4), built hastily and powered by springs of weak rubber, much inferior to sinew or hair, shot over 300 yards against the wind when it was new.

Payne-Gallwey constructed an *onager* which hurled an eight-pound shot about 500 yards, and this impressive superiority in performance over Schramm's one-armed stone-thrower was due, as I have suggested elsewhere,[1] to the much greater angle through which the arm and the spring were allowed to operate. In his two-armed, arrow-shooting, euthytone catapults, too, Schramm only seems to have given the arms an angle of $37\frac{1}{2}$ degrees through which to recoil.[2] This is approximately correct for a Mark IIIA or IVA arrow-firer,[3] but the arms of a Vitruvian euthytone can work through an angle exceeding 45 degrees,[4] and this must produce a significant increase in performance. Also, Schramm's interpretation of the design for the hole-carrier (περίτρητον) of a palintone stone-thrower only allows the arms movement through about 45 degrees,[5] whereas it should be possible to produce an angle of 50 degrees.[6] This will again lead to a significantly greater output of power. Incidentally, Schramm's two-armed stone-thrower was a very small one by any standards, and small models usually fail to match the performance of larger originals.

Let us now consider the question of materials for the springs. Schramm did not succeed in an attempt to manufacture sinew-cord;[7] therefore, he used horse-hair and maintained that sinew could not have provided greater power.[8] Of course, the Greeks and Romans employed hair extensively, probably horse-hair as a general rule;[9] but I think sinew must have been at least a little more powerful, and, because supplies of it appear fairly modest in comparison with hair, it was probably reserved for special machines. Heron obviously considered sinew to be the best material for springs,[10] since he includes women's hair more or less as an afterthought in his discussion of the matter.[11] Vitruvius does not distinguish between the merits of hair and sinew, though he indicates that, of the former material, women's hair is the best.[12] In an account of siege-warfare descended ultimately from Hellenistic sources,[13] and perhaps based directly on Frontinus' lost *de re militari*,[14] Vegetius strongly emphasizes the importance of sinew for artillery; to him hair from the manes and tails of

---

[1] See *Technical Treatises*, The Onager, § 3.

[2] Cf. Schramm, *Μονάγκων und Onager*, 267.

[3] See above, p. 21 and fig. 11 (p. 21).

[4] See *Technical Treatises*, Heron's *Cheiroballistra*, fig. 12a.

[5] See Schramm, *Poliorketik*, Abb. 68.   [6] See above, p. 22 and fig. 12 (p. 22).

[7] Schramm, *Saalburg*, 20 n. 5.   [8] Ibid. 29.   [9] See above, p. 75 n. 7.

[10] Heron, *Bel.* W 110, mentions sinews from the shoulders and backs of all animals except pigs.

[11] Ibid. W 112.   [12] Vitr. x. 11. 2

[13] See F. Lammert, 'Die antike Poliorketik und ihr Weiterwirken', in *Klio* 31 (1938), 399 ff.

[14] Schenk, *Vegetius*, 81.

horses is merely a useful substitute, and women's hair is excellent in emergency.[1] Heron's remarks about sinew are summarized by Anonymus Byzantinus, who adds two possible alternatives, silk and hemp.[2] In view of the prominence given to sinew by all the technical writers, it seems clear that this material provided the longest range in practice.

The evidence for range supplied by the ancient sources may now be examined against the background of the figures actually achieved by Schramm and Payne-Gallwey and the above considerations which suggest that Schramm's ranges were rather on the low side. The earliest claim about range is, in fact, also the most extravagant. It was made by Agesistratus and recorded by Athenaeus Mechanicus:

In his 'Artillery', Agesistratus so far surpassed his predecessors that a person passing on the information about him is not easily believed. His three-span catapult shot 700 yards (three and a half stades); its springs weighed twelve minae. His four-cubit, a palintone engine, shot 800 yards (four stades).[3]

Schramm simply did not believe these claims,[4] and most people agree with him. But it is noteworthy that the weight of sinew (12 minae, 5·18 kg.) in the springs of Agesistratus' three-span catapult greatly exceeds the weight of horse-hair (3·5 kg.) that Schramm managed to insert in the springs of his three-span.[5] The difference in material cannot altogether account for the excess. Agesistratus came after a long line of great artificers who spent most of their lives with catapults and other machinery; there are probably few master craftsmen of any sort in the world today who could match his ability, or that of a Ctesibius, or a Dionysius of Alexandria; also, Agesistratus had the advantage of an improved design for the washers (χοινικίδες).[6] Therefore, I believe that the figures mentioned do represent the absolute maximum ranges achieved by him, his machines being laid at an angle of elevation of 45 degrees.

To be effective, however, an arrow-shooting engine must discharge its missile at an angle much nearer the horizontal, and, consequently, its range in action will be distinctly shorter. For instance, if Agesistratus' three-span catapult projected its missile at an angle of 20 degrees, the bolt would travel about 400 yards and be quite effective at that range if it

---

[1] Veg. *Mil.* iv. 9.   [2] Anon. Byz. *Pol.* W 253, 14 ff.

[3] Ath. Mech. W 8. 5–9: ἐν γὰρ τοῖς Βελικοῖς τοσοῦτο τοὺς πρότερον ὑπερήγαγεν ὥστε καὶ τὸν ἐξαγγέλλοντα ὑπὲρ αὐτοῦ μὴ ῥᾳδίως πιστεύεσθαι. ὁ γὰρ τρισπίθαμος αὐτοῦ καταπάλτης ἔβαλλε τρία στάδια καὶ ἡμιστάδιον ἔχων τόνου μνᾶς δυώδεκα. ὁ δὲ τετράπηχος, παλίντονος ὤν, τέσσαρα στάδια. Hultsch, in *RE* Suppl. i (1903), 'Athenaeos (23)', col. 220, denied Wescher's assumption that the words τοῖς Βελικοῖς ('Artillery') indicated the title of a book by Agesistratus, proposing that Athenaeus merely heard him lecture. In that case, Vitruvius must have listened to his lectures too, and must have taken down notes absolutely identical with those of Athenaeus.   [4] Schramm, *Saalburg*, 25 n. 1.   [5] Ibid. 76.   [6] See above, p. 42.

hit something. Philon is much more modest in his statement concerning the range of Dionysius of Alexandria's repeating catapult. 'It shot,' he says, 'at longest range, slightly more than 200 yards [one stade].'[1] We are not told whether this was longest effective, or longest absolute, range. At any rate, its design would obviously not be conducive to long range, and Philon himself continues: 'It has not found a noteworthy use, for we must direct most of our research, as I have strongly insisted, to achieving long range and to tracking down the parts of the engines which impair their efficiency. By the means just mentioned [i.e. the repeating catapult], I see no advance achieved in these respects.' We may justifiably take this to mean that the repeater was substantially inferior in performance to ordinary catapults.

Different sizes of machines had different ranges. Justus Lipsius goes into the matter in some detail and reasonably maintains the view that, among arrow-firers, the scorpion or three-span (probably the larger scorpion) had the longest range.[2] He cites Sisenna's statement: 'longius scorpio catapulta se concitans',[3] and produces two further passages to confirm that the scorpion had an extremely good range. Both occur in Diodorus' description of the siege of Rhodes by Demetrius. The latter put on board his ships, preparatory to attacking the Rhodian harbour, 'those of his three-span arrow-firers that shot the furthest' (τῶν τρισπιθά-μων ὀξυβελῶν τοὺς πορρωτάτω βάλλοντας).[4] When actually inside the harbour, he hindered the Rhodians, who were trying to improve their fortifications in that area, by firing at them with 'the lesser arrow-firers capable of long range' (τοῖς μὲν ἐλάττοσιν ὀξυβελέσι μακρὰν φερομένοις).[5] Neither of these excerpts says in so many words that the three-span engines had longer range than other catapults; but, taken together, they imply that Demetrius, wanting long range, chose the best possible machines for that purpose. It is significant, too, that Agesistratus achieved his range of 700 yards with a three-span machine, having selected that size because it usually shot further than the others.

Stone-throwers, likewise, had ranges varying according to size; but, in their case, it mattered little whether the angle of projection was large or small. The kinetic energy of a missile at any point along its trajectory is given by the formula MV^2 (M = mass of the missile, V = its velocity). If a missile is projected at an angle of 45 degrees, it will meet the earth

---

[1] Philon, *Bel.* 76.

[2] Justus Lipsius, *Poliorceticon*, iii (Antwerp, 1614), 2.

[3] Sisenna, *ap.* Non. 553. 25. Lewis and Short seem in error when they take *scorpio* as the ablative from the form *scorpius* in this context.

[4] D.S. xx. 85. 3.   [5] Ibid. 86. 2.

again at approximately the same angle. It is true that we are only taking gravity into account and are neglecting air-resistance and the factors that affect it; but these things seem pretty well negligible when a comparatively small missile is moving a comparatively short distance. If a missile hits the target a few feet above the earth, it will strike it at an angle of about 45 degrees, and its forward momentum on impact will be half its total

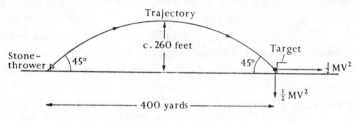

FIG. 1. Trajectory of stone-shot

momentum. For a catapult bolt with a relatively light weight, $\frac{1}{2}MV^2$ will not amount to much, and, of course, its blow will be a glancing one; but a comparatively heavy stone ball, weighing some 30 or 60 minae, will have considerable momentum, so that $\frac{1}{2}MV^2$ on impact will be quite useful. For this reason, there will often be no difference between the actual and the effective maximum ranges of stone-throwers.

When describing the siege of Jerusalem by Titus (A.D. 69), Josephus relates: 'the stone balls that were being hurled weighed one talent [about half a hundredweight] and travelled two or more stades [400 yards or more]'.[1] It seems, however, that they were being used against personnel. Philon provides a better idea of the effective range of the one-talent engine when trained against a wall. He explains that it is essential to have at least three ditches in front of all fortifications.[2] According to his measurements, the exterior lip of the outermost ditch must be at least 178 yards away from the city wall. 'If ditches of this size and type have been dug, they will not be filled in quickly, and the one-talent stone-thrower, which is the most powerful, will either not get near the wall or, being deprived of support,[3] will topple over.'[4] Probably a large stone-thrower had to stand within 150 yards of a wall to be effective, the

[1] Joseph. *BJ* v. 270.
[2] Philon, *Pol.* 84. 43 ff. On an artillery fortification incorporating a ditch-system very similar to Philon's see A. W. Lawrence, 'Archimedes and the design of the Euryalus fort', in *JHS* 66 (1948), 103 ff.
[3] *LS*, s.v. ἔκλυτος, gives 'deprived of force' as the meaning in the present context. But there is obviously no question of the power of the engine being affected. It just could not find a sufficiently large and stable platform.
[4] Philon, *Pol.* 85. 6 ff.

machine being forced to shoot at a very low angle of elevation so that its shot would have the maximum possible forward momentum.

Though the one-talent stone-thrower was the most useful against fortifications, the engine that carried the palm for all-round efficiency (except against walls, though perhaps fairly effective against battlements) was the 30-mina stone-thrower. 'Above all', insists Philon, in

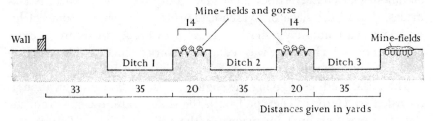

FIG. 2. Philon's ditch-system

advice to defenders, 'you must take most care of your 30-mina engines.'[1] 'They have the most appropriate dimensions and are the most forceful in their blows.'[2] This calibre was particularly useful against hostile machinery, approach-works, and personnel.[3] Its popularity is further attested by the numbers of shot belonging to it (83 out of 353 at Rhodes; 118 at Pergamum).

We may conclude, then, that arrow-shooting and stone-throwing catapults could operate normally up to 400 yards. Particularly powerful machines were perhaps effective at a range of 500 yards, especially after the introduction of the modifications included in Vitruvius' account.[4] Certainly, I think that the arrow-shooting *ballistae* issued to the Roman army after A.D. 100 would be effective at 500 yards. But against reasonably solid fortifications nothing less than a one-talent engine within 150 yards would be much use.[5]

There are two possible ways of altering the range of a piece of ancient artillery. Firstly, we can pull back the arms to varying distances or tighten the springs to varying degrees, while maintaining the same angle of projection. Secondly, we can change the angle of elevation, while keeping to the same amount of pull-back and retaining the same tension

[1] Philon, *Pol.* 95, 49 ff.   [2] Ibid. 96. 10 ff.
[3] See below, p. 114.   [4] See above, pp. 41 ff.
[5] On suggested ranges for the earlier non-torsion machines see above, pp. 12, 15. For further remarks on the range of torsion artillery see Schambach, *Bemerkungen*, 16 f. The large double-purpose engine, built by Archimedes and mounted on Hieron's great ship 'Syracosia' (Moschion, *ap.* Ath. 208c), could hurl either a three-talent shot or a twelve-cubit bolt to a range of 200 yards (one stade).

in the springs. There are only one or two negligible hints, as far as I know, to indicate the former method was ever used.[1] Since ancient artillerymen always desired the blow to be as powerful as possible, they would draw their engine back to its most efficient extent on almost all occasions and keep the springs at the tension required to provide the maximum propulsive force. But they did alter the design of certain machines in order to obtain special characteristics for a given purpose. For instance, Archimedes, during the siege of Syracuse (213–211 B.C.), made some of his scorpions with unusually short springs (βραχύτονοι) to secure a more powerful blow.[2] The range was reduced in consequence; but he was prepared to sacrifice this because he did not need it for his object.

The usual method of laying the engines, both for line and elevation, is recorded by Heron: 'They pull back the slider, raise the case from the rest, traverse [for line] by means of the universal joint, depress and elevate through the pin ΥΦ, look along at the target, load the missile, and pull the trigger.'[3] Elsewhere, he informs us: 'We shall aim at the target by looking down the length of the case [i.e. the stock].'[4] The word for 'look along' and 'looking down' is διοπτεύειν, which corresponds to Philon's word for the aperture between the centre-stanchions (or in the middle of a Vitruvian composite centre-stanchion), διόπτρα, the window.[5] This served two purposes, of which the essential one was to allow the missile to fly out at the front; but also, as the term implies, it was the only approximation to a sighting arrangement which the ancients had. In point of fact, formal sights were not introduced in gunpowder artillery until 1801, before which time sighting had been accomplished by looking along the 'line of the metal', that is, the outside edge of the barrel. For arrow-shooting catapults the window offered a fairly satisfactory method of aiming. But it could not usually be applied in the case of stone-throwers, where the normal angle of projection tended to exceed 30 degrees. It is possible that stone-throwers were roughly aligned on the target, and that adjustments were made after observation of the fall of shot.

Modern field guns are mostly engaged with targets which are not

---

[1] Cic. Tusc. ii. 24. 57: 'ut enim ballistae lapidum, et reliqua tormenta telorum eo graviores emissiones habent, quo sunt contenta atque adducta vehementius.' Hier. adv. Jovin. (ed. Migne, 22), i. 3: 'ballista (probably the arrow-shooting ballista of the Roman empire) quanto plus retrahitur tanto fortius mittit.'

[2] Plut. Marc. 15. For another method of securing a powerful blow see Philon, Bel. 53, and Vitr. x. 10. 6: 'bracchii brevitas facit plagam vehementiorem.'

[3] Heron, Bel. W 89.

[4] Ibid. W 86, 7: διὰ γὰρ τοῦ μήκους τῆς σύριγγος διοπτεύοντες ἐπιτευξόμεθα τοῦ σκοποῦ.

[5] Philon, Bel. 64.

visible from the gun-position, and their fire must be directed from a distance by an officer who can see the target. The ancient artilleryman,
however, could simply peep round the shield of his machine after firing
and observe, from a few hundred yards away, exactly where his shot fell.
An illuminating passage from Lucan may supply confirmation of this
view. In the first sea-battle off Massilia, between Decimus Brutus and the
city's navy in 49 B.C., a certain Massiliot, Tyrrhenus, lost his sight when
hit on the temple by a sling-bullet. Not wishing to miss any of the
engagement:

> 'Vos', ait, 'O socii, sicut tormenta soletis,
> me quoque mittendis rectum componite telis'.[1]

It is probably justifiable to assume that Tyrrhenus expected his comrades
not only to point him in the right direction, but also to observe his performance and tell him what adjustments to make so that he could hit the
enemy. There is no doubt that efforts were made by the defence to observe the flight of hostile shot so that warning of its approach could be
given.[2]

There is good reason for supposing that ancient pieces of artillery were
extremely accurate.[3] The Rhodians not only managed to knock off some
of the iron plates from Demetrius' *helepolis* (304 B.C.), which required a
steady stream of balls on the same spot, but also had no difficulty in
directing blazing bolts at the wooden framework thus exposed and setting
it alight.[4] Caesar reported an excellent piece of sharp-shooting at the
siege of Avaricum, three bull's-eyes, perhaps more, possibly in the same
number of shots:

> Visum praetereundum non existimavimus. Quidam ante portam oppidi
> Gallus per manus sebi ac picis traditas glaebas in ignem e regione turris
> proiciebat: scorpione ab latere dextro traiectus exanimatusque concidit . . .
> eadem ratione ictu scorpionis exanimato alteri successit tertius et tertio quartus.[5]

It is important to note here that Caesar records the incident not as an

---

[1] Luc. iii. 716 f.

[2] *BHisp* 13. 7: 'ita corona circumdata pugnatum est aliquamdiu vehementissime, simulque
ballista missa a nostris turrem deiecit, qua adversariorum qui in ea turre fuerant quinque
deiecti sunt et puer, qui ballistam solitus erat observare'; Joseph. *BJ* v. 271 ff.

[3] I cannot wholly agree with the views of Schramm (*Saalburg*, 25 f.), who believed that
artillery normally operated at a range of 150 yards and that, at greater ranges, accuracy
was so poor that only large targets (e.g. groups of people) were engaged. It is true that
stone-throwers shot at large targets, one difficulty being the variations in the weights of shot
available. But I think artillerymen who had lived with arrow-shooting and stone-throwing
catapults for several years, shooting constantly in practice and in action, would have been
able to do remarkable things even at ranges in the region of 400 yards.

[4] D.S. xx. 96. 6–7.

[5] Caes. *BG* vii. 25. 2–3.

outstanding instance of accurate shooting, but as an example of the desperate efforts the Gauls were prepared to make at what they regarded as the turning-point in the siege. The scorpion could not fail to hit them—there was nothing extraordinary about that; but a few Gauls were still ready to sacrifice their lives for the safety of Avaricum.

Was this scorpion a repeater like the one described by Philon?[1] There is no reason why it need have been, because experience with a full-scale model of a three-span arrow-firer has shown that the pulling back, loading, and shooting of a small engine is by no means a long process. One minute is a very generous time to allow for each aimed shot. Philon complains that the repeater's ability to shoot a large number of missiles rapidly at a given target is, if anything, a disadvantage. He continues:

> Perhaps the argument that it is useful for firing into a group would persuade many; but this, too, will be found untenable. The missiles will not have a spread, since the window [or aperture] has been laid on a single target and produces a trajectory more or less along one segment of a circle; nor will they have a very elongated dropping zone.[2]

The shells from a twenty-five-pounder field gun, firing at a range of, say, 5,000 yards, do not land on the same spot. The 100-per-cent zone at this range, that is, the area within which all shells fired at the same angle of projection will land, can be represented by the rectangle illustrated below. Strange as it may seem, this is an excellent characteristic of the

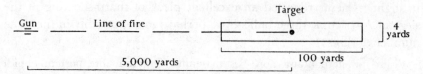

FIG. 3. Plan of 100-per-cent zone of field gun shooting at a range of 5,000 yards.

twenty-five-pounder's performance, for field guns are normally used for plastering an area or taking part in a barrage. Philon criticizes the repeating catapult because its missiles did not spread out either laterally or longitudinally—in other words, it was too precise. Schramm's model of the repeater confirmed this precision.[3] If anything, it would be less accurate than ordinary catapults; but the latter did not waste several shots on a single target. I suggest, then, that ancient artillery, when operated by skilful hands, could achieve a high standard of accuracy right up to maximum effective range.

[1] i.e. Dionysius of Alexandria's πολυβόλος, Philon, Bel. 73.   [2] Ibid. 76.
[3] Schramm, Saalburg, 62; see Technical Treatises, Philon, n. 125.

The best way of discovering how valuable pieces of artillery are is to study their effects. Most people will agree that, in the case of artillery in every age, the difference between promise and performance is somewhat disappointing. But the effectiveness of artillery must not be measured by its capacity for destruction alone. Effects may be divided into two main sections, actual and moral. The latter may be subdivided into two further parts, moral effect of artillery on the troops which it is supporting and its moral effect on the enemy. In some ways, the impression artillery makes on morale is just as important, if not more so, than the actual destruction it causes.

First, let us see what ancient artillery could actually do. Having mentioned the range attained by the stone-throwers of the tenth legion at Jerusalem (A.D. 70), Josephus continues: 'and their impact was not only irresistible to the front rank, but also to the men behind, to a considerable distance'.[1] At 400 yards, the one-talent shot ploughed its way through several ranks. Moreover, at the siege of Jotapata in Galilee, where Josephus was in command of the city against Vespasian, he tells us that one of his friends, who was standing beside him on the walls of the city, had his head snapped off suddenly by a ball from a stone-thrower; the head was thrown three stades.[2] At the siege of Massilia (49 B.C.) Caesar comments on the excellence of the town's war-apparatus. No light sheds (*vineae*) could stand up to its artillery: 'Asseres enim pedum XII cuspidibus praefixi atque hi maximis ballistis missi per IV ordines cratium in terra defigebantur.'[3] The Massiliots were using palintone engines for shooting huge bolts with tremendous force, just as Agesistratus employed a palintone to achieve his range of 800 yards with a four-cubit bolt. Lucan refers to the same incident at Massilia, but relates a different effect:

> Sed maior Graio Romana in corpora ferro
> vis inerat. Nec enim solis excussa lacertis
> lancea, sed tenso ballistae turbine rapta
> haud unum contenta latus transire quiescit;
> sed pandens perque arma viam perque ossa relicta
> morte fugit, superest telo post vulnera cursus.[4]

Alexander the Great was fortunate to escape this sort of death at Gaza (332 B.C.). He successfully stemmed a retreat; 'but was himself struck by a catapult bolt right through his shield and breastplate and into his

[1] Joseph. *BJ* v. 270.
[2] Ibid. iii. 245. The three stades is hard to swallow; but a head could easily be smashed at 400 yards. Perhaps Josephus actually wrote 3 plethra, not stades; i.e. 100 yards (three times 100 feet).
[3] Caes. *BC* ii. 2. 2. [4] Luc. iii. 463 ff.

shoulder'.[1] Another impressive story is told by Procopius, the artillery in question being a Roman arrow-shooting *ballista*. During Vitiges' siege of Rome (A.D. 536) a Goth was hit by a bolt as he sat half-way up a tree, shooting arrows from a hand-bow. The bolt nailed him to the tree and he hung there, pinned to the trunk.[2] These scraps of information afford some idea of what artillery could do against personnel.

A somewhat macabre find from the excavations at Maiden Castle in Dorset strikingly illustrates what the literary sources have to say about the effect of catapult bolts, reminds us of a fragment from the comic poet Caecilius Statius,[3] and proves the accuracy of Lucan's account, just quoted. Around the east gate a number of skeletons and arrow-heads came to light—relics of the Roman attack on the hill-top fort which was one of the twenty towns that Suetonius says Vespasian destroyed on his march south-west from London with *legio II Augusta* in the early years of the invasion of Britain.[4] One skull (see below, Plate 5) had a square hole in its temporal left squama.[5] It seems fairly certain that this could only have been caused by a bolt from a catapult. Roman bolt-heads had a square cross-section at their bases, and several were found near the skull which fit the hole exactly. Moreover, the missile must have been moving at high speed to pierce the bone without shattering it, which is what would probably have happened if the missile had been an arrow from an ordinary hand-bow.

One artificer, Zoilus of Cyprus, produced two breastplates ($\theta\acute{\omega}\rho\alpha\kappa\epsilon\varsigma$) that could resist a catapult-bolt and provided a demonstration of their efficiency in which a bolt was shot from a machine at one of them at a distance of twenty paces. The only effect was a small scratch.[6] The catapult employed by Zoilus would have been a Mark IIIA arrow-firer, not necessarily a very efficient machine; and he would not, I imagine, have gone out of his way to find a particularly powerful catapult for the demonstration. Demetrius Poliorcetes acquired both breastplates when he was besieging Rhodes, wearing one himself, and giving the other to a prominent soldier. It is always possible, of course, to find some counter even to the most devastating weapons, and it is significant that only two breastplates of this type were available. A few years later, Demetrius had a lucky escape at the siege of Thebes (290 B.C.) when a catapult bolt

[1] Arr. *Anab.* ii. 27. 2. The machine was probably a non-torsion catapult.
[2] Procop. v. 23. 9–12.
[3] Caecil. fr. 27 Ribbeck[3] (from the *Demandati*) : 'si unquam quisquam vidit quem catapulta aut ballista icerit'.   [4] Suet. *Vesp.* 4. 1.
[5] Wheeler, *Maiden Castle*, 63 and 119 (text); 282, fig. 93 (bolt- and arrow-heads); 351, pl. liiiᴅ (the skull). See Plate 5, below.
[6] Plut. *Demetr.* 20. 3–4.

struck him in the neck.[1] We are not told whether he was wearing his special breastplate, but, even if he had been, it would not have helped him much.

The effects achieved by stone-throwers, when firing at walls, will be discussed in the next chapter. But, since the first half of Philon's seventh book (παρασκευαστικά) is devoted almost exclusively to wall-building with a view to withstanding stone-throwers, it seems that their blows were not to be despised. He recommends 10 cubits (about 15 feet) as a thickness which would be unaffected by stone-shot.[2] At the very least, therefore, it may be said that stone-throwers had some effect against walls of dimensions less than those suggested by Philon.

Let us now investigate the moral effects of artillery and, first, how it improved the morale of its own troops. In the case of modern guns, both the noise and appearance are comforting and inspiring. Obviously, ancient weapons could not compete with the modern ones for noise of discharge; but a passage from Seneca proves that they did make some noise as they fired: 'nam ballistae quoque et scorpiones tela cum sonitu expellunt.'[3] It would be surprising if this noise did not produce, on a small scale, the same feelings in soldiers of ancient times as the explosions of their own guns provoke in modern soldiers. But, in old times, confidence and morale were increased principally by the appearance of the artillery and the sight of the damage it wrought. That is why Philon, when introducing a new type of engine, claims: 'It has an appearance not a whit less awe-inspiring than the others', and later hastens to assure his reader that it 'would be no less imposing than that of the older machines'.[4] Speaking of a cover for the frame, he continues: 'Let it be of elm or of ash wood, or anything one prefers for the sake of appearance.'[5] If the engines on one's own side are 'awe-inspiring' and 'imposing', the troops must advance with greater confidence.

Conversely, the enemy will be downcast by the sight of fine engines arrayed against them. The noise of shooting may have had some influence, while the noise of the missile on impact was certainly discouraging. Archimedes threw at the Romans 'immense masses of stone that came down with incredible noise and violence'.[6] The most considerable moral effects, however, are those which follow immediately upon ridiculously small actual effects. Alexander the Great, for example, wished to cross the River Jaxartes in Russian Turkestan in the face of Scythian

---

[1] Ibid. 40. 3.   [2] Philon, *Par.* 80. 45 ff.
[3] Sen. *Q.N.* ii. 16.   [4] Philon, *Bel.* 56; 61.
[5] Ibid. 62. For a reconstruction of this cover, see *Technical Treatises*, Philon, diag. 7.
[6] Plut. *Marc.* 15. 1.

forces on the opposite side. In order to clear a space for landing, he stationed his artillery along the river and 'the machines kept firing salvoes at the Scythians riding along the bank, of whom some were wounded by the missiles and one, stricken right through his shield and breastplate, fell from his horse. Thereupon, terrified by the range of the missiles and because a noted warrior had fallen, they retired from the bank a little.'[1] The actual effects were one man dead and a few wounded; but the moral effect led to withdrawal from the bank and the achievement of the object. This is a fine example because it shows the proportion between the actual and the moral elements in the complete effect of artillery.

Admittedly, the enemy on that occasion were not accustomed to artillery, and equally successful results could not really be expected against soldiers trained to face it. But this objection cannot be raised in the case of a similar incident during the Civil War in Africa which is recorded by Hirtius and concerns Roman cavalry: 'A scorpion bolt was discharged rather accurately; their officer was hit and nailed to the ground; the remainder fled back to camp, thoroughly panic-stricken.'[2] Again, the moral effect was much greater than the actual. At the siege of Adrianople by the Goths in A.D. 378 the defenders hurled a huge stone ball from an *onager* at a dense group of Goths. The shot fell harmlessly to the ground, but Ammianus reports: 'visus tamen ita eos metu exanimavit, ut stupore spectaculi novi, cedentes e medio, abire temptarent.'[3]

Thus, ancient pieces of artillery had a useful range, reasonable accuracy in the hands of skilled layers, and could often achieve impressive results. Intelligently used, they could contribute significantly to the success of a military operation. Above all, their moral effect must be stressed and, if not specifically mentioned, can usually be inferred from the account of an action. There can be no more noteworthy example of the effect of artillery and the genius of that famous artificer Archimedes than the words of Plutarch explaining why Marcellus abandoned active assault on Syracuse:

In fine, when such terror had seized upon the Romans that, if they did but see a little rope or a piece of wood from the wall, instantly crying out that there it was again, Archimedes was about to let fly some engine at them, they turned their backs and fled, Marcellus desisted from conflicts and assaults, putting all his hope in a long siege.[4]

[1] Arr. *Anab.* iv. 4. 4.
[2] *BAfr* 29. 3: '... scorpione accuratius misso, atque eorum decurione percusso et ad terram defixo, reliqui perterriti fuga se in castra recipiunt.'
[3] Amm. xxxi. 15. 12.   [4] Plut. *Marc.* 17. 3 (Dryden's translation).

V

ARTILLERY IN SIEGES

ARTILLERY is a supporting arm. By itself it cannot win battles or take cities, for, in all cases, the final blow must be delivered by infantry and cavalry. But artillery enables the force which it is supporting to achieve with a minimum of loss an object which, without that support, would have been either attainable only with heavy sacrifice or even absolutely impossible. Modern artillery assists by a variety of methods which can, however, be conveniently reduced to two, destruction and neutralization. It may try to destroy the enemy and his material, or it may endeavour simply to keep him occupied and prevent him paying too much attention to the troops it is supporting. The latter process, neutralization, naturally involves casualties and damage, but these effects are not the primary purpose of the shooting. It will be interesting to see how far the Greeks and Romans subscribed to these ideas in sieges.

First, we shall analyse, from the point of view of artillery, the accounts of a selection of important Greek and Roman sieges during the last four centuries B.C. Then the use of artillery in practice will be compared with the theoretical advice of Philon. The sieges considered are: Motya (397); Perinthus (340); Halicarnassus (334); Tyre and Gaza (332); Megalopolis (314); Munychia and Cyprian Salamis (307); Rhodes (305–304); Syracuse (213–211); Echinus (210); Carthage (147–146); Athens–Peiraeus (87–86); Massilia (49). All the principal uses of artillery in static warfare are illustrated in the history of these operations. It is as well to bear in mind that all sieges can be considered from two angles, that of the besieger and that of the besieged.

§ 1. *Analysis of Sieges*

The first siege in which artillery ever participated was the assault on Motya, the Carthaginian island fortress at the west end of Sicily. Dionysius I of Syracuse commenced his attack in 397 and, owing to the nature of the place, had to build a mole out to the island. 'He gradually brought his machines towards the wall in proportion as the mole increased.'[1] Reaching the wall eventually, he applied his rams; 'but, with the catapults, he forced back those fighting on the ramparts.'[2] Mobile towers of six storeys were employed, yet we are not told whether the artillery was in them or not. The besieged had no answer, and Motya fell. Bolt-shooting non-torsion artillery, that is, *gastraphetae* and, perhaps, early advanced non-torsion catapults of small calibre, simply provided covering fire.

Although advanced non-torsion engines, now including stone-throwers, had certainly been developed by the middle of the fourth century, Aeneas Tacticus, who wrote a treatise on the subject of city defence about that time, only mentioned artillery once.[3] We should probably not attach too much importance to this neglect of catapults, because he was an expert in intrigue rather than armament. On the other hand, it is possible that the constructional development and the diffusion of artillery had not yet reached a stage which would justify more extensive treatment of the subject. Certainly, he could not have virtually ignored artillery if he had written a decade or so later.

In some ways Philip II of Macedon's siege of Perinthus (340) followed much the same lines as that of Motya. He constructed eighty-cubit (120-feet) siege-towers which far exceeded the towers of the city in height.[4] The walls were shaken with rams and undermined by means of galleries. Meanwhile, 'the king, who had many arrow-shooting catapults of all sizes, destroyed with these the enemy fighting on the battlements, so the Perinthians, after experiencing many losses every day, secured alliance, missiles, and catapults, from the Byzantines'.[5] Thus, the besieged had soon realized that the most satisfactory reply to a hail of bolts was a return of the compliment in kind; but the fact that Perinthus, a fairly important city, had no catapults of her own indicates that artillery had

---

[1] D.S. xiv. 49. 3. The machines were the mobile siege-towers. On this siege in general see J. I. S. Whitaker, *Motya* (London, 1921), 75 ff. Recent investigations on the site are recorded in the *Illustrated London News* of 21 September 1963, 425 ff.: a splendid air-photograph shows the causeway linking the island to the mainland (*c.* 1,860 yards long); it is suggested that Dionysius probably repaired this causeway and made it the basis of his mole; eighteen bronze and iron arrow-heads were found that had apparently rebounded off the fortifications at the time of the siege. I am inclined to wonder whether some of these might not be the heads of bolts projected from *gastraphetae*.

[2] D.S. xiv. 51. 1.

[3] Aen. *Tact.* 32. 8. On Aeneas' work and date see Tarn, *HMND* 102 and 105; L. W. Hunter, *Aeneas on Siegecraft* (Oxford, 1927), xi ff.

[4] Philip's towers no doubt caused the Perinthians to experience the feelings indicated by Vegetius, *Mil.* iv. 17: 'quid enim auxilii superest, cum hi, qui de murorum altitudine sperabant, repente supra se aspiciant altiorem hostium murum?' On the siege of Perinthus see F. R. Wüst, *Philipp II. von Macedonien und Griechenland* (Munich, 1938), 123 ff.

[5] D.S. xvi. 74. 4.

not yet spread very widely. The borrowed equipment seems to have done something to restore the situation and the experience of a soldier, Antigenes, who was hit in the eye by a catapult bolt in this siege, who but survived to accompany Alexander to Asia, bears witness to the accuracy of the Perinthian shooting, which was apparently supporting a sally.[1]

Philip's store of ammunition and engines was considerable, however, and he perhaps had the benefit of Mark II torsion catapults as against the Byzantine non-torsion machines. 'He beat the walls continuously with rams and brought them down; also, he restrained the men on the battlements by means of his arrow-shooting catapults.'[2] This gives a very neat picture of early siege-methods with artillery—the catapults neutralize the defence, rams destroy the walls. Arrow-firers only were employed, and the siege was unsuccessful. It has been reasonably suggested that it failed because of the activity of the inhabitants, the splendid position, the fortifications, and the assistance supplied by Byzantium and Persia; all these things outweighed Philip's tactical ability and siege-technique.[3] It may be, however, that the available siege-appliances were not yet efficient enough to give the besieger a full opportunity to exploit decisively the natural advantages of his position.[4]

The siege of Halicarnassus by Alexander (334) marks the beginning of a transition to a new stage in the development of siege-technique supported by artillery. For the first time the use of stone-throwers in operations before a city is recorded. One of the Persian sallies was repulsed by other means and also 'by large stones flying from the machines on the towers and by the shooting of bolts'.[5] In addition to using siege-towers, Alexander filled in the ditch, 30 cubits wide by 15 deep (45 by 22½ feet), with mobile siege-sheds of a type expressly designed for this purpose (χωστρίσι χελώναις),[6] so that his rams could reach the walls. He used his stone-throwers against personnel, just like the arrow-firers, but in other respects followed the old procedure. The Persian defenders made several sallies, supported by arrow-firers (probably non-torsion engines),[7] and, when part of their wall was breached, built another inside which incorporated a tower 100 cubits in height (150 feet), full of arrow-firers,[8] to repel the assaults coming over the dilapidated wall in front. They also set the besieging machines on fire, not by shooting blazing bolts, but by making sallies with torches in their hands. Therefore, covering fire seems to have been the dominant role of artillery still, though it was

---

[1] Plut. *Alex.* 70. 3.   [2] D.S. xvi. 75. 3.   [3] So Wüst, op. cit. 130.
[4] On these advantages see the neat summary by Schambach, *Bemerkungen*, 8 f.
[5] Arr. *Anab.* i. 22. 2.   [6] D.S. xvii. 24. 4.   [7] Ibid. 6.
[8] Ibid. 26. 6.

particularly applied to the support and repulse of sallies and stone-throwers came into the picture.

Alexander was successful; but, by comparing the accounts of Arrian and Diodorus, we can see that he had a difficult time, and the experience gained here undoubtedly stood him in good stead at Tyre (332) which was his masterpiece. Tyre was in an excellent natural position, in those days, on an island like Motya, and could boast a substantial armament of catapults (probably non-torsion) and other machines, which filled the whole perimeter of the city.[1] It was plainly a hard nut to crack. Alexander began to construct a mole, on the end of which he had two towers which were fitted with hide coverings 'so that they could not be damaged by flaming missiles shot from the wall'.[2] When the mole came within range of the city, he put machines on the end of it, 'and with his stone-throwers tried to beat down the wall, while he interfered with the personnel standing on the battlements by means of his arrow-firers'.[3] Against this barrage the Tyrians took anti-catapult measures, making huge wheels which whirled round and stopped or broke the bolts, while buffers lessened the force of the stone shot.[4] In spite of these precautions, the Macedonian shooting must have had serious effects because the Tyrians made a rather desperate sally by sea, in which they succeeded in burning the towers on the mole with fire-ships.[5]

Alexander repaired the mole, widening it at the same time, and arranged for the construction of more towers and machines.[6] He also set out to collect a fleet, for the obvious reason that he wished to prevent the Tyrians having free access to the sea, but, in addition, because he wanted to avail himself of the privilege of all attackers—the right to choose the point where they will make the assault. His previous efforts had been confined to the small length of wall opposite the mole where the enemy naturally exerted all their energy with a view to strengthening that part of the perimeter. Wishing to test the wall where it might not be so carefully constructed and improved, Alexander fitted his horse-transports and the slower triremes with machines, so that he could approach it anywhere.[7]

Arrian does not tell us precisely what the ship-mounted machines consisted of; but one passage seems to imply that the ships had some stone-throwers on board. Apparently they found difficulty in approaching the

[1] D.S. xvii. 41. 3.   [2] Arr. Anab. ii. 18. 6.   [3] D.S. xvii. 42. 7.
[4] Ibid. 43. 1.   [5] Arr. Anab. ii. 19. 1–5.
[6] Ibid. 6. Some of the siege-towers used here may well have been constructed to the design of Poseidonius, of which we have a description in Biton, W 51. See Technical Treatises, Biton, diag. 3.   [7] Arr. Anab. ii. 21. 1–2.

Tyrian circuit at some points because of heaps of stones which lay at the base of the wall under the sea. The heaps were cleared away as follows:

ἐξάπτοντες οὖν βρόχους τῶν λίθων ἀπὸ τοῦ χώματος ἀνέσπων αὐτοὺς ἔξω τῆς θαλάσσης. ἔπειτα μηχαναῖς μετεωρίσαντες κατὰ βάθος ἀφίεσαν, ἵνα οὐκέτι προβεβλημένοι βλάψειν ἔμελλον.[1]

Most reasonably interpreted, this means that stones in the sea round Tyre formed a mound (χώματος is not Alexander's mole), from which the ships dragged with nooses as many as necessary to make sufficient draught for themselves, and that they hurled them off into the open sea with stone-throwers (strongly implied by the word ἀφίεσαν), so that they would not be in the way again. This passage offers important corroboration of the much more numerous references to artillery, stone-throwers in particular, which Diodorus supplies.

Alexander could then test the wall of Tyre at various points with both rams and stone-throwers, and his mole eventually reached the city.[2] He shook the fortifications at a number of points with his stone-throwers, while his arrow-firers, set up in the wooden towers, wounded the rampart fighters.[3] Finding a weak stretch of wall by the Egyptian harbour on the south side of the city, he concentrated his efforts in that area, and the machines on the ships made a substantial breach. He then withdrew these vessels and brought up others carrying drawbridges, which assisted the marines to land in the breach.[4] While he delivered his main assault here, other ships were ordered to heave to at different places round the walls and create diversions. This assault proved successful.

The siege of Tyre is of prime importance because stone-throwers were employed to shake walls for the first time. The besieged used blazing bolts (πυρφόροι) against towers and ships.[5] Arrow-firers again provided covering fire, some being housed in the towers on the mole. The excellence of Alexander's siege-apparatus, particularly his artillery, and the way in which it was handled constituted the two vital factors in the capture of an almost impregnable city.

After this grim struggle, Alexander took Gaza with relative ease. Diodorus dismisses the siege in a single sentence.[6] Arrian is detailed

[1] Ibid. 21. 7.   [2] D.S. xvii. 43. 5.   [3] Ibid. 45. 2.
[4] Arr. *Anab.* ii. 23. 1–2. On drawbridges (ἐπιβάθραι) and *sambuca* see *Technical Treatises*, Biton, n. 37. Diades, one of Alexander's leading engineers, claimed to have invented the ἐπιβάθρα (Ath. *Mech.* W 10. 10 ff.), and this was probably the occasion on which he did it. An ancient list of famous engineers, *Laterculi Alexandrini*, called Diades—justifiably, it would seem—'the man who took Tyre with Alexander' (see Diels, *Antike Technik*, 30; Tarn, *HMND* 107).
[5] Arr. *Anab.* ii. 21. 2.   [6] D.S. xvii. 48. 7.

enough, but shows his usual tendency to include all siege-engines in the vague term 'machines'. Alexander brought his siege-train from Tyre by sea and built a circular mound to bring his machinery level with the town which was on a plateau 250 feet high. His machines and mines effected a breach, while his arrow-firers gave valuable covering fire.[1] The men of Gaza had catapults, probably non-torsion engines, which they used in support of a sally, and Alexander was wounded by a bolt when trying to repel it.[2]

Alexander unquestionably exhibited tenacity, energy, and tactical skill in the conduct of sieges; but Philip II had surely possessed the same qualities to an approximately equal degree. The former owed his greater success to the superior siege-machines and artillery (especially the recently developed Mark IIIB stone-throwers) with which his artificers, Diades and Charias, the pupils of Philip's Polyidus, and other engineers like the shadowy Poseidonius, were now able to provide him.

Polysperchon's attack on Megalopolis arouses interest chiefly because he employed elephants—not a normal siege-weapon. Before his army arrived on the scene, the Megalopolitans had a brief chance to make hasty preparations and, among other things, they constructed some arrow-shooting catapults.[3] Even at this early stage they expressed concern at the size of Polysperchon's force and at the prospect of facing elephants.[4] Although the Macedonian general built siege-towers and equipped them with all sorts and sizes of artillery in order to neutralize the defenders on the ramparts, he effected a substantial breach in the city wall by mining operations.[5] The Megalopolitans succeeded in stemming the first Macedonian assaults through the breach and effectively engaged Polysperchon's siege-towers, which probably moved into close range in support of those assaults, with their arrow-shooting catapults, archers, and slingers.[6] Polysperchon next began to clear a track through the breach so that his elephants could charge decisively along it. But the Megalopolitan leader, Damis, had served with Alexander and knew a few tricks of the trade. He organized a mine-field inside the breach, burying planks thickly studded with nails in an area which the Megalopolitans purposely left undefended. Catapults, archers, and slingers were stationed on the flanks of the breach so that the elephants and drivers would be caught in cross-fire.[7] Damis' plan worked perfectly,[8] and Polysperchon

---

[1] Arr. *Anab.* ii. 27. 4.   [2] Ibid. 2.   [3] D.S. xviii. 70. 2.   [4] Ibid. 3.
[5] Ibid. 4–5.   [6] Ibid. 6–7.
[7] Ibid. 71. 2–3. Vegetius (*Mil.* iii. 24) maintains that arrow-firers are particularly effective against elephants: 'latius tamen contra eas (bestias) et firmius praefigitur ferrum, ut in magnis corporibus maiora sunt vulnera.'   [8] D.S. xviii. 71. 4–6.

departed, leaving a part of his army to continue the siege, which, in fact, was never brought to a successful conclusion.

Demetrius the Besieger, who fully merits this title (Poliorcètes) and the magnificent tribute paid to him in Diodorus,[1] sailed from Ephesus in 307 B.C. to free the cities of the Greek mainland, principally Athens, from the control of Cassander.[2] Entering the Peiraeus suddenly with twenty ships, while other units forced their way in along the shore, he gained the port of Athens within the day, though Cassander's commander, Dionysius, shut himself up in the subsidiary fortress of Munychia.[3] A few weeks later Demetrius commenced his attack on Munychia, a position naturally strong and well fortified artificially, with stone-throwers and other machines.[4] After two days of continuous bombardment and assault, 'the defenders being wounded by catapults and stone-throwers', Demetrius' men forced their way in, 'since the walls had been cleared by means of the stone-throwers'.[5] Both types of catapult, therefore, provided covering fire.

Very shortly afterwards, Demetrius laid siege to Salamis in Cyprus, where Menelaus, Ptolemy I's general, had prepared for the investment. Demetrius decided to build gigantic machines, arrow-firers, stone-throwers, and a *helepolis*, 90 cubits high (135 feet) with nine storeys.[6] 'Into the lowest floors of this he introduced all sorts of stone-throwers, of which the largest were three-talent engines; into the middle floors, the largest arrow-shooting catapults; into the highest, the smallest arrow-firers and a number of stone-throwers . . .'[7] 'Bringing the machines up to the city, and putting down a barrage of missiles, he tore away the battlements with his stone-throwers and shook the walls with rams.'[8] Thus, arrow-firers provided the normal neutralizing shooting. Though the stone-throwers were not, apparently, employed against the walls themselves, they sheared off the battlements and so completely exposed the rampart walk. The situation became desperate for the besieged, and they only managed to stave off the evil hour by burning the besieger's machines with blazing bolts.[9] After Demetrius had defeated Ptolemy's navy off Salamis as it came with a relief force, Salamis surrendered.

The siege of Rhodes began a year or so later. It lasted about twelve months (305–4), and failed partly because the Rhodian harbour was never firmly closed and supplies of all kinds could be brought in. Also,

[1] Ibid. xx. 92. 1–2.   [2] For the following events see Ferguson, 63.
[3] D.S. xx. 45. 1–3.
[4] Ibid. 5.   [5] Ibid. 7.
[6] D.S. xx. 48. 1. On the *helepolis*, see *Technical Treatises*, Biton, n. 24.
[7] D.S. xx. 48. 3.   [8] Ibid. 4.   [9] Ibid. 6.

units of the city's fleet could put out to sea to harry Demetrius' com-
munications. For example, one Rhodian captain, Amyntas, intercepted
many transport-ships carrying material for Demetrius' siege-engines and
captured many artificers expert in artillery construction and eleven very
experienced artillerymen (καταπελταφέται).[1]

Demetrius fully realized the necessity of blocking the harbour, and
most of his early attacks were directed towards this end. But the Rhodians
equally understood the importance of keeping it open so that, when
Demetrius sailed in with stone-throwing and arrow-shooting catapults on
his ships, he found them busy rebuilding and improving the defences
there. Using his best arrow-firers 'and bringing his vessels within range,
he kept inflicting casualties on the city-folk who were increasing the
height of the fortifications in the harbour area'.[2]

The Rhodians replied by putting machines on the mole and arrow-
firers and stone-throwers on three merchant ships to prevent soldiers and
engines being landed there. Nevertheless, Demetrius managed to disembark a force of marines and engines on the end of the mole during the
night. At daybreak he attacked with the machines on his ships and 'with
the smaller catapults that had long range he hindered those working on
the wall by the harbour, while with his stone-throwers he shook considerably the enemy's machines and the wall across the mole; in fact, he
knocked this down in some places since it was weak and low at the time'.[3]
The faithful arrow-firers gave their usual covering fire; the stone-throwers
operated against hostile machines—counter-battery fire; finally, the
stone-throwers, unassisted by rams, and within the day apparently,
breached a wall. This last is not a bad achievement when we consider that
it took James I three hours and 286 'shott' from seven or more heavy
guns to make a breach for three men to enter abreast in the wall of Elfs-
borg in Sweden (1612).

Demetrius maintained his assault for eight days. 'He broke the artillery
on the mole with his one-talent stone-throwers and shook down the
curtain of the cross-wall, towers and all',[4] so that his infantry was able to
take part of it. But his hold was precarious, and he was eventually
forced to retire altogether, while the Rhodians were left to lick their

---

[1] D.S. xx. 93. 5; H. von Gaertringen, 'Aus der Belagerung von Rhodos 304 v. Chr.', in
SBBerlin (1918), 755. Von Gaertringen's elucidation of the papyrus fragment with which he
deals shows that Diodorus' account should end, as it does in the Florentinus MS., as follows:
. . . ἐν οἷς ἑάλωσαν καὶ τεχνῖται τῶν ἀξιολόγων πρὸς βέλη καὶ καταπελταφέται τῶν ἐμπειρίᾳ
διαφερόντων ἕνδεκα. I take βελέων in the papyrus, and βέλη in Diodorus, to mean artillery,
not just the missiles. Understandably, the Rhodians retained the services of these captured
experts.

[2] D.S. xx. 85. 3.   [3] Ibid. 86. 2.   [4] Ibid. 87. 1.

wounds and repair the damaged sections of the wall on the mole.[1] One
week later, Demetrius penetrated the harbour again. 'Once within range,
he fired upon the Rhodian vessels at their moorings with blazing bolts
in large numbers, while he shook the walls with his stone-throwers and,
with the arrow-firers, tried to injure those who exposed themselves.'[2]
This second attack on the harbour area also failed, and Demetrius
decided to try the landward fortifications. The architect Epimachus of
Athens designed for him a larger mobile siege-tower (*helepolis*) than had
ever been constructed before.[3] Like all other similar machines, it was
intended principally to hold artillery and raise it to a sufficient height for
doing effective damage to the walls. The top storeys rose far higher than
the city's curtains and towers so that the covering fire from the upper
floors would be as devastating as possible.

It was fitted on three sides with iron plates to protect it from the
Rhodian stone-throwers and blazing bolts; its apertures or windows had
movable visors, so that the catapult detachments would be shielded when
not actually shooting. It was intended that this *helepolis* should provide the
main covering fire to facilitate the approach of tortoises ($\chi\epsilon\lambda\dot{\omega}\nu\alpha\varsigma$ $\chi\omega\sigma\tau\rho\acute{\iota}$-
$\delta\alpha\varsigma$), rams, and galleries ($\sigma\tau\circ\dot{\alpha}\varsigma$), on a front equal to six curtains and seven
towers of the Rhodian city wall. The Rhodians, for their part, were so
certain that the wall would be breached that they began to construct
another inside. This precaution was justified, because Demetrius, shaking
the walls with stone-throwers as well as rams,[4] succeeded in knocking
down the strongest of the towers, built of four-foot stones, and a whole
length of curtain. The Rhodians were in a critical position, but relief
arrived from Ptolemy and Cassander at this opportune moment. Their
spirits revived, and they prepared an enormous quantity of artillery on
their wall opposite the siege-works. When night fell they shot flaming
bolts against the *helepolis* and stone-shot against enemy personnel. 'Since
the night was moonless, the fire-bolts flashed in their swift flight, while the
ordinary catapult bolts and the stone shot, whose movement could not be
spotted, killed many of those unable to detect the oncoming blow.'[5] Some
of the iron plates on the *helepolis* were broken off, presumably by stone
balls, so that the fire-missiles could take effect on the exposed woodwork.

---

[1] Ibid. 4.   [2] Ibid. 88. 2.
[3] See *Technical Treatises*, Biton, n. 24.   [4] D.S. xx. 95. 4.
[5] Ibid. 96. 6. In daylight, the approach of a hostile missile could often be observed. The
Jews in Jerusalem spotted the Roman shot, Joseph. *BJ* v. 269. This was also possible with
shot from gunpowder artillery, certainly as late as 1743. A certain Sam Davies wrote to a
friend about the battle of Dettingen in that year: '. . . the balls came whistling about my
ears. Then I saw the Oysterenns dip their heads and look about them for they doge (dodge)
the balls as a cock does a stick, they are so used to them . . .'

Demetrius elected to draw the great tower out of range in the end.[1] The next morning he ordered his men to collect the Rhodian missiles so that he could estimate the Rhodian position with regard to supply. More than 800 fire-bolts of several sizes were picked up, and about 1,500 cata- pult bolts.[2] Demetrius was much impressed by the city's armament.

Although Demetrius made one more big attack, he despaired of taking the city by storm and, in view of the situation elsewhere and the wishes of his father, came to terms with Rhodes. The lessons of the siege are roughly as follows. However powerful his resources and his military engines, no besieger can afford to allow a besieged city access to the world outside. Also, the possession of artillery hardly, if at all, inferior to that of the besieger in quality and quantity gave a city a very good chance of withstanding even the most energetic, determined, and well-equipped besieger. It must be remembered, however, that few individual cities could match the Rhodian engineering tradition, or afford lavish expendi- ture on fortifications and defensive artillery.

Syracuse was one of the few such cities. In 213–211 B.C. the Romans pitted what they had learned of Hellenistic siege-craft against the mechanical skill of that notable scientist and artificer Archimedes. The latter's ingenuity and Hieron II's financial support had turned Syracuse into a fortress of the first order,[3] which embodied all the latest ideas for defence and some extra contrivances invented by the great engineer himself. Most of the city's circumference was naturally protected by the imposing heights of the Epipolae and Achradina; but Archimedes 'fitted places which could be approached by low-lying hollows with every kind of artillery, as seemed appropriate for each point'.[4] The first Roman assaults, by sea under Marcellus against the Achradina fortifications, by land under Appius against the Hexapylon, were formidable enough to strike terror in the hearts of the Syracusans until they saw the effect of Archimedes' machines.

Marcellus had artillery, too, but it was very moderate in quantity compared with the Syracusan ordnance. He supported his first attack with archers, slingers, and artillery, posted on ships near his four *sam- bucae*—large mechanically operated scaling-ladders, carried on vessels in this case.[5] When the defenders on the walls had been neutralized,

---

[1] For the ultimate fate of Demetrius's *helepolis* see Vitr. x. 16. 4–8.

[2] D.S. xx. 97. 2.

[3] See A. W. Lawrence, 'Archimedes and the design of the Euryalus Fort', in *JHS* 64 (1948), 99 ff.

[4] Livy, xxiv. 34. 3: 'quae planis vallibus adiri possent, ut cuique aptum visum est loco, ita genere omni tormentorum instruxit.'

[5] On *sambucae*, see *Technical Treatises*, Biton, n. 37.

ANALYSIS OF SIEGES

Marcellus brought up the vessels carrying the *sambucae*. At least one of them was smashed, and its supporting pair of vessels sunk, by ten-talent stones. In spite of Plutarch's phraseology, it is plain that these stones were dropped from large cranes, not hurled by stone-throwers.[1] Meanwhile, the land assault fared no better, for Appius' men were raked by bolts and shot when still at some distance from the wall.[2] Marcellus, therefore, decided to creep up at night and establish himself at the foot of the Achradina wall, because it had been pointed out at a council of war that Archimedes' artillery was all tuned to throw missiles at relatively long range; if the Romans advanced right up to the walls they would be within shot (ἐντὸς βέλους) in an unusual sense of that term, that is, too near to be hit by artillery which could not shoot effectively at an angle of depression.[3] To the surprise of the Romans, when their plan was put into practice, a regular hail of missiles came from slits arranged at all heights in the walls, slits 1 cubit wide according to Livy,[4] and 4 dactyls according to Polybius.[5] Plutarch comments that the majority of Archimedes' engines were under the wall (ὑπὸ τὸ τεῖχος) which probably means they were in front, and at the base, of the walls among the outworks (προτειχί-σματα), just where we shall find Philon recommending them to be placed.[6] The surprise of the Romans indicates that they had not experienced this type of fortification before.

It is significant that no attack was directed against the Euryalus fort, which guarded the best natural approach to the Epipolae plateau, the approach which the Athenians had used 200 years previously. After these repulses Marcellus decided that he could only take the city by blockade.

At the siege of Echinus on the Malian Gulf (210 B.C.), Philip V concentrated his efforts on a relatively short front. Opposite two towers in the city wall he constructed two tortoises (χελῶναι χωστρίδες); opposite the intermediate curtain, and parallel to it, he built a long gallery, which thus ran from one tortoise to the other.[7] Each tortoise was a small mobile siege-tower and had three compartments, one above the other. In the lowest compartment, and standing, of course, actually on the ground, were the men levelling a path for the vehicle, and a ram was installed ready for operation.[8] Into the first floor were packed fire-appliances and arrow-shooting catapults.[9] Finally, on the second floor, stood soldiers,

---

[1] Plb. viii. 5. 8; Plut. *Marc.* 15. 4. [2] Plb. viii. 7. 1–2.
[3] Ibid. 5. 5; Livy, xxiv. 34. 10: 'interiores ictibus tormentorum'.
[4] Livy, xxiv. 34. 9. F. W. Walbank suggests that Livy's figure is due to mistranslation and that he probably did not understand what a παλαιστή (a palm = 4 dactyls) was and did not appreciate the need for a narrow slit.
[5] Plb. viii. 5. 6. [6] Plut. *Marc.* 16. 2.
[7] Plb. ix. 41. 1–3. [8] Ibid. 4. [9] Ibid. 5.

presumably archers and slingers, who were to prevent any attempt to interfere with the working of the ram.[1] Each tortoise was about the same height as the towers of the city. Philip also built three platforms (βελοστά-σεις) for stone-throwers, one of the latter being a one-talent, the other two thirty-mina engines.[2] It is extraordinary how closely Caesar's works at Avaricum resembled the above arrangements.[3] Caesar, or his military architects, must have studied Hellenistic sieges carefully and chosen the most appropriate model for his purpose.

The Romans probably possessed a much better supply of artillery than usual for their siege of Carthage (147–146 B.C.), because they had forced the surrender, in 149 B.C., of all Carthaginian ordnance,[4] and could now turn these engines against their former owners. Nevertheless, the Carthaginians contrived to build more machines, employing women's hair, in emergency, for the springs.[5] Scipio Aemilianus, the Roman commander, tried to capture a mole, situated to control the harbour, and from which the city wall was in easy range. He beat the mole's protective wall with rams, while his artillery gave the normal covering fire. The Carthaginians were driven to make a sally to burn Scipio's engines. They issued forth, wading through the water or swimming, under heavy fire. Some were struck in the eye or the chest by bolts, but they kept moving all the same.[6] In spite of these desperate tactics the Romans captured the mole and built on it a wall equal in height to that of Carthage, from which their artillery could engage the enemy on favourable terms. Although precise information is lacking, we may presume that the Roman catapults played a significant part in the final assaults which led to the fall of the city.

Sulla started his siege of the Peiraeus and his simultaneous blockade of Athens with no artillery at all (87–86 B.C.). After an initial assault, in which the storming parties carried no more complicated machinery than ordinary scaling-ladders, he retired to establish workshops at Eleusis and Megara, obtaining artillery from the city of Thebes at the same time.[7]

---

[1] Plb. ix. 41. For the construction of tortoises (χελῶναι, testudines), particularly the one designed by Hegetor of Byzantium, see Vitr. x. 14 and 15.

[2] Plb. ix. 41. 8.

[3] Caes. BG vii. 17 ff. Of course, Caesar built a mound (agger), composed mainly of wood, in place of the covered gallery (στοά) here. On στοά (= porticus; e.g. Caes. BC ii. 2. 3) see Hobein in RE 2. vii (1931), 'Stoa', cols. 2–3; Walbank, Polybius, i. 111. A stoa or porticus was most easily made by placing a number of siege-sheds (vineae) in line.

[4] App. viii. 80.

[5] Tarn (HMND 114 f.) believed that, normally, only slave-girls sold their hair for catapult-springs, but that, in this time of crisis for Carthage, noble ladies gave their hair freely. However, Strabo (p. 833) specifically says 'slavegirls provided hair for the catapults'.

[6] App. viii. 124.

[7] App. Mithr. 30. On this siege in general see Ferguson, 447 ff.

The strength of the fortifications, which were 40 cubits (60 feet) high, it was said,[1] the sizeable Mithridatic garrison under Archelaus, and the support sent in by Mithridates by sea made the Peiraeus a most formidable proposition. The Romans planned, as usual, to build a siege-mound and towers housing artillery for covering fire. Sulla actually constructed two siege-towers, and Archelaus also made one, which he filled with catapults, to counter their effect. He also used artillery to support his sallies,[2] and to damage the Roman works, so that a duel took place between the artillery in the rival towers. This continued 'until Sulla, by means of catapults which shot about twenty very heavy lead balls at the same time, shook Archelaus' tower and made it insecure'.[3] It is more probable that these catapults were firing salvoes than that each shot twenty balls simultaneously, like grape-shot.

Although Sulla's artillery severely damaged a tower on this occasion, the main work of destruction was accomplished by rams and mining. The Romans breached the first wall and then found that Archelaus had rapidly constructed subsidiary, crescent-shaped fortifications behind every gap. Nevertheless, they assaulted these immediately while still damp and weak; but lunettes are admirably suited to defensive operations, since the attackers can be subjected to a concentrated hail of missiles from both the front and the flanks.[4] The Romans were driven back with losses, and Sulla reluctantly decided to abandon, for the time being, his attempts to storm the Peiraeus.

Athens, however, which had been blockaded all the time, now fell, principally through shortage of food,[5] and Roman hopes revived. Sulla renewed his efforts against the Peiraeus, breached the wall again, pressed home a series of assaults against one lunette after another which Archelaus built behind this breach, and finally forced the Mithridatic garrison to withdraw into Munychia. The Romans could not expect to take this fort without a fleet; but the object had been achieved, because Munychia was too small to make an effective Mithridatic base, and Archelaus soon departed from it by sea.

The Mithridatic generals intended, it would seem, to apply hammer-and-anvil strategy. They pinned Sulla down before a fortress which they considered impregnable, especially as the Romans had no fleet with which to block the harbour. Meanwhile, Mithridates' son, Ariarathes

---

[1] App. *Mithr.* 30.   [2] Ibid. 32.   [3] Ibid. 34.   [4] Ibid. 37.

[5] Ferguson, 449, says spies within the Peiraeus inscribed messages on leaden balls which they then hurled to Sulla by catapult to inform him when a supply-convoy was leaving for Athens. Appian really says, however, that the spies used slings for this purpose (*Mithr.* 31 : . . . ἠφίεσαν ἀπὸ σφενδόνης, and ibid. 34 : . . . ἐσφενδόνησαν . . .).

(Plutarch) or Arcathias (Appian), brought another Pontic army round by land through Thrace and Macedonia. Eventually, Sulla would be caught between Arcathias' hammer and Archelaus' anvil, after his troops had been worn out by their futile attacks on the latter. The basically sound Mithridatic plan was upset by the sluggishness and untimely death of Arcathias and by the skill and tenacity with which the Romans prosecuted the siege. Employing the resources of Hellenistic siege-craft, supported by artillery, Sulla overcame a powerful fortress, fully garrisoned,[1] and defended with no little ingenuity and resolution.

Unlike Sulla, Caesar probably possessed some artillery right from the start of his investment of Massilia (49 B.C.); but, initially at least, the city's catapults were superior, because there was a famous artillery arsenal there, and Caesar had not needed to maintain large quantities of machines for his Gallic campaigns against far less sophisticated fortifications. Hence, the early Roman attempts to approach the walls were met by such galling fire that Caesar's men directed their efforts to erecting powerful protective barriers, for the usual type proved ineffective. Even so, Massiliot shooting constantly hindered the siege-works.[2] If we walk westwards down the Rue de la République in modern Marseilles, we can easily appreciate the natural strength of the heights on our left, on which stood the old city, and the difficulty of constructing a mound towards this from the eminence on our right, the Butte des Carmes, where Caesar probably established his base camp. Trebonius, left to supervise operations in Caesar's absence, built a brick tower of six storeys, protected against hostile missiles, and fitted with apertures for artillery.[3]

From this tower a *musculus* was constructed towards the walls of the city, and the artillery in the tower covered its approach with neutralizing fire.[4] When soldiers working under the *musculus* brought down a portion of a Massiliot tower, the defenders asked for a truce, but used this to make a treacherous sally in which the Roman works were partially burnt.

---

[1] Ferguson, 448, following Kromayer (*Antike Schlachtfelder*, ii. 388), speaks of Sulla's 'decisive superiority in numbers'. Numbers are never decisive in sieges, and a besieger who attacks with too small a force needs his head examining. Although Appian possibly exaggerates a little (*Mithr.* 31), there can be no doubt that Archelaus' force was perfectly adequate for the defence.

[2] Caes. *BC* ii. 2. 5: 'sed magnitudo operum, altitudo muri atque turrium, multitudo tormentorum omnem administrationem tardabat.'

[3] Ibid. 9. 9: '... fenestrasque, quibus in locis visum est, ad tormenta mittenda in struendo reliquerunt.'

[4] Ibid. 11. 3: 'musculus ex turri latericia a nostris telis tormentisque defenditur; hostes ex muro ac turribus summoventur; non datur libera muri defendendi facultas.' The construction of the brick tower at a distance of about 20 yards from the city-wall was a really remarkable feat of military engineering.

Though hotly pursued by the Romans as they rushed back to the shelter of their walls, they reached the city in safety under cover of their artillery.[1] The Caesareans repaired and enlarged the siege-works, and the Massiliots then surrendered, for the reason, among others, that the Romans were operating more and more in an area so close to the walls that their artillery, in which they had placed great hopes, could not depress sufficiently to cover it.[2]

It appears, therefore, from this summary analysis of sieges, that a besieger who possessed efficient artillery and knew how to use it stood a very good chance of success. A city could only hope to survive if it had thoroughly up-to-date fortifications and artillery, and if it conducted an active defence. Catapults, then, played an important part in all major sieges from 397 B.C. onwards. It was not so much that they achieved anything spectacular themselves, but they gave effective support to other engines and to the assaulting infantry. At the very least, the covering or neutralizing fire of arrow-shooting and stone-throwing engines permitted besiegers to fill in ditches and build galleries, to batter and undermine the walls, and to attack them by means of scaling-ladders and so on, with far fewer casualties and with greater ease than was possible when the only support of this kind came from bows and slings alone. Stone-throwers undoubtedly provided a certain amount of purely destructive fire which could, on its own, beat down walls, especially weak ones, supplement the shaking effect of rams, shear off battlements, and smash enemy machines. It is not surprising that Philon seems pre-occupied with the threat of artillery in his books on the defence of cities.

§ 2. *Philon*

Philon constantly bears in mind the need to provide adequate defence against stone-throwers. Towers must be built, he says, with one corner projecting towards the area from which the enemy will approach, so that hostile shot will glance off, for the force of stone balls which strike the wall at right-angles (καταφόραι) is considerable.[3] The thickness of tower walls and curtains should be 10 cubits (15 feet), for that thickness can withstand stone shot.[4] Towers must not be too high because they would then be easily shaken and brought down by stone-throwers.[5] Great care

---

[1] Ibid. 14. 3: '. . . fit in hostes impetus; sed e muro sagittis tormentisque fugientes persequi prohibentur (sc. nostri)'.

[2] Ibid. 16. 3: '. . . suorumque tormentorum usum, quibus ipsi magna speravissent, spatii propinquitate interire . . .'   [3] Philon, *Par.* 79. 11–19.

[4] Ibid. 80. 45 ff.   [5] Ibid. 81. 40 ff.; cf. Hor. *C.* ii. 10. 10.

must be taken to construct a good system of outworks, including ditches, palisades, and mine-fields.[1] This arrangement of ditches has already been discussed and illustrated;[2] but even beyond the outer ditch, Philon advises defenders to bury empty pots and to cover them with seaweed which does not rot. Men can walk over this mine-field, but heavy machines break the pots and sink down.

Gates were always weak points, as Seneca testifies in his *Hippolytus*:

Nec torta clausas fregerat saxo gravi | ballista portas.[3]

Philon suggests, therefore, that they should be flanked by hexagonal, rather than rectangular, towers for three reasons: first, the obtuse-angled corners of hexagons are less liable to damage than the right-angled corners of rectangles; secondly, a pair of hexagonal towers does not have the same tendency to channel glancing shot down the intervening corridor towards the gates as a pair of rectangular towers; thirdly, hexagons afford the catapults inside them better fields of fire.[4] Similarly battlements were rather vulnerable, and, we have noted for example, that Demetrius smashed them at Cyprian Salamis. Each battlement should, therefore, be constructed with a projecting angle, so that stone shot can only strike glancing blows (παραφόροι, not καταφόροι).[5] Philon concludes his description of outworks with the significant comment that a city must concentrate on these things because walls are easily taken by stone-throwers and galleries (ὑπὸ γὰρ τῶν λιθοβόλων καὶ στοῶν ῥᾳδίως ἁλίσκεται τὰ τείχη).[6]

Another important use for catapults, as we have seen, for instance, at Rhodes and the Peiraeus (86 B.C.), was against enemy artillery (= modern counter-battery fire) and other siege-engines. Philon remarks, in this connection: 'It is useful to deploy two ten-mina stone-throwers against each hostile stone-thrower, and it is essential to transfer these to whatever point the enemy move their engine, so that you may shoot at it, break it, and smash it.'[7] The besiegers, too, are advised to station two ten-mina engines and one five-span arrow-shooting catapult opposite each defensive stone-thrower.[8] Artillery is also to be employed against the enemy's galleries, towers, and ladders. The thirty-mina stone-thrower is the most effective for this work, and, if it is properly handled, 'neither a gallery nor a tortoise would easily be brought up'.[9] Flaming bolts are to be shot against hostile equipment, too,[10] as they were, above all, at Rhodes.

[1] Philon, *Par.* 84. 43 ff.   [2] See above, p. 91, fig. 2.
[3] Sen. *Hipp.* 534 f.   [4] Philon, *Par.* 79. 21 ff.
[5] Ibid. 80. 9 ff. The sense seems fairly clear in spite of the *lacuna*.
[6] Ibid. 85. 48 f.   [7] Philon, *Pol.* 91. 15 ff.   [8] Ibid. 98. 10 ff.
[9] Ibid. 95. 49 ff.   [10] Ibid. 94. 8 ff.

Philon does not specifically mention the employment of artillery in support of sallies, but he clearly implies it, for the whole idea of his various systems of defence was to provide covering fire for every nook and cranny round the walls and over an area extending well beyond the outermost ditch. His towers and walls were chambered for artillery; they were to have slits or windows like those of Archimedes at Syracuse; there were to be catapult-emplacements in front of the walls.[1] The towers project from the curtains, which could form a series of crescents, and are thus able to enfilade every part of the wall and to protect each other. Their slits or windows point in various directions, being narrow outside and broad inside to protect the operators and to allow satisfactory fields of fire.[2]

Thus, Philon's writings not only confirm what the historical accounts of sieges indicate, but also suggest that the latter give but a vague picture of the importance and effectiveness of artillery in this type of warfare. From all the available written evidence, we can tabulate the uses of catapults in sieges as follows:

NEUTRALIZATION

Covering fire	All sieges
In support of sallies	Perinthus, Halicarnassus, Massilia (implied by Philon)

DESTRUCTION

Anti-personnel	All sieges
In repulse of sallies	Halicarnassus, Carthage
Walls	Tyre, Rhodes, Carthage (?) (Philon)
Battlements	Salamis (Philon)
Counter-battery	Megalopolis, Rhodes, Peiraeus (86 B.C.) (Philon)
Other siege-engines	Tyre, Rhodes, Salamis, Syracuse, Peiraeus (86 B.C.), Massilia (Philon)

[1] Philon, *Par.* 82. 6 ff.   [2] Ibid. 81. 10 ff.

VI

ARTILLERY AND FORTIFICATIONS

In this chapter it is my intention to record a few observations on the relationship between the development of artillery and that of Greek and Hellenistic fortifications. All the fortifications that will be considered may be dated certainly, or very probably, within the last four centuries B.C., and special attention will be paid to those which were erected in the fourth and third centuries when improvement in the design of catapults was, relatively, most marked and rapid. These observations are ultimately based on the evidence supplied by the existing remains of ancient defence works, of which I studied a considerable number during two fairly extensive journeys, one to sites in the Greek mainland, the other to Greek cities in south Italy and Sicily.

§ 1. *The Siting of Catapults in City Defences*

Although Dionysius I's *gastraphetae*, the first artillery, were employed in an offensive role at the siege of Motya (397 B.C.), it cannot have been long before the Greeks generally began to appreciate that catapults would be equally valuable in defence. The successful Perinthian appeal to Byzantium for alliance, catapults, and ammunition during the early stages of Philip II's siege of their city (340 B.C.) supplies the first definite evidence for Greek application of the fairly obvious theory that artillery-supported defence is the best answer to an attack supported by artillery.[1] But it is very probable that, for some years before this siege, the designers of fortifications had been aware of the need to provide suitable accommodation for catapults at appropriate points in city defences. At this relatively early period they had no reason to think in terms of strengthening their walls and towers to resist heavy shot projected by stone-throwers of large calibre and enormous power.[2] It seems that formidable torsion

---

[1] D.S. xvi. 74. 5; see above, pp. 100 f. Byzantium had almost certainly acquired these catapults for defensive purposes, and the catapults which appear at Athens, 371/0 B.C., were probably intended for defence too (see above, p. 65).

[2] It is most improbable that non-torsion stone-throwers, even the large engine hurling a shot weighing perhaps 40 pounds and designed by Isidorus of Abydos (Biton, W 48 ff.), would be effective against walls.

machines, with Mark IIIʙ frames, made their first real impression at Alexander's siege of Tyre (332 B.C.).[1]

Where, then, are Greek builders of fortifications likely to have placed their most important batteries of bolt-shooting and stone-throwing catapults? Although it may appear self-evident that the bulk of the defensive artillery will have been set up in the chambers of towers or on the rampart walk, discussion of this question will help to clear the ground and will introduce us to several interesting factors in the siting of catapults. Now Philon gives the following advice:

Below [i.e. in front of] the curtain-walls and outworks, platforms are to be constructed for as many and as large engines as possible, some at surface level, others below ground level, so that there may be plenty of room for their operation, so that the detachments may not be hit, so that they may inflict casualties while themselves out of sight, and so that, when the enemy draws near, the aimers may not be handicapped by being unable to depress their engines.[2]

Catapults in advance of the main defences, as recommended, would certainly be useful. First, they could substantially supplement the shooting of machines on the wall and in the towers where space for artillery would be relatively limited; secondly, they could effectively engage targets at very close range in the area near the main wall which the artillerymen on that wall or in its towers could not depress their machines enough to hit. The latter point is best explained by illustration (Fig. 1).

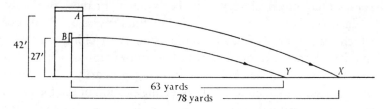

FIG. 1. Shooting from a tower and from the rampart walk.

A bolt or stone shot projected from a catapult at A, high up in a tower and with its stock laid horizontal, will only descend to ground level at X, over 70 yards in front of the wall. Similarly, missiles hurled from engines at B, on top of the rampart walk and likewise laid horizontal, will not fall to

---

[1] On Mark IIIʙ frames see above, pp. 22 ff. On stone-throwers used against walls by Alexander at Tyre see above, pp. 102 f.

[2] Philon, *Par.* 82. 6–14. There is some confusion in the text; but if, in line 9, we delete ὀρυκταί and κατώρυχοι, thus writing . . . αἱ μὲν [ὀρυκταί] ἐπίπεδοι [καὶ κατώρυχοι] . . ., the general sense becomes clear.

ground level nearer than Y, over 60 yards away. In both these instances we have assumed that the catapults were pulled back to their full extent, so that, had they been laid at an angle of elevation of 45 degrees, their missiles would have achieved a range of about 400 yards.

It may be felt that they could cover targets much nearer to the wall if their arms were not pulled back so far and if, thus, their springs were not tightened so much. This is obviously quite true; but the power of their missiles to inflict damage on impact would be so significantly reduced that it would certainly not be worth adopting such a procedure with bolt-shooting catapults, and it would be very little more useful to apply the method to stone-throwers. Further, it may be suggested that catapults might achieve really close coverage if laid at angles of depression. I have found that my full-scale and reasonably accurate model of a three-span catapult, which is well balanced on its base, can in fact be depressed to an angle of 4 degrees below the horizontal. But, if its spring-frame was plated as heavily as ancient frames clearly were, the universal joint ($\kappa\alpha\rho\chi\acute{\eta}\sigma\iota\sigma\nu$), around which it pivots, would require moving nearer the frame in order to preserve satisfactory balance, and this would eliminate any possibility of depressing the engine.

Even if ancient catapults could actually shoot at angles of depression up to 4 degrees below the horizontal, points x and y would only be brought some 10 yards nearer the main fortification. Thus, engines set up at ground level just outside the wall, and protected by ditches and palisades, would effectively cover the last vital 50, or more probably 60, yards which the besieger must cross in the final stages of his approach, and which was an area of dead ground as far as machines on the main wall and its towers were concerned. But we must emphasize here that, in offering the above advice, Philon is thinking primarily of a somewhat unusual situation in which a small projecting portion of the fortifications covers a narrow, critical front. Where there is the much more common arrangement of a series of towers and curtains in more or less a straight line, the ground immediately in front of any one tower or stretch of curtain can be covered quite satisfactorily by catapults shooting through the side windows ($\theta\upsilon\rho\acute{\iota}\delta\epsilon\varsigma$) of neighbouring towers (see Diagram 1, p. 155). Philon is perfectly aware of this point, of course.[1] Even at corners, catapults in towers adjacent to the corner tower can engage targets almost up to its base. Thus, when several towers can mutually support each other in this way, there does not seem to be much advantage in exposing any considerable quantity of valuable ordnance amidst subsidiary

---

[1] Philon, *Par.* 81. 15–25.

defences outside the principal barrier; but we shall deal with this more regular situation again below.

Meanwhile, the Euryalus fort at Syracuse provides the best example of an elaborate defensive system designed to protect a limited front and to function independently. It forms a powerful projecting bastion which blocks what would otherwise be a naturally easy route of access to the Epipolae.[1] There are no adjoining defences close enough to provide any support. Therefore, in its final design, which was most probably the work of Archimedes (c. 220 B.C.), Euryalus was equipped with permanent outworks of stone and three rock-cut ditches laid out in approximately the manner that Philon recommends.[2] Differences in measurements between Philon's theory and the actual practice at the Euryalus were due to local conditions.[3] The outworks, both behind the inner ditch and between the inner and middle ditches, no doubt contained platforms for artillery at a much lower level than the main battery on the famous 'five towers'—the final line of defence.

If a besieger was foolish enough to launch a full attack on the Euryalus,[4] his men and machines could be battered by every arrow-shooting and stone-throwing catapult in the main five-tower battery and in the permanent outworks while they were advancing from extreme range to the outer ditch. The besieging force would also have been exposed to the full defensive barrage all the time it was laboriously crossing the outer ditch and advancing across the space, over 90 yards in extent, between it and the middle ditch. If the besiegers miraculously crossed the middle ditch and seized the first outwork, they would have been sufficiently close to escape the attentions of at least some of the catapults in the main battery; but when they tried to cross the inner ditch, they would have had to face the engines mounted in the second outwork shooting at point-blank range.[5]

[1] This route was used by the Athenians in 414 B.C. before any fortifications existed there (Thuc. vi. 97). The Punic general, Hamilcar, attempted to reach Epipolae via Euryalus in 309 B.C. (D.S. xx. 29), when the approach was protected by the fort in an early form; a sally by the garrison and some shooting (though it is not stated what this involved precisely) halted the Carthaginian operation.

On Euryalus see A. W. Lawrence, 'Archimedes and the design of Euryalus Fort', in *JHS* 66 (1948), 99 ff.; F. E. Winter, 'The Chronology of the Euryalos fortress at Syracuse', in *AJA* 67 (1963), 363 ff. (older literature conveniently listed on p. 363 n. 1); F. Krischen, *Stadtmauern*, 25 ff.

[2] For illustration see above, p. 91.

[3] Lawrence, op. cit. 103 ff.

[4] Marcellus rejected the idea without hesitation in 212 B.C. (Livy, xxv. 25).

[5] Krischen (*Stadtmauern*, Tafel 32) regards the second outwork as part of an earlier defensive arrangement and omits it in his reconstruction of the fort in its final state (*Stadtmauern*, Tafel 10). But this scheme of things appears most unlikely.

Incidentally, Philon's recommended measurements for a system of
three ditches may supply additional evidence for the width of the strip of
ground in front of the main wall which could not be covered by catapults
on that wall or in its associated towers. The outer lip of the inner ditch
should lie, he says, 68 yards from the foot of the city wall[1]. This strongly
suggests that machines on the wall and towers could engage targets
provided they did not approach nearer than that point. Hence the final
ditch was placed here to prevent the enemy penetrating easily within the
main defensive artillery cover.[2]

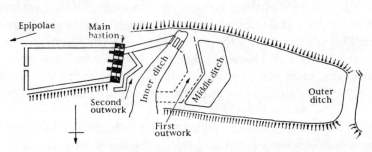

FIG. 2. Sketch-plan of the Euryalus

The above situation, however, is somewhat exceptional. The fire-plan
shown in Diagram 1 (p. 155) illustrates a more usual arrangement in which
series of towers lies in a straight line, as they do in most stretches of the
circuits at Perge and Paestum, for example, or even in the gently curving
oval of Mantinea, so that neighbouring towers can easily assist each other.
In the circumstances shown in Diagram 1 it can be readily observed that
only a narrow strip of ground right up against the bases of the towers, and
5 yards wide at the most, is not covered by artillery. Thus, there is certainly not the same need to put catapults among the outworks here.
Also, we should expect the inner ditch in such a system to be much nearer
the base of the wall than Philon's recommended 33 yards. Now the
straight north wall at Paestum contains eight towers, the intervals
between them varying from 75 yards to a little over 100 yards.[3] The
coverage attainable by catapults mounted in the eight towers would be
similar to that shown in Diagram 1. In 1961 a ditch was discovered outside Paestum's north wall, running parallel to it, its inner edge being
about 6 or 7 yards away. The ditch (see Fig. 3, p. 121) was some 22

[1] See above, p. 91, for illustration of Philon's arrangement of ditches.
[2] For further discussion of the tactical possibilities with regard to artillery at the Euryalus
see Lawrence, op. cit. 105 f.
[3] For plan of the city, see Schläger, Abb. 1.

yards from lip to lip, as against Philon's 35 yards, and 27 feet deep, as compared with Philon's 30 feet.[1] Artillery on the eight towers could easily cover every scrap of ground in front of the wall from the outer edge of the ditch to its maximum range (*c.* 400 yards). Batteries of catapults at ground level in the narrow space between the base of the wall and the ditch would not have increased the extent of the coverage, though they would have increased its density, especially over the first 100 yards or so.

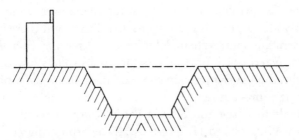

FIG. 3. Cross-section of ditch outside north wall at Paestum

Philon's advice about artillery in the outworks seems sound, but only up to a point. It would be important to deploy catapults among outworks close to the foot of a projecting bastion. But, where the main fortification consisted of the usual, continuous, more or less straight line of curtains and towers, the value of any artillery at ground level in front of the wall would be very much reduced. Also, as we shall see later, catapults placed at a height on walls and towers gain an advantage in range which it would be folly to surrender by voluntarily siting the bulk of the engines at low level.

Ancient artillery was certainly never mounted on platforms behind the main wall. In some medieval drawings, it is true, we see stone-throwing and arrow-shooting engines depicted hurling their missiles over the fortifications from inside a beleaguered city.[2] But there is no evidence that the Greeks or Romans operated their machines in this way. Philon insists that a clear space about 30 yards wide should be left between the inner face of a city wall and the houses within.[3] But his reasons are that this allows free movement for the transport of stones (ammunition, or for repairing the wall) and for relieving parties, and that it leaves room for the construction of a subsidiary ditch behind any sector of the wall that

[1] See Schläger, 23, and Tafel 7. 1.
[2] e.g. Payne-Gallwey, *The Crossbow*, 258, fig. 183.
[3] Philon, *Par.* 80. 17 (60 cubits wide).

is in danger of being brought down. He does not mention any possible use for artillery platforms, though it would have been highly appropriate for him to do so had it been applicable. In addition, in order to shoot over their own wall, catapults would have had to be at least 10 yards behind it, and at least 30 yards back if they were intended to cover a substantial area. But this means a considerable sacrifice in range, and it is clear that Greek fortification designers strove to gain for their catapults every slight advantage in range over the besieger's artillery.

Casemates for artillery within the walls themselves occur rarely. In most Greek walls at present standing to their full height there is no sign of any such arrangement. When Polybius and Livy mention that Archimedes constructed special arrow-slits for his scorpions low down in the walls of Achradina at Syracuse in 213 B.C., their accounts imply a certain novelty in the procedure.[1] At any rate, it thoroughly surprised the Romans. Only at Perge and Side in Pamphylia is it possible now to see reasonably well-preserved Hellenistic walls incorporating casemates.

The normal rampart walk along the curtains of Perge does not rest on a solid structure but on a series of piers and arches (see Diagram 2, p. 155). Underneath the arches lies a row of casemates forming as it were a second rampart walk at a lower level. Doorways in the piers provide access from one compartment to the next, and each casemate has two arrow-slits ($\tau o \xi \iota \kappa a \iota$). The upper rampart walk is wide enough (about 8 feet) to accommodate three-span catapults and allow adequate room for their operation. But the lower rampart walk, that is the floor of the casemates, is only 5 feet 6 inches wide. Thus only the very small one-cubit arrow-shooters will fit here, and, even then, the artillerymen will be in a most precarious position as they take aim. It is possible that, in emergency, the floor of each casemate could be extended rearwards by means of wooden staging; if this was done, the defenders could use three-span catapults at this lower level as well as up above. The stocks of catapults placed in the casemates would be about 18 feet above external ground level; the stocks of catapults on the upper rampart walk would lie about 28 feet above the ground outside. The fire-power produced by this means was clearly impressive, though the engines were quite small, and would provide a substantial addition to the shooting of the main batteries in Perge's towers.[2]

At Side, the lower rampart walk is supported on rectangular piers (see

[1] Plb. viii. 5. 6; Livy, xxiv. 34. 9; see above, p. 109.
[2] On the curtains of Perge see Lanckoronski, 62, fig. 49. 63; Winter, *Ikria*, pl. 4 (photograph of wall from inside the city).

Diagram 3, p. 156),[1] or on piers and arches,[2] or on a solid wall.[3] The narrower upper rampart walk is carried on smaller piers which rest on the lower walk and against the rear of the curtain's facing wall.[4] The lower rampart walk is thus divided into a series of partial compartments, each of which has one central arrow-slit and a second, smaller slit directly beside the right-hand pier. The width of the lower walk, including the covered portion, is about 10 feet, so that three-span catapults (length of stock—4 feet 6 inches) and even two-cubit engines (length of stock— 6 feet) could be comfortably operated at this level, one machine to each casemate shooting through the central arrow-slit.

It has been reasonably suggested that the smaller slit in each casemate was meant to enable an observer to direct the artilleryman on to suitable targets.[5] The aperture between the centre-stanchions of a three-span arrow-firer through which the artilleryman aimed was a mere 3 inches wide by 6 inches high, in a catapult of the third or second century B.C. Moreover, a catapult's frame was generally protected by a shield, and the aperture in the centre of this could well be smaller still. Hence an artilleryman looking down the stock of his machine gets a very restricted view of the target area. An observer peering through an adjacent slit, unimpeded by machinery, might assist greatly. If this interpretation of the purpose of the two casemate slits is correct, we can account for the apparently awkward position of the small observation-port on the ground that the observer must not be exposed to nasty knocks from a catapult's recoiling arm.[6]

The upper rampart walk at Side is only 4 feet 3 inches wide. Since the stock of the tiny one-cubit catapult is 3 feet long, we doubt whether even this engine could be operated satisfactorily here. If the higher platform was extended rearwards by means of wooden staging erected on the rear portion of the lower rampart walk, then the defenders could deploy batteries of three-span and two-cubit machines on the higher as well as the lower level; but, as things stand now, the upper rampart was designed for defending personnel (archers, etc.), not artillery. The great advantage

[1] Mansel, *Side*, 28, Abb. 15 (photo), 30, Abb. 17a (reconstruction).
[2] Ibid. 29, Abb. 16 (photo), 30, Abb. 17c (reconstruction); Winter, *Ikria*, pl. 2.
[3] Mansel, *Side*, 28, Abb. 15 (right side of photo), 30, Abb. 17b (reconstruction).
[4] For photographs of these piers, etc., in detail see Winter, *Ikria*, pls. 3a, 3b.
[5] Ibid. 191 f. Not having been to Side, I cannot tell for certain how effective the small slits would be as observation-ports; but Winter implies that they could serve this purpose satisfactorily.
[6] In Diagram 3b (p. 156) the outline of a three-span catapult has been drawn in one of the compartments. The distance from the end of one arm of the engine to the pier near by is just over 2 feet; the observer will have to be quite careful not to make a false move at the wrong time. With a two-cubit catapult the situation is even more serious.

of this system will have been that the single row of engines in each curtain, their stocks being about 31 feet above exterior ground level, and their operators were given much more protection than if they were placed on the normal, relatively exposed, upper parapet. After all, besieging stone-throwers could shatter the battlements shielding an ordinary rampart walk and then clear it of any personnel and machinery not already dislodged. If this happened at Side, the engines on the lower parapet would still be shooting, and it would not be so easy to shatter the lower portion of the battlements protecting this parapet because it was buttressed by the piers built at regular and fairly close intervals.

Philon, in his *Paraskeuastika* (*Preparations for a siege*) and his *Poliorketika*, has three passages which indicate types of casemated walls. The construction of the curtains at Rhodes, presumably in his own time, involved the use of arches, and there were certainly compartments—to be used as guard rooms—in the walls at ground level.[1] From this and other minor pieces of evidence Schramm justifiably reconstructed the walls of Rhodes with another row of casemates above the guard-rooms, each casemate housing a bolt-shooting catapult (two-cubit).[2] Above these again he put a roofed upper parapet containing more artillery.

A little later Philon briefly describes another very powerful type of curtain, and guard-rooms are again mentioned as being incorporated in the wall at ground level. They are to be covered over either by means of arches or with beams and boards,[3] so that there will have been further casemates up above for artillery and, higher still, an upper rampart to accommodate yet more catapults. Schramm's reconstruction, based on Philon's difficult account, which is not over-generous with its information, is not altogether convincing.[4] We suspect, in fact, that the whole system was a theoretical one, perhaps Philon's own proposal for a modified version of the Rhodian defensive arrangement.

Finally, in the *Poliorketika*, Philon explains a method of adapting an ordinary solid curtain with its single parapet when an emergency demands it:

Against the machines, when they draw near, against both the rams and the drawbridges, raise the wall at this point. Do not dismantle the battlements

---

[1] Philon, *Par.* 80. 45 ff.   [2] Schramm, *Poliorketik*, Tafel 25, Abb. 80.
[3] Philon, *Par.* 83. 15 ff.
[4] Schramm, *Poliorketik*, Tafel 27, Abb. 84. Philon clearly states that the width of the wall should be 18 feet; Schramm makes the wall, in his reconstruction, 33 feet wide for the first 15 feet of its height, putting the guard-rooms in an extra portion added on at the back and not in the main body of the wall underneath the artillery casemates. Also, he fails to include the special slanting battlements designed to render the blows from hostile stone shot less effective; see *Par.* 83. 18–23.

already existing, but commence building on top of them, construct others up above, and make the wall covered in on this front,[1] so that there may be two sets of battlements [and two parapets] available for use, and so that, if they bring forward the drawbridge, we may easily set it on fire from below through the [lower] battlements. Also, if they sheer off the upper battlements, we may push forward [counter-]rams and nooses from the apertures in the lower battlements and easily smite them.[2]

In other words, the defenders ought to convert their simple conventional wall into something very like the system permanently available at Perge and Side. Philon's account demonstrates the advantages of having two rampart walks when the enemy get really close; but its main significance lies in the implication that walls of solid construction with a single parapet were still very common in Philon's day (*c.* 200 B.C.).

Occasionally, elsewhere, we find isolated casemates, as at Latmian Heraclea,[3] but no continuous system of compartments. Between the two great semicircular towers in the north gate defences at Selinus there runs a wall with a continuous corridor inside—or, rather, according to Krischen's reconstruction, three corridors, one above the other.[4] The floor of the lowest of these is on a level with the bottom of the ditch; it has doors which afford access to the ditch and two peculiar arrow-slits between each pair of doors.[5] Krischen is almost certainly correct in reconstructing another corridor above this, its floor being approximately at ordinary ground level, and in assuming a row of arrow-slits in it which may well have been used by a battery of small arrow-shooting catapults.[6] This was not exactly a casemated wall, but it had the same function.

Archimedes' extempore casemates at Syracuse and the corridor-wall at Selinus were designed to enable the defenders to bring some artillery to bear on ground immediately in front of the defences which catapults on the rampart walk and towers could not cover. But the object at Perge, Side, and Rhodes (as far as we can judge), was principally to increase the fire-power. Curtains with casemates or corridors seem to have come in

---

[1] . . . κατάστεγον ποιῆσαι ταύτῃ τὸ τεῖχος . . . This seems to mean simply that the floor of the new, upper parapet will form a roof over the original rampart walk. It is not necessary to assume that Philon recommends a roof for the upper parapet as well, though this is just possible.

[2] Philon, *Pol.* 91. 47 ff. On drawbridges used for assault, ἐπιβάθραι, see *Technical Treatises,* Biton, n. 36, and diag. 3.

[3] Krischen, *Herakleia,* 16, 17, Abb. 13 (referring to points 7 and 51 of the circuit).

[4] Krischen, *Stadtmauern,* 30 f., and Tafeln 11, 19, 39 (4), 41, 42.

[5] These slits are wide on the outside and narrow on the inside instead of the other way round.

[6] Finally, there was a rampart walk on top in the form of a third corridor, according to Krischen, who gives it a roof and rear wall.

at a relatively late period (*c.* 250–175 B.C.) and certainly never became fashionable in the Greek world.[1] In the first place, they would have required careful and expensive construction.[2] Secondly, the compartments will have been more vulnerable to rams than the ordinary solid walls.[3] Hence, to outweigh this drawback, a city had to possess considerable quantities of excellent artillery which could take full advantage of the additional facilities offered. Few cities could match Rhodes in artillery production. Generally speaking, then, we find that the major portion of a town's defensive artillery will be set up on the ordinary single rampart walk and in the towers.

§ 2. *Towers and Artillery*

The fourth century B.C. witnessed a major revolution in Greek siege-technique. The introduction of the catapult and later improvements in its design constituted only a single feature, though perhaps an important one, of the general progress. Hence it is rarely possible to assert with confidence that any particular development in fortification design is due to artillery rather than to some other device or technique or even, simply, to the general advance in siegecraft. However, the need to include substantial batteries of catapults in the defences seems undoubtedly to have been the major cause of changes in the construction of towers, which tend, from about the middle of the fourth century, to become gradually higher, larger, and more numerous. The first signs of change appear at Messene.

The well-preserved and impressive towers and curtains on the slopes of Mt. Ithome have excited the admiration of all visitors to this site. Pausanias compares the defences of Messene favourably with those of Ambrossos (or Ambrysos, in Boeotia), Rhodes, and Byzantium.[4] It is true that the masonry at Messene is still strikingly beautiful and reveals

---

[1] Gabrici (*Mon. Ant. Lincei*, xxxiii. 101) dated the north-gate defences at Selinus shortly before 250 B.C. Mansel (*Side*, 39) estimates that Side's casemated walls were erected in the second century B.C.

[2] Philon (*Par.* 80. 51 f.) claims, 'When curtains are constructed thus (i.e. as at Rhodes), the expense will be less . . .'. He presumably means that the cost of a solid wall of the same height and width (15 feet) will be greater than that of a casemated wall. Even if he is right, it would surely be much cheaper to modify an existing solid wall, e.g. by increasing its thickness, than to dismantle it completely and erect a new casemated wall in its place.

[3] Casemated walls were fashionable in the tenth century B.C., in Solomon's time (Yadin, 370 ff., e.g. Hazor and Megiddo), but more effective rams made them unpopular in the ninth century.

[4] Paus. iv. 31. 5. For a plan of Messene see especially Blouet, pl. 22; smaller plans are supplied by Frazer, *Pausanias*, iii, facing p. 430, and Kirsten in *RE* 'Messene'. On Ambrossos see Frazer, *Pausanias*, v. 449 ff.

workmanship of high quality, and that the siting of curtains and towers shows full tactical appreciation of the terrain. It is very difficult to believe, however, that this city was anything like so strong as Byzantium and Rhodes.[1] The visitor must beware of letting the imposing situation and the remarkably fine state of preservation lead him into exaggerating the defensive value of Messene's fortifications.

The literary evidence tells us that the city was founded, and the building of the fortifications begun, in 369 B.C. under the auspices of Epaminondas;[2] but one or two modern authorities suggest a considerably later date for the defences now visible.[3] In the best-preserved section, comprising the north wall (excluding the Arcadian Gate) and the northern part of the west wall, two principal building periods can be distinguished on stylistic grounds. All masonry west of the Arcadian Gate is fairly regular isodomic trapezoidal; the towers east of the Arcadian Gate and, possibly, the associated curtains are isodomic ashlar.[4] There are striking differences in construction between the trapezoidal and ashlar towers.

Let us take one rectangular tower as typical of the rectangular and semicircular towers in the trapezoidal west wall.[5] It has one chamber, the floor of which lies at approximately the same level as the rampart walk. The walls of this room are one stone (1 foot 10 inches) thick. Above the chamber, joist holes still visible in the masonry suggest that there was a roof sloping gently towards the rear, so that a slightly precarious platform, protected by battlements, was available for archers and slingers at a height of about 25 feet above external ground level[6]. The chamber has a door in each side-wall, so that defenders can move freely through the tower from one section of the rampart walk to the next, and four apertures which are the most unusual features of the whole construction. They are neither true arrow-slits ($\tau o\xi\iota\kappa a\iota$) nor true windows ($\theta\upsilon\rho\iota\delta\epsilon s$).

---

[1] Byzantium's defences towards the end of the second century A.D., in much the same state as when Pausanias saw them, and being called by Herodian (iii. 2. 1) 'the strongest of city walls', withstood a vigorous and protracted siege (end A.D. 193–December, A.D. 195) by Marius Maximus (*ILS* 2935). The city was starved out (Hdn. iii. 6. 9; Dio, lxxiv. 10–14). On the excellence of Rhodian walls see Strabo, xiv. 2. 5.

[2] D.S. xv. 66. 1 and 6; Paus. iv. 27. 5–7.

[3] Maier ii. 98 n. 151, conveniently summarizes modern views.

[4] Scranton, *Greek Walls*, 112, regards Messene as an example of 'ashlar masonry in which there are occasional joints slightly out of vertical, which do not disturb the general effect'. I stand by the impression recorded in the text. For the trapezoidal style, see my reconstruction of a typical tower in the west wall in Diagram 4b, below, and the photograph of the same tower provided by Lawrence, *Greek Architecture*, pl. 120A. For the ashlar style at Messene, on the other hand, see my reconstruction of tower L east of the Arcadian gate, Diagram 5b, below, and the photographs of this tower supplied by Maier, ii, Tafel 4, Abb. 8, and Lawrence, *Greek Architecture*, pl. 121. [5] See Diagram 4, p. 156, below.

[6] See Diagram 4d which reproduces Blouet's version of the roof arrangement.

Their external width of 1 foot is at least twice as large as that of normal Greek arrow-slits;[1] on the other hand, they preserve a characteristic feature of arrow-slits in that they are wider on the inside (2 feet) than on the outside, whereas windows do not have oblique sides of this sort.[2] Incidentally, the apertures come to a point at the top, which is rather unusual. Neither photographs nor drawings do full justice to the striking and extraordinary appearance of these apertures, which can only be properly appreciated when observed on the spot. I suggest that they represent an early and somewhat crude attempt to provide convenient embrasures for pieces of artillery, which will most probably have been advanced non-torsion machines.

There was never anything to prevent non-torsion or torsion arrow-shooting catapults from projecting their missiles through ordinary arrow-slits, and obviously they often did so. But what is eminently suitable for an archer is by no means always satisfactory for an artilleryman with his catapult. A piece of artillery mounted on a base behind an arrow-slit is virtually confined to shooting along one fixed line; it has no field of fire worth speaking about. But an archer can readily move from side to side, taking advantage of the ingeniously simple arrangement of the oblique side-walls in his slit, and he can thus see and shoot through an arc of almost 45 degrees. Of course, it is quite possible for the operators of small non-torsion and torsion catapults to move their machines laboriously, base and all, from side to side in order to increase the field of fire. This clumsy procedure might not prove entirely ineffective while the besieger was engaged in slow preparatory work in the early stages of an investment; but it would be extremely inefficient, if not altogether useless, during the rapid development of a major assault—just when quick and effective shooting was most required from the defensive catapults.[3]

Again, an archer's eye, as he takes aim, is 3 feet at the most behind the rear of the slit, and only the bow, the arrow, and his left hand may possibly obscure his view of the target. The eye of the artilleryman, looking down the stock from the rear, will be at least 4 or 5 feet behind the rear of the aperture, and his vision will be impeded by the bow of his

[1] The width of Greek arrow-slits on the outside varies between 4 inches and 6 inches and, on the inside, between 1 foot 9 inches and 2 feet. Measurements in excess of these are only found where the masonry has been unduly affected by wear and damage.

[2] Windows in Greek fortifications vary in width between 2 and 3 feet, internal and external width being the same.

[3] In this paragraph, I have been thinking chiefly of apertures suitable for major batteries of artillery mounted in towers. Where a row of smaller engines stands on a straight parapet as at Side, there is obviously not the same need for each individual catapult to have a wide field of fire.

catapult and, above all, by the stock itself when it is cocked up to provide the necessary elevation (i.e. range).[1] If the artilleryman moves
his head sideways, so that he can avoid the stock, check his aim, and
even, perhaps, see that the target is still there, an ordinary arrow-slit will
not be wide enough to let him see the target from the slightly different
angle.

Thus, an arrow-slit is far from being an ideal embrasure for catapults
in towers which should be able to cover a wide front. Hence the designers
of the trapezoidal fortifications at Messene, at a time (*c.* 369–360 B.C.)
when non-torsion artillery was beginning to appear in mainland Greece,[2]
produced experimental apertures which, they hoped, would allow small
non-torsion catapults more scope than arrow-slits. From the point of
view of artillery, towers must be regarded as rather more important than
rampart walks, especially at a period when curtain walls are narrow.
This can best be demonstrated by a simple example. The stock of Zopyrus' relatively small mountain *gastraphetes*, which may well have been
roughly contemporary with the earliest defences at Messene, was 7 feet
long.[3] Four machines of this size would fit into the rectangular trapezoidal
tower that we have just examined, provided that their bases had slightly
different heights and the artillerymen carefully avoided obstructing each
other. But, since the curtains adjacent to the tower are 8 feet 6 inches
wide, and since the battlements protecting the rampart walk are at least
1 foot 6 inches thick, a space only 7 feet wide remains on top of the wall.
Therefore, no engine of the above size could possibly operate on the
rampart walk here unless its aimer stood on thin air behind it.

The unusual apertures, then, in the trapezoidal towers at Messene
represent one of the first Greek efforts to give catapults suitable embrasures.[4] The construction of the later, well-preserved ashlar tower east

---

[1] The view of the target area will be even more seriously hampered, when a catapult is
of the torsion variety, by the spring-frame.

[2] See above, pp. 65 ff.

[3] Biton, W 64 ff. Though intended as a field-piece, this engine can hardly have been
significantly different from a defensive *gastraphetes*.

[4] Woodhouse (*Aetolia*, photograph facing p. 112) observed embrasures of this peculiar
type in the remains of towers at Aetolian Chalcis. The form of the embrasures suggested, he
thought (op. cit. 111), that they were 'merely to supply an outlook for the guard'; but
he was prejudiced, because he believed the defences to be relatively early. The stone-work,
he says, is laid in 'regular courses, but the joints are oblique'. Scranton (*Greek Walls*, 169)
includes Chalcis in a class of masonry which he calls 'irregular trapezoidal verging on
irregular ashlar'. Although I failed to see Chalcis, the verbal descriptions and the photographs strongly suggest that the masonry style is not significantly different to that of the
older defences at Messene. I suggest that the apparently related styles of masonry and the
unusual embrasures point to its being roughly contemporary with the earliest stage at
Messene, i.e. mid-fourth century B.C.

of the Arcadian Gate reveals that fortification designers had now learned two most important lessons: first, the most convenient embrasure for tower-mounted catapults is the window ($\theta v \rho i s$), not a modified arrow-slit; secondly, the higher the defensive catapults can be placed, the better.[1] This tower has two chambers, one above the other. The floor of the lower room is approximately level with the adjacent rampart walk, the tower being solid up to this point—masonry facing with earth-rubble filling. The lower chamber has one door, giving access to the rampart walk on the left, and four normal arrow-slits, two in the front wall and one in each side wall.

Up above, there is what can only be described as an artillery chamber, containing six rather small windows, two in the front wall and two in each of the side walls.[2] Because the windows are situated somewhat close to the corners of the room, it seems likely that only four pieces of artillery would be set up here. The two catapults shooting through the windows in the front wall were probably turned, when required, to operate through the near-by windows in the side walls. Two further engines will have shot through those side windows which lie close to the rear of the chamber. If this reconstruction of the artillery organization is correct, and if the garrison was using non-torsion machines, then the room would comfortably hold four advanced *gastraphetae* equal in size to Zopyrus' engine. If torsion catapults were available by the time this tower was built—and this seems probable—then four three-span or two-cubit catapults could have been easily accommodated. Some boxes of catapult-bolts will have been held in readiness in the upper room, while reserve ammunition was conveniently stored in the lower chamber where the arrow-slits were for the use of archers.

In one course in each of the side walls within the tower the visitor can still see the sockets ($c.\ 3 \times 8$ inches) for the wooden beams that supported the floor of the upper chamber. In fact, we often find in Greek towers that the main joists for floors and roof run from side wall to side wall. Philon notices this feature and gives the reason for it: 'The joists of all towers must be fixed in the side walls, in order that, if the wall facing the enemy is battered and falls, the roof and flooring may remain in position and we may be able to rebuild them.'[3] The course immediately above the one containing the sockets for the joists has been made slightly thinner in all four walls than the lower courses (about 1 foot 10 inches as opposed to

---

[1] For the description which follows see below, p. 157, Diagram 5.
[2] The windows are 2 feet 4 inches high, 2 feet 4 inches wide at the bottom, and 2 feet wide at the top.
[3] Philon, *Par.* 82. 50 ff.

2 feet 1 inch), so that a lip is left (about 3 inches wide) all round.[1] Thus, the floor boards are not only supported on the joists, but are also held up at their extremities by this lip. The floor of the upper room will have fitted very snugly into position. Defenders probably climbed up to the artillery chamber by means of a ladder or simple wooden steps and through a trap-door; when the latter was closed, the entire floor-area of the chamber would be available for the working of the catapults. A simple gabled roof completed the tower; there were no battlements.[2] The windows originally had shutters on the inside, so that catapults had full protection from the weather in the upper room and could be left there for long periods without deteriorating. The shutters may also have been used to screen the artillerymen sometimes from hostile missiles.

The apertures in the earlier trapezoidal tower are just over 15 feet above the level of the ground immediately outside. But here the windows of the ashlar tower are 30 feet above external ground level. It is clear that the designers of fortifications realized more and more, as their experience with artillery developed, how valuable it was to place batteries of catapults as high as possible and thus to gain every scrap of advantage in range. The importance of this may be demonstrated by a hypothetical example, illustrated in Diagram 6.[3] We imagine a defending tower holding one arrow-shooting catapult and one stone-thrower at a height of 36 feet above the ground. But, because the fortification designers have taken full advantage of the terrain, as the Greeks did whenever possible, these machines are actually 96 feet above most of the area over which the besieger must approach (from Y). Also, we make the following assumptions:

1. The besieger's artillery has the same performance as the defending catapults.
2. The maximum effective range of all engines is 400 yards.
3. Arrow-shooting catapults achieve this range with an angle of projection of 30 degrees.
4. Stone-throwers achieve this maximum with an angle of projection of 45 degrees.

In this situation,[4] if the defending arrow-shooter discharges a missile at

---

[1] Lawrence, *Greek Architecture*, pl. 122 (B), provides a photograph of the interior of the tower which illustrates one window, one arrow-slit in the lower chamber, a part of one joist-socket, the lip, and the four small sockets to hold the framework for shutters for the window.

[2] For indication of the gable see Lawrence, op. cit., pl. 121; Maier, ii, Tafel 4, Abb. 8.

[3] p. 157, below.

[4] Naturally, the figures assumed here can only be estimates; but, even if the **real**

an angle of 30 degrees, that missile will travel along the trajectory denoted by the sign *c* and will hit the ground, or a target, at *C*, 450 yards away in terms of horizontal distance. The besieger's arrow-shooting engines, on the other hand, will not be able to reply directly to the defending catapult until they can be set up at point D and can hurl their missiles along the trajectory marked *d*. While the besieger is bringing his arrow-shooting catapults across the strip of ground from C to D or, preferably, to a point closer to the fortifications than D, the artillerymen in the tower at x can engage any suitable target in the area without the slightest interference from the enemy. It has been suggested, of course, that no great accuracy or effectiveness can be expected from catapults shooting at long ranges.[1] There is some truth in this, and certainly no one would attempt to shoot at a single individual at extreme range. But an experienced artilleryman, shooting from a tower belonging to his own city over ground that he knew intimately, would cause considerable consternation and some casualties among gangs of besiegers as they brought up, assembled, and set in position their own engines. He could achieve this even at long range.

The besieger is not, it seems, at quite the same disadvantage with regard to stone-throwers. The stone-thrower in tower X, when laid at an angle of 45 degrees, will discharge its shot along trajectory *a*, and the missile will fall to the ground at A, about 430 horizontal yards away. The besieger can first bring his stone-throwers to bear on the offending upper storey of tower X when he sets them up at B, and when they shoot along trajectory *b*. There is, therefore, a strip of ground nearly 70 yards wide, from A to B, which the defending stone-thrower can cover, but from which besieging stone-throwers cannot engage the artillery chamber in the tower. Furthermore, it will hardly be possible for attacking stone-throwers to shoot effectively even when they are set up at B. They might succeed in obtaining a fair percentage of hits on the masonry; but, at extreme range, the stone shot would be most unlikely to cause serious damage even to the relatively light stone-work of the upper storey of the tower, and the besieger would be very fortunate indeed if one of his stone-throwers managed to project a missile through one of the windows, thus damaging the defending engine.[2]

In practice, in this hypothetical example, the besieger must really set

performance of catapults was rather different, the general picture that emerges from the following discussion would still be valid.

[1] Schramm, *Saalburg*, 25 f.; see above, p. 93 n. 3.

[2] Hits achieved at long range on the more solid lower portions of the tower will not have had much effect.

up both his arrow-shooting catapults and his stone-throwers within 300 yards of the defences if they are to have any chance of neutralizing the battery in the tower. Therefore, the advantage in height gives the defenders the opportunity of shooting at the besiegers during the first 150 yards or so of their approach without fear of effective shooting in reply. Greek fortification designers certainly seem to have made efforts to increase steadily the heights of important artillery-towers, and Philon obviously recognized the value of superior height.[1]

There are several towers in Greek fortifications still standing to a substantial height which closely resemble the tower by the Arcadian Gate at Messene. Tower 6 in the north wall at Paestum may be examined first.[2] The upper storey was restored in the first century B.C. (Sulla's time),[3] and Krischen has reconstructed the tower as it must have looked after this,[4] basing his drawings on the architectural fragments found near by.[5] The lower parts of the tower, however, up to the top of the first chamber, are much earlier, dating certainly between 330 and 273 B.C. and probably, I think, between 330 and 300 B.C.[6] The original upper storey will have been simple and plain, as opposed to the somewhat ornate Sullan restoration, but will have possessed windows in much the same positions— two in the front wall, and probably two in each of the side walls. Thus, its appearance was probably very similar to that of the corresponding tower at Messene, though it did not project so far from the wall by any means.[7] It will be noticed that its windows were over 38 feet above external ground level, whereas the Messenian tower's windows are only 30 feet above the ground. However, this extra height was not really due to conscious planning, but to the fact that the rampart walk (and, consequently, the solid lower portion of the tower) at Paestum is over 7 feet higher than at Messene.

There are two towers at Tithorea in Phocis which still stand up to the level of their windows.[8] The broached trapezoidal fortifications to which they belong have been assigned to the period shortly after 338 B.C.,[9]

---

[1] Philon, *Par.* 81. 37–39.

[2] See Diagram 7, below. For plan of Paestum see now Schläger, Abb. 1. Schläger's tower 6 = Krischen's tower 5.   [3] Schläger, 25 f.

[4] Krischen, *Stadtmauern*, 24, Abb. 22, Tafeln 7 and 8. Schläger, Tafel 9. 1, provides a photograph of its present state.

[5] Krischen, *Stadtmauern*, Tafel 30.

[6] Schläger, 23. Lucanians were then masters of Paestum, but the fortification designers and masons will have been Greek.

[7] As a result of the addition later of an extra face to the curtains, this tower lost what little projection (3 feet) it originally had.

[8] See Diagram 8, p. 159, below.

[9] Tillard, in *BSA* xvii (1910–11), 54 ff., 71, figs. 9 and 10.

though this dating has been criticized.[1] The windows in the large tower at the western end of the north wall are a foot or two lower than in the similar tower at Messene; but the internal dimensions of the rooms are almost exactly the same. Again, at Lilaea in Phocis, near the lower end of the acropolis wall as it descends to the plain and the site of the main city wall, there lies a similar, though slightly smaller, tower.[2] Its front wall still rises to the level of the windows, and one window is fully preserved. The arrangements here show some variations, however. The lower chamber is below the level of the rampart walk, which was probably at the same height as the floor of the upper room. Also, in the seventh course now visible in the front wall, on the inside directly under the surviving window, there occurs what appears to be a joist-socket, 9 inches by 9 inches in size. This tower is, thus, exceptional in its flooring system, because the joists ought to run, as we have seen, from side wall to side wall.[3]

Let us now sum up the features of towers of this type. They have walls which are formed of one layer of stones; they are generally solid up to the level of the adjoining rampart walks; there are two chambers, the lower fitted with arrow-slits and the upper with windows. All these towers could accommodate a battery of four small catapults, almost certainly arrow-shooting engines, at a fair height above the ground.[4] I would tentatively suggest that towers of this type came into fashion in the period from 350 to 320 B.C. when Greek architects obviously had to grapple very seriously with the defensive problems created by the advances in siege-technique in general, and by the development of the more powerful torsion artillery in particular.

The great ashlar tower (A) at Aegosthena represents in all probability the next logical stage in the quest for height.[5] Unfortunately, no one has so far uncovered all the details of its construction. Benson found that the inner surfaces of its walls had been daubed over, so that joist-sockets and other indications of floorings were no longer visible. In fact, it apparently served as a dwelling for a hermit. In 1953 I discovered that some tramp had barricaded his possessions most effectively in an upper chamber, hence only the lowest storey could be entered and inspected from the inside.[6] However, my observations, though restricted, together with

---

[1] By Maier, ii. 98 n. 154.   [2] See Diagram 9, p. 159 below.
[3] See above, p. 130.   [4] 28 to 38 feet.
[5] Diagram 10, p. 160 below, illustrates the following description. On Aegosthena in general see E. F. Benson, 'Aegosthena', in *JHS* 15 (1895), 314 ff. and plans 1 and 2, pls. ix and x (photographs); Lawrence, *Greek Architecture*, pl. 127 (photo).
[6] This unique monument ought certainly to be carefully restored and preserved.

Benson's remarks provide enough material for a reasonably accurate re-construction.

Tower A certainly comprised three storeys. Benson, it is true, believed that it possessed two chambers.[1] He apparently assumed that the lower and middle rooms formed one extremely lofty chamber with two 'narrow oblong windows', i.e. arrow-slits. But the upper arrow-slit must have been associated with an intermediate floor, otherwise it would seem to have been particularly purposeless. Also, the joists of such a floor will have contributed significantly to the stability of the whole building—rather an important point in view of its height. Tower A is solid for a height of some 20 feet. The stone facing walls which enclosed the earth-rubble filling are of double thickness (c. 3 feet); i.e. they are formed of two layers of carefully dressed stones, only the outer face of the exterior layer being left rough (quarry face). The walls continue double in this manner at least to the top of the first chamber, as is quite evident from examination of the sides of the door and arrow-slit in this lowest room.

Whereas the earlier towers possess walls only one stone thick, this great tower requires thicker walls in its lower portion in order to allow greater height to be attained. Since the walls are now made of two layers of stone, headers are needed to bind the layers together. It will be noticed (in Diagram 10b) that courses of headers and stretchers alternate from the socle to the level of the lowest floor. Above this point headers have been so inserted that they appear from the outside in a rough quincunx formation. In fact, some headers seemingly occur in the walls of the second chamber, and this may mean that the double walls continued up to the floor of the third chamber. But, until a thorough clearing of this tower is undertaken and its construction becomes completely intelligible, the matter must remain in doubt.

The third and topmost storey, which is sufficiently well preserved to show that it had a simple gabled roof, incorporates three windows (c. 3×3 feet) in each of the three outer sides. It is not very easy to determine accurately the total height of the tower and, consequently, the height above ground level of the battery of up to nine rather small (three-span, two-cubit) arrow-shooting engines which will have operated through the embrasures. Benson gives a curious combination of measurements—under 20 feet to the floor of the lowest chamber, and then $11\frac{1}{2}$ metres (37 feet 8 inches) from that point to the gable. But I calculated 22 feet from exterior ground level to the lowest floor so that the total height may have been as much as 60 feet, a figure that has been proposed more

[1] Benson, op. cit. 316.

than once as a rough estimate. I have adopted this round figure for Diagram 10. At any rate, this tower is about the same height as the Sullan tower by the Vesuvius Gate at Pompeii (see Diagram 11) as reconstructed by the Italians (58 feet). Furthermore, the windows at Aegosthena are between 51 and 53 feet above external ground level, whereas the embrasures of the artillery-chamber in the tower at Pompeii are only $42\frac{1}{2}$ feet above the ground outside.

Unless tower A at Aegosthena has nothing whatsoever to do with artillery, Scranton's extremely tentative date for it, early fourth century, does not make sense.[1] If its construction bears any relation to the development of artillery, it will have been constructed in the final quarter of the fourth century or, more probably, in the first quarter of the third century. No other towers of this sort are anything like so well preserved as the example at Aegosthena. Dilapidated towers, which appear, at first sight, to belong to the same category, may actually have been built in accordance with a variant design. There are several variations on the three-chambered towers with double-thickness walls in their lower courses.

At Eleutherae, the Attic border fort, six fairly well-preserved towers lie along the north wall protecting the most vulnerable portion of the small circuit.[2] Four of them had three chambers each; but, unlike Aegosthena's tower A, each one carries its lowest chamber with its floor level with the ground inside the fort, and a doorway in the rear wall allows access to the room, which has no other opening (i.e. no arrow-slit or window). The tower walls are two stones (c. 3 feet) thick up to the top of this lowest chamber; above this point they are thinner (c. 2 feet), being only one stone thick. Thus, the floor of the middle room rested on the ledge (c. 1 foot wide) formed by the reduction in wall thickness. This middle chamber is level with the rampart walk to which access is provided by a doorway in each side wall, and it has arrow-slits. One tower still stands to sufficient height to reveal quite large (9×9 inches) beam sockets which provide ample evidence for another substantial floor, that of a third chamber—almost certainly intended for artillery.[3] These towers,

---

[1] *Greek Walls*, 81, 176.

[2] On Eleutherae see Wrede, *Attische Mauern*, 32 f. (on Bilden 83–6); Wrede calls the place Gyphtokastro (Panakton), the names of the border forts in this area being much disputed. By Eleutherae I mean the fort on the road from Eleusis to Thebes and guarding the southern end of the Dryoscephalae pass.

[3] We must point out that this tower with the beam sockets is not one of the four towers now under consideration. This fifth tower, however, and the sixth are similar to the first four in every way except that they are solid up to the height of the rampart walk and, consequently, have no chamber at internal ground level.

For photographs see Wrede, *Attische Mauern*, Bilden 85 (tower 3) and 86 (tower 6); Lawrence, *Greek Architecture*, pl. 119.

then, have three chambers like the great tower at Aegosthena; yet the height of the presumed artillery-chamber will only be the same, approximately, as in the later towers at Messene. The purpose of the lowest room remains far from clear. Perhaps it provided storage space; after all, in time of peace, catapults and other defensive paraphernalia must be stored somewhere. In a large city like Athens there were adequate arsenals in which important defensive equipment could be carefully preserved, but the same facilities would not have been available in a small border fort. On the whole, however, we cannot help feeling that this design for towers, which produces some weakness in the region of its base and still does not produce any advantage in height, definitely represents an error of judgement on the part of the architects.[1]

The north-east corner tower (no. 2) at Paestum belongs to the same basic type as the first four towers at Eleutherae.[2] But here both the lower and the middle chambers are below the level of the rampart walk. The lowest room has two arrow-slits in its front wall as well as a doorway in its rear wall leading to the interior of the city and thus has some offensive purpose. The extant remains show tower 2 as it was after extensive rebuilding some time in the period 273 B.C. (when Paestum became a Roman colony), at the earliest, to about 220 B.C.[3] Its design before the rebuilding may, possibly, have been basically the same.

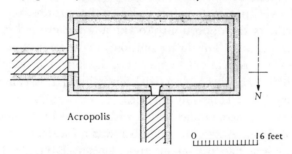

FIG. 4. Plan of large tower on the acropolis at Lilaea

In spite of these variations, some towers exist which seem originally to have resembled tower A at Aegosthena very closely. A splendid corner tower in an important position on the acropolis at Lilaea in Phocis is an extremely fine example (see Fig. 4). It has double walls (*c.* 3 feet thick), which originally retained this size at least to the top of the lowest

[1] Towers B and C at Aegosthena are also hollow down to interior ground level; but their walls are only one stone thick, and they probably had only two chambers.
[2] See Krischen, *Stadtmauern*, 20, Abb. 17 and 18. For photographs see Schläger, Taf. 4. 2 and 5. 1.
[3] Schläger, 24.

chamber. The tower is solid to the level of the rampart walk, that is to say, for the first 15 feet of its height. The lowest, and only surviving, room has a door leading on to one section of the rampart walk, an arrow-slit to enfilade the outer face of one curtain, and a slightly unusual window to cover the rampart walk of the other adjacent curtain. The tower measures 39 feet by 15 feet internally, so that its topmost chamber could have accommodated a really formidable battery of perhaps six catapults shooting out of the southern wall against a besieger's most favourable approach.

So far, then, the evidence examined suggests a very simple sequence of artillery-towers which we may summarize as follows, having first introduced one or two tentative conclusions about earlier towers:

Pre-artillery towers

Little is known for certain about their superstructure, if any; but there were probably two basic types:

1. Mere protuberances, rectangular or semicircular, from the outer face of the main wall, rising to the same height as the wall and having no chamber. Elementary towers like this served two main purposes. First, they provided at appropriate points enlarged open platforms from which larger units of archers and slingers, etc., could operate than was possible from the relatively narrow rampart walks on the curtains. Secondly, they allowed defenders the opportunity to enfilade the ground immediately outside the main wall. This latter purpose was often achieved with less expense in early fortifications by means of the indented trace,[1] a system still employed in a hastily constructed defence line in the second half of the fourth century (the Dema wall in Attica).

2. Towers with one chamber, fitted with arrow-slits, its floor being at rampart-walk level. Above the chamber was a battlemented platform. Such constructions had two main advantages over type 1. They raised the archers, slingers, etc., to a high level, which might lead to more effective shooting. Also, they offered moderately comfortable quarters for watchmen in time of crisis in the covered chamber.

Artillery towers

3. This type developed from type 2, above, which it closely resembled. The older towers at Messene are the only definite example, though the towers at Aetolian Chalcis may have been rather similar. The sole modification is the substitution of primitive embrasures for the arrow-

[1] See Scranton, *Greek Walls*, 149 ff.

slits in the chamber, so that catapults can shoot with some effect from the room which provides the machinery with reasonable protection against inclement weather.

4. The later, ashlar towers at Messene belong to this type, which has two chambers, the upper one being equipped with windows through which the catapults can shoot conveniently from a higher level. The upper chamber can be regarded as a development of the old battlemented platform which has now been provided with a light roof.

There was possibly a variant form of this type wherein a tower has two chambers but one of these lies below the level of the ramparts.

5. Towers with three chambers, the highest being built with embrasures for artillery, which has thus been given even greater advantage in range. Variant forms exist in which one or two of the chambers lie below the level of the curtain's parapet.

The above scheme may represent the basic line of development in the first phase of the defensive reaction to artillery. The principal object was to provide suitable covered batteries for relatively light arrow-shooting catapults at the greatest possible height. For various reasons, it seems improbable that any of the towers so far studied was intended to carry stone-throwers, except possibly very small ones indeed. The small square windows are most unsuitable for stone-throwing artillery which will do much of its most effective shooting at high angles of elevation (30 to 45 degrees). Stone-throwers require taller windows, somewhat more robust towers, and better facilities for getting the machines in and out of the chambers. Before discussing more advanced constructions, however, we shall next proceed to examine the possible influence of catapults on the choice of shapes for towers.

§ 3. Tower Shapes

Both rectangular and semicircular towers occur early in the Bronze Age in the Near East.[1] Both types were used in the Greek world in the classical period before the fourth-century revolution in siegecraft, the rectangular sort being the more common, mainly because semicircular towers were perhaps more difficult and expensive to build. In the west wall of Messene some of the earliest artillery-towers are rectangular, others semicircular. Even at this primitive stage, designers will have

[1] Yadin, 53 ff. In fact, there seems to have been a circular tower at Jericho about 7,000 B.C., though its exact purpose is uncertain; for a convenient summary of the evidence see Yadin, 32 ff., 115 (photo).

begun to consider which tower shapes provide the most advantageous fields of fire for catapults in any given set of circumstances.

We must first estimate the field of fire of a single catapult placed behind a window (θυρίς). The factors that will affect this are: the calibre of the catapult; the width of the window; the thickness of the wall in which the window lies. Let us take a very favourable example (Fig. 5) where

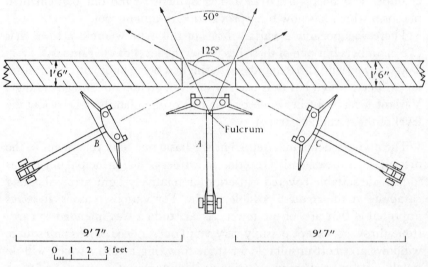

FIG. 5. Fields of fire for a catapult shooting through a window.

the wall is quite thin (1 foot 6 inches), the embrasure wide (3 feet) by Greek standards, and the catapult fairly small (two-cubit).[1] If such a catapult is set up on its base in position A in Fig. 5, its operator can aim it through the window and shoot along any line within an arc of 50 degrees simply by turning its stock around the vertical fulcrum of the universal joint. In other words, he operates his engine in the normal and most convenient manner. But, if he wishes to obtain a larger field of fire, he must move his machine, base and all, setting it up in a series of positions on either side of A. The extreme positions in each direction are represented in Fig. 5 by the outlines of catapults at B and C. In this somewhat laborious and inefficient way a theoretical field of fire of 125 degrees can be obtained.

It would have been very difficult, however, and sometimes impossible, to achieve such a wide arc in practice. A floor space at least 9 feet wide,

[1] The narrower the window, or the larger the catapult, or the thicker the wall, the smaller will be the field of fire.

starting from the nearer side of the window, is required for each of the extreme positions B and C, and this does not allow room for the operator to stand at the rear of the stock. On one side of the window, let us say towards C, the side wall of a rectangular tower would probably limit the space available to something less than 4 feet.[1] In the other direction, towards the centre of the tower, it would be possible to place the catapult in position B; but this would mean drastic interference with other catapults shooting through neighbouring windows. In fact, a field of fire of 125 degrees could only be attained when one single catapult had sole use of all the windows (normally two or three) in one wall of a tower. It would obviously be altogether better if towers and windows were so arranged that every catapult remained in position A behind its window, capable of operating without difficulty through an angle of 50 degrees, and that, nevertheless, the combined fields of fire of all machines amply covered the terrain over which a besieger would advance.[2] Greek designers were alive, it seems, to the problem of achieving this effect.

(a) Rectangular towers

Bearing the above considerations in mind, we now examine the fields of fire obtainable from a rectangular tower. The arcs of fire available with a tower (A) in a long straight wall will be as illustrated in Fig. 6, p. 142. Although there will be two or three catapults shooting through the two or three windows in each of the three embrasured sides of the tower, a single segment suffices to indicate the fields of fire covered by all catapults shooting through one side. The centre line of the arc covered by machines shooting through the front wall lies, of course, at right angles to that wall. But, if the same arrangement was employed for catapults shooting through the side walls, half the field of fire would lie uselessly behind the defences. Therefore, the catapults which provide flanking fire will be so placed behind their windows that one edge of their shooting arc runs along the base of the circuit wall, as shown in Fig. 7, p. 142. The stock of the catapult at D (Fig. 7, p. 142) can swing freely from E to F. Although its position, as can be seen, reduces the field of fire here from 50 degrees to about 41 degrees, the whole of the lesser arc is useful.

[1] Two feet from window to side wall in tower 6 at Paestum (see Diagram 7, p. 158); 3 feet 4 inches in the tower by the Arcadian Gate at Messene (see Diagram 5, p. 157) and in similar towers.

[2] If the catapult is larger than the two-cubit calibre, or if other factors are unfavourable, the readily attainable field of fire will naturally be less than 50 degrees. In very restricting circumstances it may even be reduced to as little as 25 degrees. In such conditions it would be even more important to work out the most suitable design for the fortifications holding artillery; but, for the present, we shall keep to the 50-degree arc.

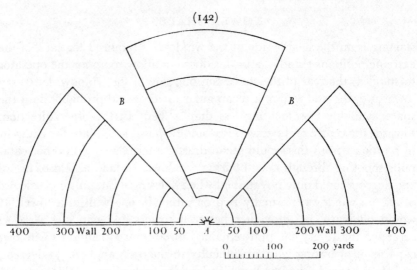

400   300 Wall 200   100 50   *A*   50 100   200 Wall 300   400

0   100   200 yards

FIG. 6. Fields of fire from a rectangular tower

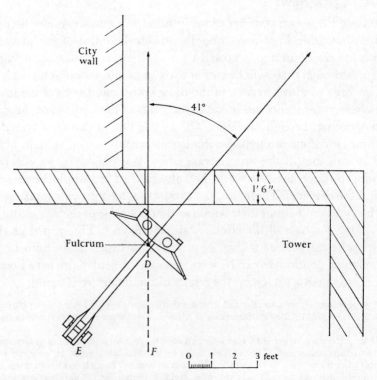

City wall

41°

1′ 6″

Fulcrum

Tower

D

E   *F*

0   1   2   3 feet

FIG. 7. Field of fire for a catapult shooting through the side window of a tower

To return to Fig. 6, p. 142; while every effort has been made to produce the best effect, the areas marked B, opposite the forward corners of
the tower, cannot normally be covered. Of course, if targets appear in the
areas BB, as they will if the enemy has his wits about him, some catapults
in the tower can be brought to bear on them with certain difficulty.
Moreover, if tower A is just one of a row of towers, then catapults in
neighbouring towers will easily cover the areas BB, and tower A will
assist its neighbours in the same way. But, when a tower is in an exposed
or isolated position, its inability to cover the areas BB may prove em-
barrassing, and then designers must look for a more suitable shape for
a tower.

(b) *Semicircular and round towers*

Semicircular and round towers now come into consideration. Fig. 8
shows how catapults in a semicircular tower (A), with four suitably

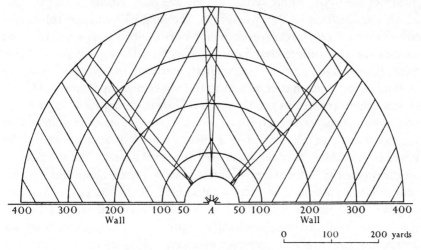

Fig. 8. Fields of fire from a semicircular tower

sited embrasures, easily cover completely a full arc of 180 degrees. If
necessary, one could so site the windows that a smaller total arc was
covered more intensively by the available artillery. In fact, it is much
easier to adjust the positions of the windows when building semicircular
towers in order to achieve the most effective coverage of selected areas.
Semicircular towers also possessed, as Philon maintained,[1] superior resistance to shot from hostile stone-throwers, which would be inclined to

[1] Philon, *Par.* 84. 24 ff.

glance off in any case. Because of these characteristics, circular and semi-circular towers were often used at exposed points in Greek circuits. There is a very good example of this feature in improvements to the defences on the Aspis hill at Argos constructed shortly after 280 B.C.[1] The additions to the older oval circuit on the Aspis took the form of a triangular salient, pointing in a north-easterly direction, with a semicircular tower at its tip. The foundations of the latter construction are still visible. The tower has a diameter of 36 feet, and its walls are 3 feet thick at its base. This shape was obviously chosen here so that a fairly formidable battery of catapults in this one tower, without much assistance, could effectively cover every portion of a wide arc.[2]

Similarly, in a rather less isolated position, the designers of the new defences outside the north gate at Selinus shortly before 250 B.C. decided on a pair of semicircular towers.[3] One of them faces approximately north, the other west. Krischen has produced valuable plans and re-constructions of the whole system of defences here outside the north gate which include, besides the two towers, the long hall with corridors dis-cussed above.[4] The larger tower, facing north, survives to a height of six courses and has an internal diameter of 64 feet. Its outer wall is $7\frac{1}{2}$ feet thick. Krischen reconstructs it as a squat, powerful, two-storeyed building with a height of just under 28 feet to the top of the upper storey. He ad-vances cogent reasons in favour of this. While it is impossible to prove or disprove the existence of a third storey conclusively, many considerations suggest that there was not one.[5] It was essential to avoid masking the tower in the older defences some 30 yards to the rear. The cross-walls, which divide the lower storey into five small compartments without em-brasures, were intended to carry a substantial floor capable of sustaining a heavy load. But, in view of the weak and interrupted rear wall of the tower, the useful thickness of which is a bare 2 feet, and because there are indications that the roof was rather heavy, it is most unlikely that the floor of a third storey plus this weighty roof could have been adequately

[1] W. Vollgraff in *Mnemosyne*, 44 (1916), 219 ff. Argos borrowed money from Rhodes to repair her walls after expelling Antigonus' garrison, 280–279 B.C.

[2] On the Aspis defences in general see W. Vollgraff, 'Fouilles d'Argos', in *BCH* 31 (1907), 149 ff. and pls. v and vi.

[3] The latest works here have often inspired comparison (somewhat to the detriment of Selinus) with the Euryalus fort at Syracuse and have been attributed to Hermocrates and the year 407 B.C. Krischen (*Stadtmauern*, 33) assigned them to the end of the fourth century (Agathocles). Gabrici's excavations have shown that the works outside the north gate belong to the period shortly before the destruction of Selinus c. 250 B.C. For a convenient brief sum-mary see A. W. Lawrence in *JHS* 66 (1948), 99 ff.

[4] See above, p. 125.

[5] Krischen, *Stadtmauern*, 29 f.

supported without the inclusion of wooden columns which would have greatly reduced the space available in the second storey and impeded the operation of catapults at that level.

Certainly the tower was capable of holding a considerable battery of catapults, both stone-throwers and arrow-firers, and of affording the machines an excellent and complete field of fire. This was definitely the main reason for the choice of shape. The rear of the tower originally had a large opening into both storeys, the entrance to the lower storey being divided into two by a stone pillar, while the opening at second-storey level was probably divided in the same way by a wooden column.[1] Krischen believed that the purpose of the frail and open rear was to reduce the chance of a besieger's making effective use of the tower if he succeeded in capturing it in moderately good condition.[2] But just as important, if not more so, is the fact that this arrangement facilitated the rapid transfer of artillery—even heavy pieces—into and out of the tower. Philon considered this essential.[3] The north tower at Selinus was capacious enough to contain at least one thirty-mina stone-thrower as well as stone- and arrow-shooting engines of smaller calibres. Its formidable battery could remain in action until the last possible minute against the successful approach of a determined besieger. Then, by means of a simple block and tackle, without any dismantling other than the detachment of the engine proper from its base, even the largest catapult could be lowered on to a wagon waiting in the courtyard behind and run rapidly to a new position within the older defences to the rear.

Philon emphasizes the defensive value of the thirty-mina stone-thrower, particularly against approach-galleries and mobile siege-sheds, and recommends that special attention be paid to erecting platforms and training detachments for machines of this calibre.[4] But in surviving Hellenistic fortifications there exist very few traces of towers or other defensive constructions capable of providing an operational area suitable for a catapult with a stock 19 feet long, a spring-frame 9 feet wide by 10 feet high, and an arm-span of 12 feet. The semicircular tower at Selinus could have accommodated such an engine comfortably.

On the evidence of Selinus we may possibly suspect that, about the middle of the third century, some designers were beginning to favour the abandonment of high, but relatively flimsy, artillery-towers and the introduction instead of low bastions with powerful walls. In other words,

---

[1] Krischen, Stadtmauern, Taf. 13.

[2] Ibid. 30; Krischen (Herakleia, 31) interprets similar wide openings in the rear of towers at Latmian Heracleia in the same way.

[3] Philon, Par. 81. 34–7.   [4] Ibid. Pol. 95. 49–96, 14.

the increasing efficiency of stone-throwers against walls caused Greek engineers to adopt, in a primitive way, some features of the famous system of ground-hugging defences which Vauban and Cormontaigne introduced in France in the seventeenth century. But the situations are quite different. In general, ancient stone-throwers never remotely approached the range or destructive power of gunpowder-artillery. Their effect on properly constructed walls is highly questionable. Even if they caused trouble when used against the upper storeys of the comparatively light towers built during the first reaction to the introduction of the catapult, there is no reason to suppose that ancient designers did not satisfactorily solve the problem by increasing the thickness of tower walls without sacrificing height. Also, at Selinus, as we have already pointed out, we are dealing with additional defences which could not be allowed to screen batteries in the older fortifications to their rear.

There exists a most interesting and instructive semicircular tower at the east end of the acropolis at *Paravola*, perhaps the ancient Boukation, in Aetolia.[1] It lies at the junction of the city wall with the defences of the acropolis, an awkward point. One chamber still remains, its floor being roughly level with the acropolis rampart walk. There was certainly another floor above this, but it is not possible to say now whether there was an upper chamber with a roof or simply a platform with battlements. The existing chamber has three windows, through which three fairly small (three-span, two-cubit) arrow-shooting catapults could operate. One of these effectively covered the approach of the enemy from the direction A in Diagram 12d, and, if the enemy penetrated into the lower city, the other engines could easily engage hostile parties approaching the acropolis from the direction B or along the rampart of the lower city wall. If a rectangular tower had been built here, it would merely have pointed ineffective corners towards the approaches *A* and *B*. Hence, the semicircular shape had great advantages in this situation.

Fully circular towers are not uncommon, but seldom survive much above the lower courses. They are often associated with gate defences, and the two best-preserved examples appear in the older main gate at Perge (third or early second century B.C.).[2] They are at least 60 feet high with an external diameter of just over 38 feet. The walls are three stones thick (7 feet 3 inches) all the way up, with a comprehensive header-and-stretcher system to bind the layers together, so that the diameter of the

---

[1] Woodhouse, *Aetolia*, 190 ff. For photograph see Lawrence, *Greek Architecture*, pls. 124–6. For the description which follows see Diagram 12d, below.
[2] See Lanckoronski, 61 ff. and figs. 46–8.

circular chambers within is practically 24 feet. The towers seem to have
been solid for the first 20 feet or so of their height; then each had three
chambers one above the other. The lowest room possessed two or three
arrow-slits. Although the superstructure in both towers is dilapidated,
windows can still be seen in both the middle and upper rooms of the
eastern tower. It appears that the intermediate chamber had two or
three windows and that there were no fewer than eight in the top
chamber. While the architectural decoration shows that the towers were
intended to impress visitors approaching the main gate of Perge, they
would clearly become powerful defences in emergency, each holding
a battery of arrow-shooting, and perhaps one or two stone-throwing,
catapults.

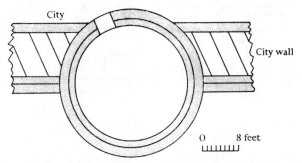

FIG. 9. Plan of round tower in the south wall at Paestum

The projecting north-east corner at Plataea was protected by a circular
tower (Diagram 12c), having an internal diameter of 31 feet. Only the
foundations survive. Since its walls are only 2 feet thick (one stone) at the
base, it must have been a somewhat frail affair. Definitely stronger,
though not so powerful as the round towers at Perge, are some circular
towers at Paestum, apparently incorporated in the defences between
273 and 220 B.C. The one illustrated above (Fig. 9) stands near the
east gate (*Porta Justitiae*). Its walls are nearly 4 feet thick, the external
diameter being practically 33 feet.

(c) Hexagonal towers

Whereas rectangular and round towers existed for centuries before the
invention of the catapult, it is possible that hexagonal and pentagonal
towers were developed specifically to offer more effective fields of fire
for artillery. Fig. 10, p. 148, shows the complete coverage that can be
obtained with catapults operating in a hexagon. The two front corners of
a rectangular tower, as it were, have been replaced by two oblique walls,

in each of which an additional window will have been fitted. Unfortunately no hexagonal tower survives above the level of the rampart walk, so that it is no longer possible to check the upper structure of this type of tower. Philon recommended the use of hexagons at gateways,

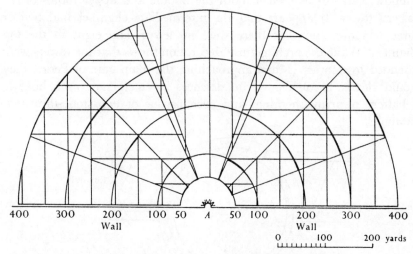

FIG. 10. Fields of fire from a hexagonal tower

partly because they could provide superior fields of fire.[1] Several instances of this usage occur at Mantinea.[2] Asine (Argolid) possesses a powerful hexagonal tower, probably put up about 280 B.C., very close to a gateway on its eastern side.[3] At Argos, the foundations of a hexagon can be seen at the junction of the lower city wall with the defences on the Aspis hill (see Diagram 12b). This situation reminds us of the similar meeting of walls at *Paravola* (Boukation?) where, as we have seen (above, p. 146), the difficulty of covering awkward approaches was overcome by the use of a semicircular tower. The Aspis hexagon could obviously solve the same problem in an equally satisfactory way.

(d) Pentagonal towers

Philon certainly does not regard pentagonal towers as abnormal.[4] He even mentions a saw-toothed system of fortification, invented by Philip II's Thessalian engineer, Polyidus, in which all the towers were apparently

---

[1] Philon, *Par.* 79. 21 ff., and see above, p. 114.   [2] See Diagram 13 below.
[3] Scranton, *Greek Walls,* 67 f., 165. Scranton classes the masonry as coursed polygonal and dates it in the late fourth or early third century.
[4] Philon, *Par.* 79. 11 f. Philon simply lists pentagons along with hexagonal and rectangular towers.

to be pentagonal.[1] But I have only seen one pentagon (built 273–220 B.C.) in the south wall at Paestum (see Diagram 12a for its plan).[2]

This tower survives only a few courses high. It was solid up to the level of the rampart walk, except for a portion towards the rear where a small flight of stone steps leads down to a little corridor and a neat sally-port. The measurements of the sides are not quite regular. Fig. 11 shows the fields of fire from a pentagonal tower. If the terrain in front

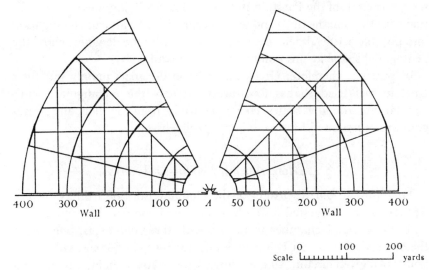

400   300   200   100 50   *A*   50 100   200   300   400

Wall   Wall

0   100   200

Scale   yards

FIG. 11. Fields of fire from a pentagonal tower

of the tower seems likely to prevent the advance of besiegers directly against it, then the fire-power of that tower can be safely directed to the flanks, thus catching the enemy in cross-fire from the side when he is approaching neighbouring stretches of the fortifications. Pentagonal towers can achieve this effect easily. Although natural or artificial obstacles, or both, prevent the besieger from moving right up to the offending pentagon, he may be able to engage it with his artillery from a point within reasonable range. But, even if this happens, the pentagonal tower will offer a most inconvenient target, because stone shot will tend to glance off the oblique front walls.

Pentagons had one or two obvious drawbacks, however. Only with great difficulty could their catapults be set up to cover the ground directly in front, and, with all the machinery available to a besieger for levelling ground, it would take a very sanguine fortification-designer indeed to

---

[1] Ibid. 83. 7–12.   [2] Von Gerkan identified another at Dura (Europus).

affirm that any given tower-site was directly unapproachable. Then again, it would be almost impossible to make full use of both the oblique front walls at the same time. The stocks of the catapults and their artillerymen behind the embrasures in one oblique wall would be inclined to interfere quite seriously with the catapults and operating detachments behind the other oblique wall. In fact, circumstances in which pentagons are ideal for batteries of catapults must be rare. A detailed study of the terrain in front of the Paestum pentagon, a careful estimate of the condition of the area in the third and second centuries B.C., and an investigation into possible artificial defences might suggest why the designers chose the pentagonal shape at this point in the south wall.

In practice, therefore, Greek fortification designers mainly put their trust in well-tried shapes for towers, namely the rectangular, semi-circular, and round varieties. Hexagons are far from common, and pentagons are represented by two solitary specimens.

§ 4. *More Advanced Artillery Towers*

To return to our discussion of the characteristics of artillery towers, we have so far suggested a simple sequence of construction from towers with one covered chamber to towers with three chambers, one above the other, the latter sort being generally confined to the most vulnerable points of a given circuit. All these towers are relatively light, any thickening of their walls in the lower portions being due entirely to the effort to produce greater height above the solid base. They have floors of the simplest possible construction, small windows (at most, 3×3 feet), ordinary doorways (*c.* 3 feet wide by 6 feet 6 inches high), and plain gabled roofs generally. Towers belonging to this series certainly remained in use until the first century A.D., especially the two-chambered sort (or the three-chambered kind where the lowest room was below the level of the rampart walk). In some places new towers of similar design continued to be built, perhaps, along the less critical sections of city circuits. But, from the end of the fourth century B.C. onwards, the evidence of existing fortifications suggests that more powerful artillery-towers were gradually developed.

One of the first notable features is an increase in the thickness of tower walls. There are three possible reasons for this. First, the thicker walls may be designed to support towers of even greater height. If walls two stones thick in the lower courses can carry a tower with three superimposed chambers, as in tower A at Aegosthena, then walls three stones thick near the base might conceivably be suitable for a tower with four superimposed chambers, and so on. A second possibility is that the greater thickness was meant to provide not more height, but greater stability, so that heavier artillery could be accommodated. Thirdly, the stouter walls may represent an effort to build towers that would be more resistant to heavy stone shot.[1]

As far as the possible desire for even greater height is concerned, the evidence of the existing remains of Greek fortifications, fragmentary at the best of times, seems by no means conclusive. But, if we judge from the relatively few powerful towers that still stand to a fair height, we find no positive indications that any tower ever possessed more than three superimposed chambers, where the floor of the lowest room lay at approximately the same level as the rampart walk. Thus, the maximum height of important towers apparently settled down at a figure of about 60 feet above external ground level. The very powerful and imposing towers along the north-west wall at Pompeii (see Diagram 11, p. 161), built in the first century B.C., still conformed to this rule, being about 58 feet high. The thickening of tower walls, then, was due to a combination of the other two possible reasons, greater stability and more substantial resistance to hostile shot.

A well-preserved tower in the east wall at Perge, probably constructed in the third century B.C., provides a good example of a fairly early kind of strengthened construction equipped to include one or two stone-throwers in its armament.[2] The tower is solid up to the level of the rampart walk. It has two chambers and walls of double thickness (4 feet; i.e. about 1 foot thicker than in tower A at Aegosthena) up to the ceiling of the first chamber. The walls of the upper room are just under 2 feet thick, and its floor rests on the ledge formed by the contraction of the wall thickness. Thus, this tower is not so high as tower A at Aegosthena, but its artillery-chamber offers a more stable platform suitable for heavier machines. Another significant point is that the windows, 2 feet 7 inches wide, have a height of 5 feet 3 inches. They therefore provide ample opportunity for small stone-throwers to shoot at high angles of elevation. For instance, each tower of this type could incorporate in its armament at least one five-mina stone-thrower (with a stock about 10 feet 6 inches long; an arm-span of about 7 feet). Thirteen towers like this originally lay along

---

[1] Philon (Par. 81. 9) recommends 10 cubits (15 feet) for the thickness of tower walls. He even says they should be 'not less than ten cubits'. In practice, the walls of ancient towers nowhere approach this figure which seems unnecessarily large.

[2] See below, Diagram 14; also Diagram 2a for restored rear of the tower. For photographs see Lawrence, Greek Architecture, pls. 128, 129A; Maier, ii, Taf. 7.

the more or less straight east wall at Perge, producing coverage of the ground outside in a manner similar to, but approximately twice as dense as, that illustrated in Diagram 1, below. It would seem that Demetrius Poliorcetes' assaults on the landward side at Rhodes ran into an artillery barrage of this density.[1] The tower at Perge possesses advantages in stability and weight-carrying capacity which almost certainly outweigh a certain sacrifice in height. I have not discovered any evidence for the size of the opening in the rear of the tower. It may have been considerably wider than the mere doorway shown in Diagram 2a, below.

At Latmian Heracleia there still exist a few moderately preserved examples of extremely powerful artillery towers.[2] These are basically rectangular and semicircular, though some towers have certain variations. Sturdier floors seem to be a new feature. The floors in older towers were constructed very simply of two elements. The floor boards were laid directly on the joists and at right angles to them. At Heracleia the floors had three elements. Smaller beams were laid at more frequent intervals across the main joists and at right angles to them; then the floor boards were laid on these smaller beams.[3]

The large artillery towers at Heracleia generally have large openings in their rear walls to allow for speedy introduction or removal of heavy and bulky equipment. Their walls are of much more robust construction than those built during the first reaction to artillery. Krischen does not appear to think that the upper chambers, equipped with windows, were meant for catapults. A novel feature associated with most of the existing windows apparently led him on a false trail. Two small rectangular holes pass right through the tower wall beside the lower corners of each window, one close to each corner. Krischen was inspired to account for them by reconstructing a type of external shutter for each window for which he adduced evidence from medieval times. He thought that iron bars were pushed through the holes to open the shutter partially at the bottom and thus allow defenders to pour, drop, or hurl all manner of unpleasant things on the heads of besiegers, or on top of their machinery, when they had already penetrated to the base of the tower.[4]

While there can be no doubt that the defenders would use their windows for this purpose at the appropriate juncture in a siege, I think it would be a gross and absurd waste if an embrasured chamber, constructed with considerable labour and expense at a fair height above the ground, was not used for artillery and only benefited the defenders when

---

[1] See above, p. 108.   [2] See Krischen, *Herakleia*, 30 ff.
[3] Ibid., 23.   [4] Ibid. 24 ff.; N.B. especially 25, Abb. 18.

the enemy had actually reached the foot of the city walls. The embrasured chambers must primarily have provided accommodation for catapults. But, if the enemy succeeded in advancing up to the fortifications and was too near to present satisfactory targets, then the windows would naturally be available for other defensive purposes.

Tower 18 at Heracleia exhibits all the main features indicated above.[1]

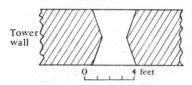

FIG. 12. Plan of embrasure in lower chamber of tower 18, Heracleia

It had two chambers for certain and, I should think, a third also, though Krischen reconstructs it confidently with two only. The lowest chamber is at internal ground level, the entrance to it being a corridor, just under 5 feet wide, through the main wall. The walls of the room are three stones thick (4 feet 7 inches), and the room itself is about 23 feet by 25 feet. It has two arrow-slits and one rather unusual embrasure (Fig. 12) in each outer wall.

In his reconstruction Krischen reasonably puts an arrow-shooting catapult behind each 'arrow-slit' and a stone-thrower behind each embrasure. The shape of the latter was due to the fact that a proper window would have been too vulnerable to infiltration and hostile shooting at this low level. An ordinary arrow-slit, on the other hand, would have been too small to allow even a light stone-shot to pass safely through. Since the designer wanted artillery at a low level, he had to resort to unusual expedients to accommodate it—not very satisfactory expedients, either, from the artilleryman's point of view. After all, the intriguing shape does not really allow anything but a narrow field of fire, unless the unfortunate artillerymen constantly manhandle their stone-thrower from side to side, base and all.[2]

[1] Krischen, *Herakleia*, 31, Abb. 24.

[2] Krischen (in Abb. 24) draws a very small stone-thrower behind one of these embrasures (in side elevation). But the machine is rather too small and stands far too low on its base, so that it can only shoot at one angle of elevation. This is useless. A four-mina stone-thrower (for this calibre see Philon, *Pol.* 95. 17—at least one editor is inclined to dispute the reading), with a base about 5 feet high, could shoot satisfactorily through one of these embrasures at all angles of elevation from the horizontal to 40 degrees (at least). The artillerymen might need to stand on a wooden platform sometimes to load their engine.

Above this chamber, at rampart-walk level, lies a capacious artillery-chamber, about 28 feet square, with two windows (5 feet high by 3 feet wide) in each outer wall. The side walls of the room are 3 feet (two layers of stone) thick. It could easily have accommodated four five-mina stone-throwers and two two-cubit arrow-shooting catapults. In the rear wall a really large opening, 12 feet wide, gives access to the rampart walk. Thus, even a twenty-mina stone-thrower could have passed through without any need for dismantling. Of course, a twenty-mina or, for that matter, a ten-mina stone-thrower in this chamber would have greatly limited the space available for other engines.

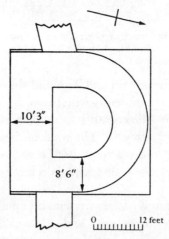

FIG. 13. Plan of semicircular tower in the north wall at Hipponium

Semicircular and round towers occur with really substantial walls. The round gate-towers at Perge, with walls three stones thick, represent a fairly early effort to increase stability.[1] The semicircular towers outside the north gate at Selinus have colossal outer walls $7\frac{1}{2}$ feet thick.[2] But the semicircular and round towers in the latest phase of the north wall at Hipponium in south Italy are probably the most powerful, though not the largest, buildings of this type.[2] Unfortunately, not one of these towers stands higher than the level of the rampart walk. They appear to have been solid up to that point with walls well over 8 feet thick (five inter-locking layers of stones). They may well have possessed three super-imposed chambers originally. If so, the walls of the third or topmost room could easily have been over 3 feet thick, thicker than the walls of tower A at Aegosthena at its base.

[1] See above, p. 146. [2] See above, p. 144.

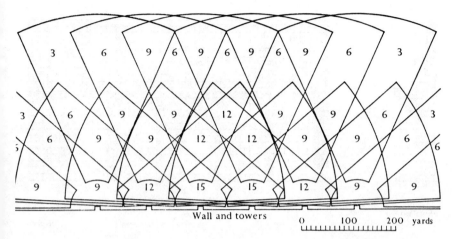

DIAGRAM 1. Coverage provided by catapults mounted in six towers 100 yards apart in a straight wall; nine catapults per tower, three in each outer wall; fifty-four engines in all. Each segment represents the area covered by three catapults. The figures in the larger spaces formed by the interlocking segments represent the number of engines that can be brought to bear on each particular space

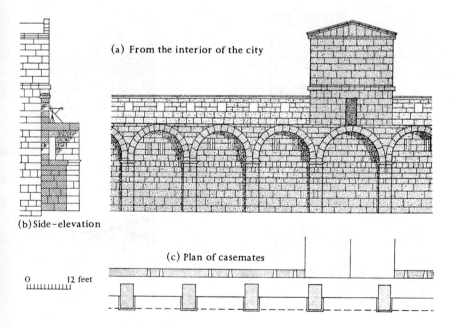

(a) From the interior of the city

(b) Side-elevation

(c) Plan of casemates

0 ————— 12 feet

DIAGRAM 2. Perge—Portion of east wall with casemates and rear of one tower

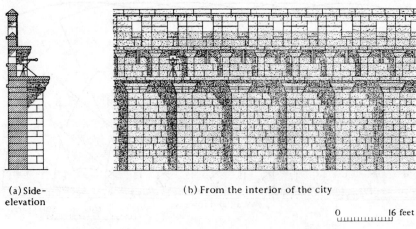

(a) Side-
elevation

(b) From the interior of the city

0 _____ 16 feet

DIAGRAM 3. Side—One type of wall with casemates

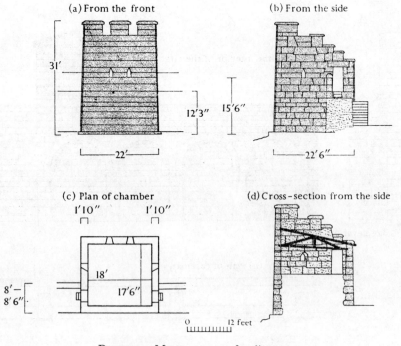

(a) From the front

(b) From the side

31'

12'3"   15'6"

22'

22'6"

(c) Plan of chamber

1'10"   1'10"

(d) Cross-section from the side

18'

17'6"

8'—
8'6"

0 _____ 12 feet

DIAGRAM 4. Messene, tower of earlier type

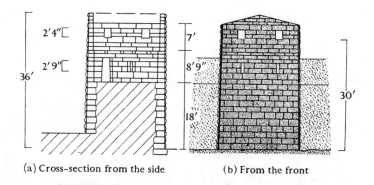

(a) Cross-section from the side   (b) From the front

0 [scale] 12 feet

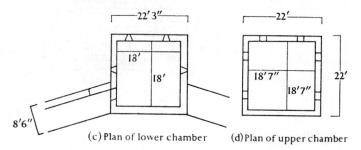

(c) Plan of lower chamber   (d) Plan of upper chamber

DIAGRAM 5. Messene, tower east of Arcadian Gate

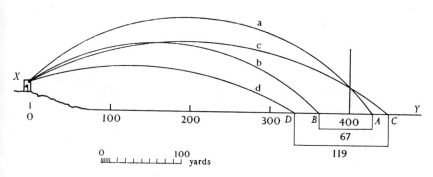

0 [scale] 100 yards

DIAGRAM 6. Simple ballistics

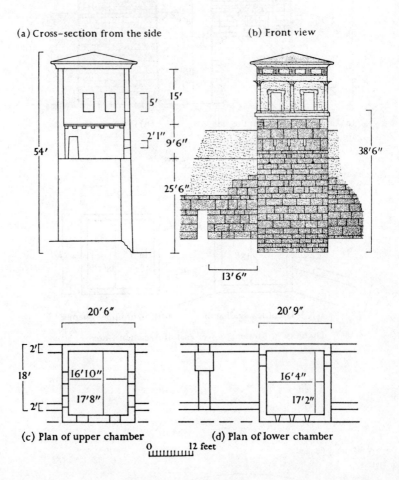

(a) Cross-section from the side   (b) Front view

(c) Plan of upper chamber   (d) Plan of lower chamber

0   12 feet

DIAGRAM 7. Paestum, tower 6.

Tower A

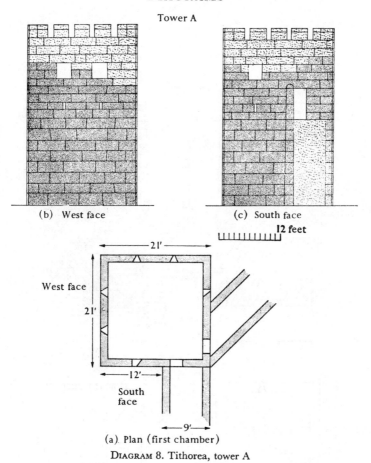

(b) West face   (c) South face

12 feet

21'

West face

21'

12'

South
face

9'

(a) Plan (first chamber)

DIAGRAM 8. Tithorea, tower A

Tower H

(b) Reconstruction (front)

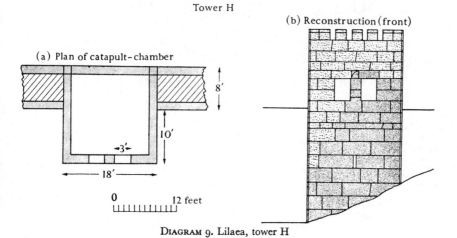

(a) Plan of catapult-chamber

8'

10'

3'

18'

0   12 feet

DIAGRAM 9. Lilaea, tower H

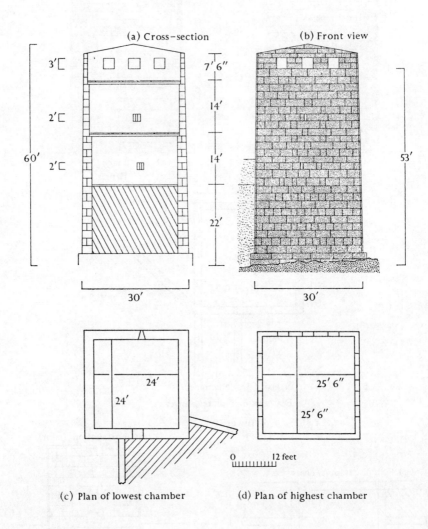

(a) Cross–section

(b) Front view

(c) Plan of lowest chamber

(d) Plan of highest chamber

DIAGRAM 10. Aegosthena, tower A

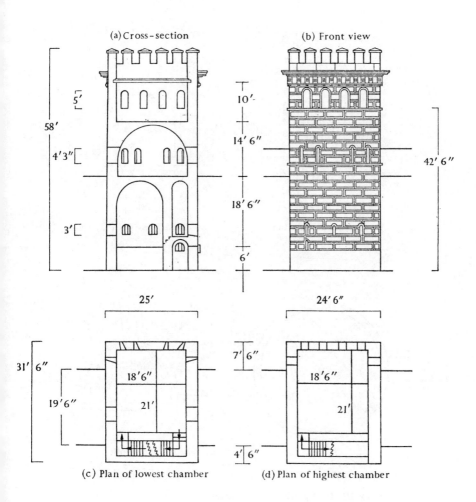

(a) Cross-section

(b) Front view

(c) Plan of lowest chamber

(d) Plan of highest chamber

0   12 feet

DIAGRAM 11. Pompeii, tower by Vesuvius Gate

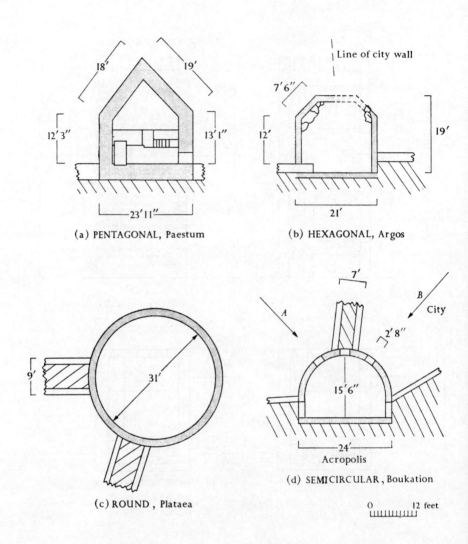

(a) PENTAGONAL, Paestum

(b) HEXAGONAL, Argos

(c) ROUND, Plataea

(d) SEMICIRCULAR, Boukation

DIAGRAM 12. Tower shapes

City

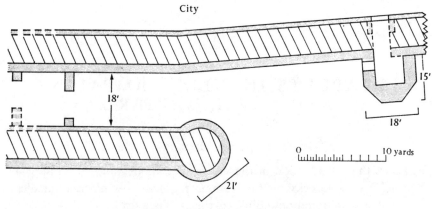

18'

15'

18'

0   10 yards

DIAGRAM 13. Plan of gate at Mantinea

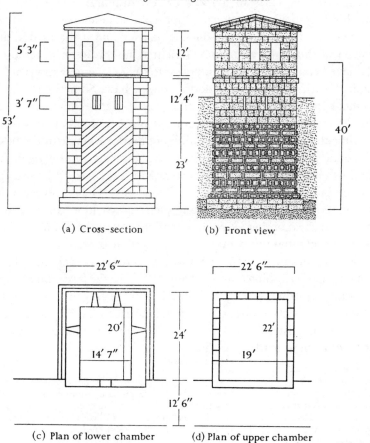

5' 3"   12'

3' 7"   12' 4"

53'

23'   40'

(a) Cross-section   (b) Front view

—— 22' 6" ——   —— 22' 6" ——

20'   22'

14' 7"   24'   19'

12' 6"

(c) Plan of lower chamber   (d) Plan of upper chamber

0   12 feet

DIAGRAM 14. Perge, tower in east wall

VII

CATAPULTS IN FIELD CAMPAIGNS
AND NAVAL WARFARE

§ 1. *Field Artillery*

BEFORE the introduction of the *carroballista* about A.D. 100,[1] it appears
that neither the Greeks nor the Romans possessed any pieces of artillery
permanently mounted on mobile carriages. They transported their catapults on ordinary carts in a more or less dismantled state.[2] A small
arrow-shooting machine such as a three-span (τρισπίθαμος, *scorpio*) could
easily be carried in two parts—the engine itself and its base; but, at the
other end of the scale, a large one-talent stone-thrower will almost certainly have been split up for transport into the following sections at least:
the pair of spring-frames; the ladder; table; base. Sometimes it proved
convenient to carry artillery and other heavy siege-equipment by sea.[3]
Thus, the transport of machines from one place to another presented no
great difficulty; but it was quite a different matter when artillery became
involved in pitched battles or lesser engagements in the field. Since
catapults operated at relatively short ranges, they had to be set up for
action in fairly close proximity to the enemy. Hence, every minute
wasted in unloading them and setting them up would mean a significant
reduction in the number of rounds that they could shoot off at a vital
stage in the combat; and every minute lost in dismantling them and
loading them into the wagons again would increase their chance of falling
into enemy hands if things were not going well for the force they had been
supporting. In other words, the difficulty of getting catapults quickly
into, and out of, action might make them more of a liability than an asset
in fluid warfare. Intelligent Greek and Roman generals understood the
limitations of their artillery in this respect.

---

[1] See below, p. 190.

[2] e.g. D.S. xx. 73. 3; Plb. xi. 12. 4; Tac. *Hist.* iii. 25 (*vehiculis tormentisque*); Joseph. *BJ*
ii. 546 (the mules and donkeys there mentioned were probably pulling carts). Technical
writers recommend that catapults should be so designed that they can be easily assembled
and dismantled: Heron, *Bel.* W 90. Philon (*Bel.* 56) thought it worth pointing out that his
wedge-machine was particularly well designed from this point of view.

[3] e.g. D.S. xiv. 47. 7; xvii. 22. 5 (on disbanding his navy at Miletus in 334 B.C., Alexander
retained a few ships 'which he used for the transport of siege-engines'); 24. 1; Arr. *Anab.* ii.
27. 3; D.S. xx. 73. 2; 74. 1.

For instance, on the first recorded occasion when catapults were used in the field, in his battle with Philip II in the south of Thessaly, the Phocian general Onomarchus deployed non-torsion stone-throwers on hills to either side of the battle-field, which he had chosen with great care, and provided them with infantry for their local protection.[1] There had presumably been plenty of time to prepare these stone-throwers for action before the Macedonians arrived on the scene, and, being in positions on rocky hillsides which were difficult to assail, they took an effective part in the battle without fear of enemy interference. Thus, their lack of mobility in action was of no great moment. Similarly, Alexander the Great appreciated the value of artillery both for covering a withdrawal, and supporting an advance, across a river in the face of the enemy. During his demonstration in force through Thrace and Illyria in 335 B.C., he was compelled to abandon the siege of Pelium, an Illyrian fortress, by shortage of supplies. As the Macedonian army withdrew, the troops of Cleitus from Pelium and of his ally Glaucias pressed hard on its rear, so that Alexander found himself somewhat embarrassed when it became necessary, in the course of the retreat, to ford the River Eordaicus. Although the main body of the Macedonians managed to cross safely, the Agrianians and archers in the rearguard had difficulty in disengaging themselves from the attentions of the enemy. Alexander then adopted the following plan:

He deployed his artillery on the bank of the river and ordered his men to shoot, at maximum range, all the types of missile that are hurled from machines. He also ordered the archers, who had already plunged in, to shoot from mid-stream. Glaucias' men did not dare to advance within range. Meanwhile, the Macedonians crossed the river safely, so that not one casualty was suffered in the withdrawal.[2]

A few years later (329 B.C.) Alexander employed catapults to support his crossing of the yellow Jaxartes (Syr-Daria) on the far borders of Sogdiana against a Scythian horde on the other bank. The machines fired salvoes right across the river (αἵ τε μηχαναὶ ἀπὸ ξυνθήματος ἐξηκόντι-ζον) and cleared a space for landing, principally as a result of the moral effect they produced.[3] This seems the best interpretation of Arrian's version of the action;[4] but Curtius says that the artillery was set up on the rafts which carried the Macedonians across.[5] However, Arrian's

---

[1] Polyaen. ii. 38. 2 (already considered above, p. 59, in another connection).
[2] Arr. *Anab.* i. 6. 8.   [3] See above, pp. 97 f.   [4] Arr. *Anab.* iv. 4. 4.
[5] Curt. vii. 9. 3 ff. Curtius calls the river the Tanais as a result of a deliberate confusion which had already been criticized by Strabo (xi. 507 ff.) before Curtius' time. Tarn, *Alexander*, i. 68, follows Curtius in putting the artillery on boats; but Curtius' account may well

circumstantial account, particularly his mention of the very few Scythian casualties and of the impression made on the enemy by the extraordinary range of Alexander's artillery, strongly suggests that the Macedonian engines were set up on the bank of the river. Archers did not supplement the barrage on this occasion, but formed the first unit to land on the Scythian side, so that they could immediately protect the area in which Alexander intended to disembark the main body. The salvo procedure was probably employed so that the catapults would fire a volley whenever a large group of Scythians, who were riding up and down on the opposite bank, presented a suitable target in a reasonably favourable position. This method was probably calculated to inspire additional terror and avoided the waste of ammunition which would have accompanied haphazard individual shooting against moving targets at long range.

In both these cases the presence of a river between the catapults and the enemy ensured the safety of the machines. In a somewhat similar manner, Perseus sought to defend the line of the River Elpeus with artillery in 168 B.C., shortly before the battle of Pydna. Admittedly, he put up fortifications along the bank, possibly because the river-bed was dry, so that the situation resembled siege-warfare to some extent.[1] Deterred by the natural obstacles, the fortifications, and the numerous artillery, Aemilius Paullus decided not to make a full attack on Perseus' position,[2] but to find an alternative route into Macedonia. Nevertheless, to keep Perseus occupied on the Elpeus, he once or twice ordered his men to advance across the river-bed towards the Macedonian side. The resulting combats took place mainly in the dry bed of the river, which was over a Roman mile wide, but when the Romans approached the other bank they suffered numerous casualties when Perseus' artillery opened fire from the fortifications, the bolts and shot reaching even to the rear of the Roman force.[3]

In using field-works and artillery to strengthen what was basically a field position, Perseus seems to have been applying a tactical plan that had become traditional, at any rate for Macedonians. Earlier, in 198 B.C., his father Philip V adopted somewhat similar arrangements in an even more appropriate position when he sought to block the narrows of the River Aous (Aoi Stena, Epirus) against the Romans.[4] In the slender corridor of

have been influenced by his knowledge of contemporary Roman imperial practice in the crossing of wide rivers. See below, p. 186, on Corbulo's passage of the Euphrates, for example.

[1] Livy, xliv. 32. 10.

[2] Ibid. 35. 9: 'quod tormenta ubique disposita essent'.

[3] Ibid. 35. 22: 'ubi propius ripam hostium subissent (sc. Romani), tormentis missa etiam ad ultimos perveniebant'.

[4] On what follows see now N. G. L. Hammond, 'The opening campaigns and the battle

the Aous valley, particularly on the north bank, and in advance of his main forces, he deployed pickets of light troops and a considerable number of catapults at suitable points on the difficult rocky slopes to dominate the principal passage lower down alongside the river itself.[1] T. Quinctius Flamininus' first assaults on this carefully prepared battlefield did not penetrate these outer defences, Philip's arrow-shooting and stone-throwing engines giving a good account of themselves along with javelineers and archers.[2] These will all have hurled their missiles into the flank of the Roman attackers. The artillery-emplacements appear to have been well sited in positions which the Romans could not easily attack, and the catapults were locally protected by the light troops. The Macedonians were only dislodged from their position when Flamininus sent a force round by a long mountainous route to descend on the enemy's lines from flank and rear, and after he had delivered a simultaneous frontal assault in which the Romans probably suffered severe casualties. Thus Philip's artillery seems to have performed excellently the tasks assigned to it.

Onomarchus, Alexander, Philip V, and Perseus used artillery successfully in field engagements because they recognized the need to set it up where it was not exposed and easily assailable. Sulla and Caesar also understood this. They both attempted to use artillery in a pitched battle, but only when the catapults were placed, for security, in small temporary fortlets on each flank of their battle-lines.[3] Caesar once employed an arrow-shooting catapult in field operations against the Bellovaci; but, like Onomarchus, he put the machine high up on a ridge well out of harm's way, and the legions were drawn up near by.[4]

Machanidas of Sparta, however, apparently did not appreciate the vulnerability of artillery when exposed in the field. As he led his army to the battle of Mantinea against the Achaeans under Philopoemen in 207 B.C., a number of catapults were conveyed in carts immediately behind the vanguard in his column of march. When Machanidas began to deploy his troops, 'he stationed the catapults at intervals in a long line in front of the whole army'.[5] Realizing at once that this artillery might cause serious casualties and, perhaps more important, confusion among his

of the Aoi Stena in the Second Macedonian War', in *JRS* 56 (1966), 39 ff., especially 49 ff. and fig. 5 (map iv).

[1] Livy, xxxii. 5. 13: 'magna tormentorum etiam vis, ut missilibus procul arcerent hostem, idoneis locis disposita est.'

[2] Plut. *Flam.* 4; Livy, xxxii. 10. 11: 'catapultae ballistaeque in omnibus prope rupibus quasi in muro dispositae'.

[3] See below, p. 178 and n. 3.   [4] Caes. *BG* viii. 14. 5.

[5] Plb. xi. 12. 4; cf. Kromayer, *Antike Schlachtfelder*, i. 300 ff.

own men, Philopoemen attacked without delay, probably before the catapults were fully prepared for action. Even if they had been ready to shoot, the machines could only have discharged a few rounds before their positions were overrun, and their artillerymen cut down, by the determined enemy.[1] We note without surprise that they do not figure again in the account of the battle.

It is very probable that catapults were used in the field on a great many more occasions than those specifically recorded by historians, and, when employed intelligently, in favourable circumstances, they supplied quite effective support; but, certainly before the Roman imperial period, artillery had no significant effect on the tactics used in pitched battles.[2] Apart from lack of mobility in action, catapults also had one or two other drawbacks which tended to reduce their efficiency in the field. Philon emphasizes an important characteristic of Ctesibius' bronze-spring engine as follows: 'in the exigencies of the field, and in naval operations, they [sc. bronze-spring machines] remain undamaged because they are unaffected by breakage or wetting. Anything like this is harmful to sinew. When springs of sinew are wet or broken, engines cannot avoid detrimental effects. Often engines kept with every precaution in covered places deteriorate considerably through change in the atmosphere.'[3] Incidentally, there is no evidence that the bronze-spring catapult ever went into general production. Further, even when the weather was favourable, catapults required careful maintenance, repairs, and adjustments at the best of times, and the requisite facilities might not be readily available in the field.[4] Philon explains the matter thus:

But occasions often arise of a kind where catapults are urgently required; if the springs are broken, however, or anything else is damaged, the re-stringing cannot possibly be effected in any way because of the delay caused by the above-mentioned stretchers. This happens not infrequently in land-campaigns, and is common in naval warfare.[5]

---

[1] Before the production of Roman imperial *carroballistae*, there was no chance of ancient artillery operating in the same way as the British guns, especially Mercer's Troop, at Waterloo (for example); see Arthur Bryant, *The Age of Elegance* (London, 1950), 238 f.

[2] For artillery in the field in the Roman Empire see below, pp. 187, 190 f.

[3] Philon, *Bel.* 72.

[4] With the standard allotment of artillery to each imperial legion (see below, pp. 179 ff.), which could set up a field-workshop whenever and wherever necessary, the Romans went a long way towards solving the problem of maintenance. Also, the production of catapults with metal frames, wherein the springs were protected by metal cylinders, did much to preserve the springs from bad weather and dampness in the atmosphere.

[5] Philon, *Bel.* 57.

§ 2. *Artillery in Naval Warfare*

In spite of the fact that the above disadvantages interfered even more seriously with their employment in naval engagements than in field warfare, catapults were undoubtedly mounted on ships and played their part in operations on rivers and on the open sea. Ptolemy I resisted the attempted invasion of the Nile delta by Antigonus and Demetrius late in 306 B.C. partly by the strategic disposition of strong garrisons at important landing points, and partly by preparing a powerful river flotilla, some of the vessels being triremes possibly,[1] and by mounting on his boats catapults of many different calibres and the necessary detachments for operating them.[2]

It was not unusual for merchant ships and other vessels normally engaged in peaceful occupations to carry artillery both for their own protection and to enable them to assist warships. For the sea-battle off Massilia (49 B.C.) the authorities of that city sought to strengthen their navy by fitting out fishing vessels in an appropriate manner and by arming them with catapults.[3] When, in the battle itself, one of Decimus Brutus' Caesarian warships laid alongside a Massiliot naval vessel, these small boats poured a hail of bolts from considerable range on to the Roman deck and inflicted serious casualties.[4]

A year or so later, as M. Antonius was bringing Caesar's reinforcements over from Brundisium to Greece, Pompeian warships sighted his convoy of transports and threatened to catch him up by rowing, because a calm fell on the Adriatic just at that moment. 'Great fear fell upon them [sc. Antonius and his men], as it would in a calm, because the warship might damage or sink them with their beaks. They made suitable preparations and were already beginning to shoot sling-shot and artillery missiles ($\beta \acute{\epsilon} \lambda \eta$).'[5] At this point, however, the wind sprang up again and carried Antonius out of danger. The term $\beta \acute{\epsilon} \lambda \eta$ may not definitely indicate catapult-bolts, but such an interpretation is very probably correct, and it is attractive to imagine Antonius' ships engaging the approaching men-of-war with their stern-chasers.

Catapults were commonly mounted on ships in order to assist in the siege of a maritime city. There were three main reasons for this. First, it helped the besieger to block the harbour and thus cut the city off completely from outside contacts. Secondly, the besieger could compel the

---

[1] Paus. i. 6. 6.

[2] D.S. xx. 76. 3: πάντων δὲ τούτων [sc. σκαφῶν] ἐχόντων βέλη παντοῖα καὶ τοὺς χρησο-μένους αὐτοῖς ἄνδρας (for the latter phrase in other Ptolemaic artillery contexts see above, p. 76).

[3] Caes. *BC* ii. 4. 2.   [4] Ibid. 6. 3.   [5] App. *BC* ii. 244.

defenders to expend considerable energy in protecting the maritime area of their city and thus prevent them concentrating their entire defensive effort against his assaults by land. Finally, if conditions were favourable, the besieger might actually direct his principal attack, properly supported by artillery, against a selected point on the seaward side, having taken fuller advantage of the privilege, naturally enjoyed by all besiegers, of choosing which section of the circuit to attack. The accounts of Alexander's attacks on Tyre in 332 B.C., where artillery was set up on horse-transports and the slower triremes,[1] and of Demetrius' attempts against the harbour area at Rhodes (305–304 B.C.) give a very good idea of what ship-mounted artillery could achieve in the siege of a coastal city.[2] In circumstances somewhat similar to those observed in a regular siege from the sea, Caesar sought to blockade Pompeius in Brundisium in 49 B.C. by closing the harbour entrance with two mounds and, where the water was deeper, with a row of rafts moored in pairs. On every fourth raft he erected a two-storey tower which, though he does not specifically say so, no doubt housed pieces of artillery.[3] To prevent the completion of these works Pompeius seized some large merchant vessels lying in the harbour and fitted them with three-storey towers, each lavishly equipped with artillery (multis tormentis). With the help of these he succeeded in hindering Caesar's building operations, so that he kept the harbour open until his fleet returned and he and his army were able to slip away on it to Dyrrhachium.[4]

The warships of both Caesar and Pompeius may well have been regularly furnished with artillery. There is a record of the latter's fleet bombarding the right flank of Caesar's army, on one occasion, as it marched along the shore.[5] The incident perhaps occurred during the first stages of Caesar's withdrawal from Dyrrhachium.[6] Artillery was also used, then as now, for neutralizing a hostile shore and supporting the disembarkation of an invasion force upon it. Catapults on Caesar's warships put down an effective barrage on the British beach (perhaps near Sandwich on the east coast of Kent) in 55 B.C. and thus cleared a suitable

---

[1] Arr. Anab. ii. 21. 1; and see above, pp. 102 f.

[2] D.S. xx. 85 ff.; and see above, pp. 106 f. We may also note further examples of this use of ship-mounted artillery as follows: Livy, xxvi. 44. 10 and Plb. x. 12. 1 (artillery on Laelius' ships at New Carthage, 209 B.C.); Livy, xxvi. 26. 3 (on Laevinus' vessels at Anticyra, 211 B.C.); ibid. xxvii. 14. 5 (on warships and merchantmen in Laevinus' fleet at Tarentum, 209 B.C.); App. Lyb. 16, and Livy, xxx. 4. 10 (at Utica, 204 B.C.); Livy, xxiv. 34. 5 (at Syracuse, 213–211 B.C.).

[3] Caes. BC i. 25. 5–10.   [4] Ibid. 26. 1 ff.

[5] Polyaen. viii. 23. 13; cf. Frontin. Strat. i. 4. 1 (Tarentine fleet engaging the army of Aemilius Papus from the sea in 282 B.C.).

[6] So Schambach, Bemerkungen, 13.

landing-area.[1] Likewise an artillery barrage from warships (*tormentis ex navibus*) successfully prepared the way for the disembarkation of three cohorts on the city end of the Heptastadium at Alexandria.[2]

Finally, while there can be no question that catapults were mounted both on warships and other vessels for subsidiary naval operations, doubts have been expressed about the employment of artillery on warships in full-scale battles at sea. Tarn stated categorically that Hellenistic warships never carried catapults into a proper sea-battle.[3] But, in the major engagement off Cyprian Salamis against Ptolemy I in 307 B.C., Demetrius Poliorcetes put stone-throwers of unspecified size on his ships, almost a third of which would seem to have been quinqueremes or larger, and three-span arrow-shooting catapults in their prows.[4] Before the fleets closed for ramming and boarding, Demetrius' men, 'using bows, stone-throwers, and numerous javelins, kept inflicting casualties on those who came within their field of fire'.[5] This evidence counts heavily against Tarn's theory. It is true, as Tarn has well explained, that ancient warships were relatively light and unstable contraptions; but even triremes were capable of carrying a fair load of marines ($\epsilon\pi\iota\beta\acute{a}\tau\alpha\iota$) and other troops, sometimes in considerable numbers.[6] There is sound evidence that a complement of 120 marines, in addition to its normal crew, was not too much for a quinquereme going into battle.[7] If we take the average weight of a marine in fighting equipment to be 12 stones, a moderate figure, then 120 men will weigh 9 tons altogether.

The much favoured three-span catapult weighed, I estimate, about 1 hundredweight when fully plated and ready for action.[8] Hence, when an admiral considered that the situation warranted it, each of his quinqueremes could accommodate, for example, ten three-span arrow-firers (10 cwt.), two comparatively small stone-throwers weighing 2 tons apiece (4 tons), expert artillerymen and ammunition ($1\frac{1}{2}$ tons), and still be able to carry forty marines (3 tons). Obviously, warships larger than the quinquereme could have done even better. Since Philon, in the

[1] Caes. *BG* iv. 25. 1: 'quod ubi Caesar animadvertit, navis longas, quarum et species erat barbaris inusitatior et motus ad usum expeditior, paulum removeri ab onerariis navibus et remis incitari et ad latus apertum hostium constitui atque inde fundis, sagittis, tormentis hostis propelli ac summoveri iussit; quae res magno usui nostris fuit. nam et navium figura et remorum motu et inusitato genere tormentorum permoti barbari constiterunt ac paulum modo pedem rettulerunt.'
[2] *BAl* 19. 3.
[3] Tarn, *HMND* 120 f., 152.
[4] D.S. xx. 49. 4.
[5] Ibid. 51. 2.
[6] Cf. Hdt. vi. 15. 1; Thuc. i. 49. 1–2.
[7] Walbank, *Polybius*, i. 86.
[8] This estimate is based on the fact that my full-scale model of a three-span catapult weighs about three-quarters of a hundredweight complete; but it has very little iron plating.

passages recently quoted,[1] clearly regarded the use of torsion artillery as normal in naval engagements about 200 B.C., catapults probably featured fairly regularly in sea-battles throughout the Hellenistic period, particularly when the opposing admirals decided mainly to adopt the tactic of laying their ships alongside the enemy vessels and boarding them.[2] It is most unlikely, I think, that Roman tactics at the battles of Naulochus (36 B.C.) and Actium (31 B.C.) were vastly different to those employed many Hellenistic commanders.

At the former battle off the north coast of Sicily, between Octavian's fleet under Agrippa and the navy of Sextus Pompeius, both sides possessed ships fitted with artillery of all kinds, and even towers and other machines.[3] Agrippa is credited with the invention, for this engagement, of a special grappling-hook which was fitted to the end of a five-cubit shaft. The apparatus was fired from a catapult, and a line connected to the rear end of the shaft was paid out as the weapon flew towards a hostile vessel. Immediately the grapple landed on its target, its operators pulled in the other end of the line, thus jamming the device firmly somewhere in the target, and gradually drew the enemy vessel alongside their own.

The actual battle started with heavy shooting, some of this being done by artillery. When the fleets came to close quarters, some ships attempted to ram their opponents, while others sailed through the enemy line hurling stone shot and bolts (βάλλουσαί τε καὶ ἀκοντίζουσαι) as they passed.[4] Some of these missiles were very probably fired from catapults. The grappling-hook apparently gave a good account of itself in action.[5] At Actium Octavian's fleet was no doubt equipped in much the same manner as it had been at Naulochus. There was no spectacular difference between the ships of Octavian and those of Antonius, though the average tonnage of the latter may have been slightly higher.[6] There is very little evidence for artillery on either side. Antonius' sailors undoubtedly employed it,[7] shooting from ship-mounted towers, and it is possible that the flaming bolts (πυροβόλοις) used by Octavian's men were hurled from catapults.

In view of the paucity of evidence for important naval engagements between Demetrius' victory at Salamis in 307 B.C. and the battle of Naulochus in 36 B.C., any conclusions about the employment of artillery

---

[1] Above, p. 168.   [2] On Hellenistic naval tactics see Tarn, *HMND* 144 ff.
[3] App. *BC* v. 118: βέλη τε παντοῖα φέρουσαι καὶ πύργους καὶ μηχανάς. In this context, I take βέλη to mean artillery.
[4] They were operating, in fact, in the same way as Nelson's vessels at Trafalgar.
[5] App. *BC* v. 119.
[6] On the two fleets see C. G. Starr, *The Roman Imperial Navy*² (Heffer, Cambridge, 1960), 7 f.
[7] Plut. *Ant.* 66. 2.

in major sea-battles and its effect on tactics must be speculative to some extent. We can state at once, however, that no Greek or Roman captain ever contemplated attempting to sink or even seriously to disable a hostile vessel by delivering a series of broadsides with his stone-throwers. The weight of the really heavy and numerous engines which such feats would have required was certainly far beyond the capacity of the largest ancient warships. On the other hand, at least some commanders certainly believed that a number of smaller arrow-shooting catapults and stone-throwers, which their ships could comfortably accommodate, would effectively prepare the way for, and support, the successful boarding of hostile vessels. In specific terms, a captain was ready to replace forty, say, of his marines with artillery and artillerymen in the hope that these machines would cause more than forty casualties among the marines on the warship he was about to board. Consequently, even those admirals who put their main trust in ramming rather than boarding would be compelled to arm their ships with catapults too, in case they were caught at a disadvantage by hostile vessels possessing overwhelmingly superior fire-power. Therefore it is possible that, during the Hellenistic period, the employment of artillery may have been one of the factors which led commanders to concentrate on boarding tactics and to build larger ships that could carry more catapults.[1]

[1] On the enormous warships constructed in the Hellenistic Age see Tarn, *HMND* 132 ff.

VIII

ROMAN IMPERIAL ARTILLERY

IN his well documented study of Roman artillery Schambach drew the following conclusions which he considered particularly valid for the last two centuries of the republic, though he seems to regard them as true, also, for the imperial period, in a general way. The Romans obtained their knowledge of catapults from the Greeks, but never attained the mechanical standards of their masters.[1] Likewise, the former did not display the same energy in their employment of artillery in sieges, preferring to put their trust in their slow, but sure, traditional methods, *obsidio* and *circumvallatio*, perhaps combined with a formal assault, in which, however, artillery played only a relatively minor part.[2] The Romans confined themselves almost exclusively to using catapults of small calibre, and this helps to explain why artillery had a smaller role in their sieges.[3] Because transport of catapults over long distances was tedious and difficult, and because engines could not be constructed rapidly on the spot when need arose, they developed the habit of requisitioning artillery from cities near the zone of operations.[4]

There is some truth in several of the above assertions, but on the whole they create a somewhat inaccurate impression. In the first place, there was no such thing as a separate Roman brand of artillery. As their dominions extended, the Romans of the republic obtained catapults, when they needed them, in three principal ways: they requisitioned or borrowed them from Greek cities or cities influenced by Hellenism; they employed Greek artificers to build them; or they used Roman artificers thoroughly conversant with Greek methods.[5] Hence, however they came by them, the Romans had pieces of artillery which were either Hellenistic or absolutely identical with contemporary Hellenistic machines. The remains of the mid-second-century catapult found at Emporiae (Ampurias), the Roman arsenal in Spain, show convincingly that the machine to which they belonged was fully up to the best mechanical standards of

---

[1] Schambach, *Bemerkungen*, 5.
[2] Ibid. 5, 10–11.   [3] Ibid. 5, 11.   [4] Ibid. 8.
[5] There is nothing to exclude the possibility that the Romans continued to use Greek mechanical brains throughout the imperial period.

its time.[1] The artillery chapters of Vitruvius demonstrate that Roman technicians kept abreast of the latest Hellenistic developments in the construction of arrow-shooting and stone-throwing catapults. In quality, therefore, Roman artillery was just as good as the ordnance possessed by anybody else.

The Romans certainly did not neglect catapults and *ballistae* of heavy calibres, either in the late republican or early imperial period. Lucilius, who served in the Numantine war as *contubernalis* of Scipio Aemilianus, mentions 100-pound *ballistae* (which mean, in the context, stone shot weighing 100 pounds).[2] A fragment of Sisenna, probably relating to Roman operations in the Social War, refers to 'four one-talent *ballistae*'.[3] A famous incident at the second battle of Bedriacum (A.D. 69) involved a '*ballista* of extraordinary size', which must have been larger than a one-talent engine.[4] In connection with Titus' siege of Jerusalem (A.D. 70) we hear of other one-talent stone-throwers.[5] On occasion, then, the Romans were quite prepared to use large *ballistae* and, no doubt, large catapults. The occasions were probably far more numerous than the extant sources suggest. From this point of view the loss of most of Sisenna's work is to be regretted, for he seems to have resembled Diodorus Siculus in paying rather more attention than usual to artillery.

Roman weakness lay in the quantity of artillery available, and I think this was due to inadequate and ill-organized facilities for production. In the East there were great arsenals at Pergamum, Rhodes, and Alexandria, all with long traditions of craftsmanship and capable of satisfying the needs of their states in every foreseeable circumstance. The Antigonids and Seleucids probably controlled similar workshops.[6] Rome possessed *armamentaria publica*,[7] but the space allotted to artillery construction would appear to have been small. Cities in Italy perhaps had workshops

[1] See Schramm, *Saalburg*, 40 ff. for technical analysis of the Ampurias catapult.

[2] Lucil. *ap.* Non. 555. 26: 'Quid fit?' 'Ballistas iactant centenarias.' The figure 100 pounds may be used here simply to indicate very large shot; but there is some evidence for the actual existence of stone-throwers of this calibre (*c.* 90–100 Roman pounds, 65–75 minae) though, strangely enough, Vitruvius (x. 11. 3) does not include it in his otherwise comprehensive list of standard sizes for *ballistae*. Both at Pergamum (see the table in *Alt. Perg.* x. 50–1) and at Carthage (see Rathgen's table, *Punische Geschosse*, 240), a small but significant number of shot were found having a weight intermediate between 1 talent (80 Roman pounds) and 1½ talents (120 Roman pounds).

[3] Sisenna, frg. 92: *histor. lib. IIII*: 'ballistas quattuor talentarias'.

[4] Tac. *Hist.* iii. 23: 'magnitudine eximia . . . ballista . . . ingentibus saxis'.

[5] Joseph. *BJ* v. 269; cf. iii. 166.

[6] As the Romans gradually extended their eastern possessions after *c.* 150 B.C., these arsenals fell into their hands one by one. But there is no evidence to suggest that they made much use of them.

[7] e.g. Cic. *pro Rab.* 7.

sufficient to meet local requirements,[1] and those in the provinces, particularly the Greek cities, likewise attended to their own defensive artillery.[2]
But it is fairly clear that there was no large, officially regulated arsenal at
Rome or anywhere else, from which Roman republican generals could
draw reasonable supplies of catapults as they set out on campaign.[3]
Hence, the provision of artillery, when need for it arose, depended mainly
on the initiative of the individual Roman commander. As we have
already observed, he could requisition catapults from subjects or borrow
them from friends. But many Greek cities, from Perinthus in 340 B.C.
onwards, and even one Hellenistic monarch, had been forced to do this
from time to time.[4] There was nothing new, therefore, about the Roman
policy of requisitioning, though they adopted it perhaps more consistently than anyone else. Secondly, the Roman general could hire technicians, establish a field workshop, and build himself batteries of catapults
at the scene of the fighting. The apparent preference of the Romans for
their older, surer, but slower methods was caused not by their failure to
appreciate the value of artillery, but by their inability to secure enough
catapults by the irregular and haphazard means open to them. In point
of fact, it is a great mistake to imagine any significant difference between
a Roman and a Hellenistic siege. In both cases, the besieger sought, for
obvious reasons, to sever all contact between the beleaguered town and
the outside world; he then delivered a series of assaults making every
possible use of siege-works and machinery. The republican Roman
commander could not deploy such a lavish store of the more complicated
machinery in general, and of artillery in particular, because his resources
were not quite so extensive as those of some Hellenistic generals. But the
difference was one of degree not of kind.

Let us look at a few examples. For his siege of Utica (204 B.C.) Scipio
determined to collect adequate supplies of artillery; but he had to
employ three methods in order to obtain it. He brought some engines
(*tormenta*) with him. Even if these came from Rome and were not picked
up on the way to Africa, it is possible that they originated ultimately in
New Carthage and formed part of the war material captured in that city.[5]

---

[1] e.g. Livy, xxvi. 6. 4 (Capua); Caes. *BC* i. 17. 3 (Corfinium); in general see Schambach,
Bemerkungen, 7.
[2] e.g. Sall. *Jug.* 57 (Zama); App. xii. 30 (Thebes); *BAfr* 29 (Leptis).
[3] Even the arsenal at Emporiae was a small Greek one in origin, the city being a colony of
Massilia. I think it was exploited by individual Roman generals in the second century,
notably Scipio Aemilianus.
[4] e.g. D.S. xviii. 51. 6 (Cyzicus); Plb. iv. 56. 3 (Sinope); ibid. 70. 2 (Philip V).
[5] For the artillery seized at New Carthage see above, p. 78. The Romans may have made
a point of acquiring artillery by capture and keeping it for their own future use. N.B. the

Secondly, additional catapults came over in provision-ships from Sicily where they had been requisitioned from the Greek cities. Finally, he had purposely hired specialist technicians to construct new catapults in a field workshop set up outside Utica.[1] At the siege of Oreos in Euboea (200 B.C.), the Romans and Attalus I of Pergamum shared the burden of assault, the former providing tortoises, galleries, and rams, while the latter supplied artillery of all kinds.[2] This causes no surprise if we remember that Pergamum had a splendid arsenal which specialized in the construction of artillery.

After an extremely optimistic attack on the Peiraeus with scaling-ladders only (87 B.C.), Sulla retired to Eleusis and Megara, requisitioned catapults from Thebes, and set up workshops to build siege-engines, probably including additional artillery.[3] He apparently brought none with him, but soon realized the need for it. Similarly, Pompey borrowed artillery from Tyre in order to prosecute the siege of Jerusalem (63 B.C.).[4] When Julius Caesar, and later Octavian, wished to provide themselves with catapults, they had to invite expert artificers, including Vitruvius and his three friends,[5] to serve them as constructors and repairers of artillery. Thus, Roman generals in the last two centuries of the Republic seem fully to have appreciated the value of catapults and to have known how to use them; but they proceeded on campaign with little or no ordnance and depended to a very great degree on rather opportunist methods for scratching a few batteries of machines together when it became impossible to do without them. It appears that Julius Caesar was the first Roman commander to keep at least a few catapults constantly with his army, fully prepared for action.[6] In this respect he returned to the practice of Alexander the Great and the leading Hellenistic monarchs, though on an admittedly smaller scale, and, consequently, he could exploit artillery rather more ambitiously, and on a greater variety of occasions, than most of his Roman predecessors.

Caesar employed his *tormenta* to put down a barrage on the British

machines carried in the triumphs of M. Claudius Marcellus (211 B.C., Livy, xxvi. 21. 7) and M. Fulvius Nobilior (187 B.C., Livy, xxxix. 5).

[1] Livy, xxix. 35. 8: 'tormenta machinasque et advexerat secum, et ex Sicilia missa cum commeatu erant; et nova in armamentario multis talium operum artificibus de industria inclusis fiebant.'

[2] Ibid. xxxi. 46. 10.   [3] See above, p. 110.

[4] Joseph. *AJ* xiv. 62; *BJ* i. 147.

[5] Vitr. i, *praef.* 2: 'itaque cum M. Aurelio et P. Numisio [*s.* Minidio] et Cn. Cornelio ad apparationem ballistarum et scorpionum reliquorumque tormentorum perfectionem fui praesto . . .'

[6] Admittedly it may simply be that we are better informed about the operations of Caesar.

beach before he landed his troops for the first time in the island,[1] just as
Alexander cleared a space on the far bank of the River Jaxartes to facilitate his crossing.[2] He even attempted to include catapults in his tactical
plan for a major battle, mounting them in temporary fortifications to
guard the flanks of his small army against the far more numerous Belgae.[3]
The plan was not put to the test because the Belgae, not unnaturally,
refrained from attacking the Romans in their well-prepared position.
Caesar perhaps went further than anyone else in popularizing the use of
catapults for the defence of camps, an extension of the long-established
employment of artillery in permanent fortifications.

In this role catapults gave a spectacular account of themselves in
a famous episode during the abortive siege of Gergovia. Caesar himself,
taking four legions and all the cavalry, had to leave the area for a time
and march some distance away in order to prevent the defection of an
Aeduan contingent. C. Fabius was left behind with only two legions to
hold the two Roman camps and the field-works connecting them outside
Gergovia. As Caesar hastened back, having successfully accomplished his
mission, he received a full report from Fabius giving details of the vigorous
series of Arvernian attacks on the camps during his absence and concluding with the statement: 'in withstanding these, the artillery was of
great value.'[4]

From incidents like this, the great value of artillery, which could
compensate for shortage of man-power by its superior fire-power, must
have impressed itself not only upon Caesar but on other intelligent
soldiers, too.[5] During the last two or three decades of the Republic,
catapults appear on a fair number of occasions in naval contexts,[6] in the
various phases of sieges,[7] and in fighting of a static nature as at Dyrrhachium.[8] Pompey was beginning to appreciate the need to have
artillery constantly available. He did not want to march away from his
base at Dyrrhachium while Caesar was in the neighbourhood because,
among other things, it would have meant abandoning most of his *tormenta*
and ammunition.[9] Even Cicero, trying to play the role of *vir militaris* in

---

[1] *BG* iv. 25 (55 B.C.). N.B. artillery used in connection with the landing near the Hepta-
stadion at Alexandria, *BAl* 19. 3.
[2] Arr. *Anab.* iv. 4. 4.
[3] *BG* ii. 8. Sulla is reputed to have done something similar (Frontin. *Strat.* ii. 3. 17).
[4] *BG* vii. 41. 3: 'ad haec sustinenda magno usui fuisse tormenta.'
[5] Other occasions when artillery defended camps: *BG* ii. 8; vii. 81; *BC* iii. 51. 8; 56. 1;
BAfr 31. 7.
[6] e.g. *BC* i. 26. 1; ii. 4; Polyaen. *Strat.* viii. 23. 13; Plut. *Ant.* 66; App. *BC* v. 106.
[7] e.g. *BG* vii. 25; viii. 40 f.; *BHisp* 13; *BC* ii. 9. 4; 11. 3; 14. 2–3.
[8] *BC* iii. 63. 6; 55. 1–2.
[9] Ibid. 44. 1.

Cilicia, reports with gusto to Cato,[1] and to Atticus,[2] about his use of military paraphernalia, including a large quantity of catapults,[3] at the siege of Pindenissus.

In view of these circumstances, those responsible for the establishment and early development of the Roman imperial army, like the successors of Alexander the Great, simply could not ignore artillery, an important subordinate arm. But they had to remedy obvious defects in the production and maintenance of catapults and in the provision of expert artillerymen which had been distinct weaknesses throughout the late Republic. Above all, it was essential to provide for the allotment of artillery on some regular basis to the new standing professional army. The best evidence for the imperial organization of artillery occurs in Vegetius' *Epitoma Rei Militaris*, published in the latter half of the fourth century A.D. At the end of his description of the legion of the good old days, *antiqua legio*, he writes:

Nam per singulas centurias singulas carroballistas habere consuevit (legio antiqua), quibus muli ad trahendum et singula contubernia ad armandum vel dirigendum, hoc est undecim homines, deputantur. Hae quanto maiores fuerint, tanto longius ac fortius tela iaculantur. Non solum autem castra defendunt, verum etiam in campo post aciem gravis armaturae ponuntur; ante quarum impetum nec equites loricati nec pedites scutati possunt hostium stare. In una autem legione quinquaginta quinque carroballistae esse solent. Item decem onagri, hoc est singuli per singulas cohortes, in carpentis bubus portantur armati, ut, si forte hostes ad adpugnandum venerint vallum, sagittis et saxis possint castra defendi.[4]

Vegetius may not, of course, be quite accurate with regard to details. For instance, Parker made the reasonable proposal that he misinterpreted the number of machines: the old legion really had fifty-five machines altogether, the ten stone-throwers (*onagri*) being included in this figure, not additional to it.[5] Moreover, we should not attach too much importance to the number fifty-five, which depends on Vegetius' assumption that his old Roman legion had fifty-five centuries. It is better, therefore, to take Vegetius' statement as valid evidence that the imperial legion had roughly one piece of artillery per century, one century in each cohort possessing an *onager*, the remaining centuries *carroballistae*. There is no

[1] *Ad fam.* xv. 4. 10.   [2] *Ad Att.* v. 20. 5.
[3] Schambach, *Bemerkungen*, 8, reasonably suggests that Cicero requisitioned his *tormenta* from the cities of his province.   [4] Veg. *Mil.* ii. 25.
[5] H. M. D. Parker, 'The *Antiqua Legio* of Vegetius', in *CQ* 26 (1932), 148. It must, however, be admitted that the proportion of stone-throwers to arrow-firers, 1:4½, will then be a little on the high side.

need to discuss here the source of Vegetius' information or the precise period to which his *antiqua legio* belonged.[1]

We may simply note that it existed somewhere between A.D. 100 and A.D. 300; the illustrations on Trajan's Column provide the earliest evidence for the *carroballista*;[2] under Constantine, at the latest, ordinary legions were no longer equipped with any form of artillery, special legions of *ballistarii* being created to look after field-ordnance. Therefore, during some or all of the period from Trajan to Diocletian inclusive, Roman legions were allotted artillery on a standard scale. Did a similar arrangement exist before Trajan also? It is true that the standard arrow-shooting engines of the early empire were the *catapultae* and *scorpiones*, and that the normal stone-throwers were still the two-armed *ballistae*. Nevertheless, the early imperial legions could easily have been equipped with *catapultae* and *ballistae* on something like the same scale as Vegetius' old legion was with *carroballistae* and *onagri*.

There is sufficient evidence to prove that this was, in fact, the case. It has often been pointed out that Josephus' figures for the artillery of the three legions with which Vespasian began his Jewish campaign (A.D. 66) correspond very closely to those of Vegetius. At the siege of Jotapata in Galilee, Vespasian had 160 pieces of artillery altogether.[3] Three of Vegetius' old legions would have possessed 165 machines. Three early imperial legions, with sixty centuries each, may have had 180 pieces of artillery in all, though it is not worth insisting on a precise figure. If Vespasian's legions were theoretically equipped with sixty catapults each, then we can account satisfactorily for the absence of twenty machines on the ground that some would inevitably (in any army) be undergoing repair while others will have been left behind to protect the legionary base-camps. Further, Josephus makes it quite clear that each legion had its own particular artillery when he notes the outstanding efficiency of the arrow-shooting catapults and the size of the stone-throwers belonging to the tenth legion at the siege of Jerusalem (A.D. 70).[4]

In connection with the second battle at Bedriacum (A.D. 69), Tacitus refers to a large *ballista* which he specifically records as belonging to the fifteenth legion.[5] To go back even earlier, it appears that *Legio II Augusta*

---

[1] Schenk, *Vegetius*, 26, concludes that his second book reproduces the arrangements of the Hadrianic epoch and is completely taken from Tarrutenius Paternus' *de re militari*. Parker, op. cit. 147, attributes the *antiqua legio* to the period between Gallienus and Diocletian (i.e. A.D. 260–90).

[2] *TC* 104–5, 163–4.   [3] Joseph. *BJ* iii. 166.

[4] Ibid. v. 269: θαυμαστὰ δὲ (τὰ ἀφετήρια) πᾶσι μὲν κατεσκεύαστο τοῖς τάγμασι, διαφόρως δὲ τῷ δεκάτῳ βιαιότεροί τε ὀξυβελεῖς καὶ μείζονα λιθοβόλα . . .

[5] Tac. *Hist.* iii. 23: 'magnitudine eximia quintae decumanae legionis ballista . . .'

possessed its own catapults in the year or so after Claudius' invasion of Britain (A.D. 43). Vespasian, then commander of this legion,[1] led it in the rapid conquest of Wessex, including the seizure of more than twenty *oppida*.[2] Excavations at Maiden Castle, Dorset, one of the twenty 'towns', have revealed a number of catapult-bolt heads at the level representing the Roman siege.[3] The second legion, therefore, covered its assault on the hill-top fort with the artillery allotted to it. The Praetorian Guard seems to have had artillery by the reign of Claudius, for they used *catapultae* and *ballistae* in the celebrations which marked the opening of the Fucine lake drainage scheme.[4] Whether Caligula's deployment of *ballistae* on the shore of the English Channel is taken as evidence of legionary artillery or not,[5] Tacitus' account of Germanicus' campaigns in Germany from A.D. 14 to 16 strongly suggests that his legions carried substantial batteries of artillery with them constantly.[6]

Although the evidence does not become entirely conclusive until the latter part of Nero's reign, the most likely occasion for the introduction of the standard legionary allotment of artillery seems to be the principate of Augustus. He created the imperial army and issued the first military *constitutio*.[7] In military matters, as in other respects, Augustus was a standardizer and not a radical reformer.[8] He and his military advisers, having examined minutely Hellenistic and Roman theory and practice in the art of war, paying particular attention to the achievements of Julius Caesar and other generals of the recent past, evolved an army organization embodying all the most effective, well-proved features from former military systems.

Every possible advantage had to be given to the imperial army because of the enormous task it was to perform. It had to defend a land frontier of something like 4,000 miles. The most critical sections of this were the lines of the rivers Rhine and Danube, throughout their entire lengths, and the middle and upper Euphrates.[9] Augustus proposed to protect the empire with only twenty-eight legions, about 168,000 men at the absolute maximum, and a number of auxiliary units whose total numerical strength

---

[1] Dio, lx. 20. [2] Suet. *Vesp.* 4.

[3] Wheeler, *Maiden Castle*, 61 ff. Wheeler calls them *ballista*-bolts.

[4] Tac. *An.* xii. 56. [5] Suet. *Cal.* 46.

[6] e.g. Tac. *An.* i. 56; ii. 6; 20.

[7] Army affairs seem to have concerned him particularly in 13 B.C., and, at least from the financial point of view, in A.D. 6. Syme, *Roman Revolution*, 352; Dio, liv. 25. 5 f.; lv. 25. 2 f.; *RG* 16. 17.

[8] Cf. Schambach, *Bemerkungen*, 4.

[9] The frontier in central Europe would still have been enormous even if the Romans had succeeded in establishing the Elbe–Danube line, which seems to have been Augustus' intention until the Varian disaster in A.D. 9.

was at approximately the same level. Thus, 336,000 men, an army of much the same size as the British expeditionary force which was successfully evacuated from Dunkirk in 1940, were meant to guard the extensive frontiers indicated above. We inevitably gain the strong impression that the size of the imperial army was dictated solely by financial considerations. It appears that the difficulty lay not so much in finding the money to pay the serving soldiers, but in providing bounties for veterans on discharge.[1]

But the impression is utterly misleading. A nicely balanced military budget would have made no sense if the army could not effectively perform its task. Augustus' primary concern was to decide what numerical strength the army would need in order to do its job. Financial considerations entered into the question to the extent that Augustus could not afford to be lavish; the imperial army had to be the smallest which could fulfil its primary function. Augustus' successors made no significant increase in the army's size (in the number of legions, at any rate) during the next 200 years or so, and thus endorsed the original arrangement. It follows, therefore, that expert military opinion, upon which the emperors no doubt depended, considered an army of about 350,000 men sufficient.

The effectiveness of a relatively small army can be increased if ingenuity is exercised in its strategic disposition. But, because they lacked forms of transport which could move large bodies of troops rapidly over long distances, ancient states were severely restricted in what they could do. Augustus, therefore, opted for a linear system of defence. This was by no means so inflexible as it sounds, but it has serious weaknesses. Once an enemy breaks the imperial shell, the way into the heart of the empire lies wide open. If the linear scheme is to work, it is essential to guard each sector of the frontier with a force powerful enough to withstand any normally foreseeable attacks without assistance and equipped to engage in any type of military operation. In other words, a series of complete armies was required. How could this be managed when the entire strength of the imperial frontier army was less than 350,000 men?

In the early empire, each sector of the frontier was covered by a legion, or by two legions in rare instances.[2] A Roman imperial legion, with its complement of auxiliary cavalry and light infantry, constituted a full

---

[1] The *aerarium militare* was founded simply to provide bounties (*RG* 17; Suet. *Aug.* 49). Tiberius stated the financial difficulty plainly (Tac. *An.* i. 78. 2) : 'imparem oneri rem publicam, nisi vicensimo militiae anno veterani dimitterentur', i.e. if, as previously happened, soldiers were released after sixteen years, the need to pay bonuses more frequently to discharged veterans would have laid an intolerable burden on the treasury.

[2] e.g. there were two at Moguntiacum until the Flavian period.

army in miniature, a well-balanced mixture of the necessary main and subordinate arms. Because the soldiers of all but the highest ranks were long-term professionals, this little army worked as an excellently trained team. Vegetius sums the situation up very neatly:

Legio autem propriis cohortibus plena cum gravem armaturam, hoc est principes hastatos triarios antesignanos, item levem armaturam, hoc est ferentarios sagittarios funditores ballistarios, cum proprios et sibi insitos equites legionarios isdem matriculis teneat, cum uno animo parique consensu castra muniat, aciem instruat, proelium gerat, ex omni parte perfecta, nullo extrinsecus indigens adiumento, quantamlibet hostium multitudinem superare consuevit.[1]

Each legion was regularly equipped with all sorts of tools and probably some basic materials, so that, wherever it happened to be, it could construct any type of military engine, any kind of temporary or permanent fortification, any field-work imaginable.[2] Nero's general, Domitius Corbulo, was in the habit of saying that victory was to be attained by the use of one of these tools, the *dolabra*.[3] Although all its members were trained as heavy infantry, the imperial legion may also be regarded as a group of unskilled labourers, semi-skilled labourers, and expert technicians (e.g. *architecti*, *mensores*). It is not known precisely how many of the latter there were, but they need not have been numerous. The legion thus had experts who could design any fortification or machine, supervise the rough work, and construct vital or complicated parts themselves.[4]

Hence a legion could confidently undertake the vigorous siege of any hostile position, from a hill-top *oppidum* like Maiden Castle, with its

---

[1] Veg. *Mil.* ii. 2. Although Vegetius' remarks refer to the second and third centuries, broadly speaking, it is clear that they must have applied equally to the legions from the time of Augustus onwards.

I take 'propriis cohortibus plena' to mean 'complete with its regular complement of auxiliary cohorts'; these provide the 'ferentarios sagittarios funditores'. Likewise, 'proprios ... matriculis' means 'the regular complement of auxiliary cavalry and the horsemen actually incorporated in the legion and on the legion's nominal roll'.

[2] Veg. *Mil.* ii. 10: 'vehicula sagmarii necnon etiam ferramenta, quibus materies secatur vel caeditur, quibusque aperiuntur fossae, contexitur vallum aquaeductus . . .'

[3] Frontin. *Strat.* iv. 7. 2: 'Domitius Corbulo dolabra hostem vincendum esse dicebat.'

On heads for *dolabrae* see J. Curle, *A Roman Frontier Post and its People* (Glasgow, 1911), 278 and pl. 58. Each head has an axe at one end and a pick at the other. The axe cut and trimmed logs for palisades, etc. (Juv. viii. 248), and for machine-construction. The pick split the logs into rough planks (Curt. viii. 4. 11).

[4] Veg. *Mil.* ii. 11: 'habet praeterea legio fabros tignarios structores carpentarios ferrarios, pictores reliquosque artifices ad hibernorum aedificia fabricanda, ad machinas turres ligneas ceteraque, quibus vel expugnantur adversariorum civitates vel defenduntur propriae, praeparatos, qui arma vehicula ceteraque genera tormentorum vel nova facerent vel quassata repararent.'

splendidly impressive, but somewhat outmoded defences, to an apparently impregnable fortress like Masada.[1] It could rapidly throw a bridge across a river.[2] The now impoverished vestiges of many a Roman camp reveal the strong defensive positions that legions could manufacture for themselves. In short, in every phase of warfare, the legion, with its associated auxiliary units, was capable of giving an extremely good account of itself. The legions mostly fought against barbarians to whom machinery of any sort was completely baffling. As Tacitus puts it: 'nihil tam ignarum barbaris quam machinamenta et astus oppugnationum: at nobis ea pars militiae maxime gnara est.'[3] Nor were the barbarians, as a rule, quick to become mechanically minded.[4] In its day, therefore, the imperial legion stood in the same relation to most of its opponents as a modern armoured division stands to a mass of irregulars armed with rifles alone.

The sort of legion discussed above, so admirably suited to the linear system of defence, was very probably established, in all essentials, by Augustus. The idea of giving every legion an allotment of artillery on a definite scale will also have originated with him. It is impossible to say what the original scale was, but, by A.D. 66, legions possessed approximately one machine per century. Until about A.D. 100, the machines allotted were the arrow-shooting catapults and scorpions and the stone-throwing *ballistae*, all engines resembling in construction those described by Vitruvius (x. 10 and 11). Within each legion, the artillery of both types would belong to several convenient calibres, possibly varying from unit to unit in accordance with local requirements. Artillery was confined to the legions for two main reasons. The legionaries, Roman citizens, would have greater ability to manufacture and operate machinery than the non-Roman auxiliaries. Secondly, the possession of this important subordinate arm could not fail to add to the prestige of the legions.

The former shortcomings in production and maintenance of catapults had been removed, because every legion could set up its own workshop, at almost any time or place, to repair or replace damaged ordnance. A large arsenal was also established in Rome, which possibly helped to

---

[1] Joseph. *BJ* vii. 309; and see now I. A. Richmond, 'The Roman siege-works of Masada, Israel', in *JRS* 52 (1962), 142 ff.

[2] Veg. *Mil.* i. 10.   [3] Tac. *An.* xii. 45.

[4] There are exceptions, as F. Lammert has shown (in *Klio* 31, 1938, 406 f.): e.g. Caes. *BG* ii. 12; 30; v. 42; Tac. *An.* iv. 23. But barbarian attempts to imitate the Roman use of machines generally appear laughable: e.g. Tac. *An.* xv. 4. Even in the third century A.D. barbarian employment of siege appliances, relatively simple ones at that, was neither impressive nor successful; see Dexippus' accounts in *FGrH* iiA, 452 ff. (frgs. 25, 27, 29). Cf. Joseph. *BJ* v. 268; 359.

supply the legions with artillery, at any rate in emergency.[1] There exists a most interesting record of an artificer from this central workshop, whose tombstone has a bas-relief of an arrow-shooting catapult at the top and, underneath, the following inscription (c. A.D. 100):

C. Vedennius C. f. / Qui. Moderatus Antio, / milit. in leg. XVI Gal. a. X, / tranlat. in coh. IX pr., / in qua milit. ann. VIII, / missus honesta mission., / revoc. ab imp. fact. evoc. Aug., / arcitect. armament. imp., / evoc. ann. XXIII, / donis militarib. donat. / bis, ab divo Vesp. et / imp. Domitiano Aug. Germ.[2]

Gaius Vedennius Moderatus, from Antium (Anzio), joined the army in A.D. 60 and served until A.D. 69 with *legio XVI Gallica* stationed at Novaesium (Neuss) in Lower Germany.[3] We may guess that, during this time, he rose to the rank of *architectus* or, at least, of *discens architecti*. When the legions of the German frontier supported Vitellius against Otho, Vedennius marched to Italy with a *vexillatio* of his legion and was one of the many legionaries from Germany who were rewarded by Vitellius with transfer into the praetorian guard. His value as a competent artificer enabled him to survive Vespasian's subsequent purge of the guard. Further, on discharge,[4] he was invited to remain in the army as *evocatus Augusti*, clearly because of his technical skill, and he remained in service for another twenty-three years as a senior artificer in the imperial arsenal at Rome. His military decorations indicate that, in all probability, he distinguished himself in the production and maintenance of artillery during frontier campaigns under both Vespasian and Domitian.

Artillery appears fairly prominently in fighting during the first century A.D. particularly, as usual, in sieges, where it was always useful for providing covering fire. Corbulo delivered an energetic and spectacular assault on the Armenian fortress of Volandum under the protection of a barrage of catapult-bolts and fire-darts; he took the place in less than four hours.[5] Vespasian, during sieges at Jotapata and elsewhere in Galilee (A.D. 67), and Titus, during the great siege of Jerusalem, were well served in this respect by their catapults which, in spite of strong opposition, generally succeeded in keeping the defenders' heads down and thus

---

[1] Cf. M. Durry, *Les Cohortes prétoriennes* (Paris, 1938), 115. For obvious reasons, I cannot agree with Durry's implication that this arsenal supplied the whole Roman army all the time. [2] *ILS* 2034.

[3] On this legion and the career of Vedennius cf. Ritterling in *RE* 12 (1925), 'Legio', col. 1763.

[4] Probably in A.D. 77; Vedennius' length of ordinary service (eighteen years) shows, incidentally, a just appreciation of the relative values of his periods in the legion and in the praetorian guard.

[5] Tac. *An.* xiii. 39. Cf. ibid. ii. 81; Joseph. *BJ* iii. 256.

facilitated the approach of siege-engines and assault-works.[1] The catapults were sometimes mounted on siege-towers to assist them in achieving their object.[2] When the frustrated enemy tried to sally forth and damage uncompleted approach-works, artillery helped to drive him back.[3] Occasionally long-range shooting interfered with life inside the besieged city.[4] Furthermore, at Jotapata, in the course of a devastating nocturnal barrage, Vespasian's stone-throwers actually achieved a certain amount of destruction, smashing battlements, damaging the corners of towers, and assisting in making a breach in the wall.[5]

When legions wished to bridge a river in the face of the enemy, catapults and *ballistae* were most useful for clearing the hostile bank. Thus, in A.D. 14, Germanicus' *tormenta* drove the Chatti away from the far bank of the River Adrana.[6] In A.D. 62, Syria was threatened by Parthian invasion, and Corbulo decided that a suitable display of force was the best means of defence. To secure a foothold on the Parthian bank of the Euphrates, he collected some large river-boats, joined them together to make a fighting platform, fitted them with towers, and put catapults and *ballistae* therein. Even the famous Parthian archers were quite outranged; the enemy withdrew from the river, Corbulo completed a bridge, and occupied a strong position on the eastern bank. The Parthians, discouraged 'tanta celeritate et ostentatione virium', sheered off.[7]

As for the employment of artillery in defence of camps, there can be no more spectacular example than the defence of Vetera by two legions against Civilis.[8] Josephus' account of the standard Roman camp shows that many types of ordnance were set up on the walls ready to shoot at a moment's notice,[9] and Hyginus offers specific recommendations about the siting of artillery in camp-defences:

Meminisse oportet in hostico ascensus valli duplices et frequentes facere et tormentis tribunalia extruere circum portas, in coxis [i.e. angulis], in loco tironum. Maxime instruendum erit vallum tormentis ab eo latere, quo novercae, si vitari non potuerunt.[10]

---

[1] At Jotapata: Joseph. *BJ* iii. 166, 219, 240; at Gamala: *BJ* iv. 19; at Jerusalem: *BJ* v. 263, 267–74, 276.

[2] Joseph. *BJ* iii. 285 (Jotapata); v. 296 (Jerusalem); vii. 309 (Masada).

[3] Ibid. iii. 211–12; v. 263, 268–9, 484; vi. 21.

[4] Ibid. iii. 166, 184–5, 246; possibly implied in v. 271–3.

[5] Ibid. iii. 242–8, 256.   [6] Tac. *An.* i. 56.   [7] Ibid. xv. 9.

[8] Ibid. *Hist.* iv. 23.   [9] Joseph. *BJ* iii. 80.

[10] Hyg. (Gromat.), 58 (probably writing in Trajan's reign). The *novercae*, as Hyginus has previously explained, are *iniqua loca*, i.e. a hill overlooking the camp, a wood, ditches, valleys, anything which might assist the enemy to approach closely to the defences. The remains of many imperial camps and forts reveal, e.g. by significant rearward thickening of the rampart, provision for artillery at the points mentioned by Hyginus, generally speaking. See, for instance, I. A. Richmond, 'The four Roman camps at Cawthorn, in the North Riding of

Apart from its use in static fighting, Roman legions were quite prepared to deploy artillery in more fluid engagements. When the Cherusci made their stand against Germanicus in A.D. 16, in the second stage of the conflict, the fighting developed in very rough country. The Cherusci took advantage of a boundary-*agger*, set up by the Angrivarii to delimit the lands of the two tribes, and proved difficult to dislodge from it. Germanicus called up his arrow-shooting artillery, which put down a heavy barrage so that praetorian cohorts were able to follow it up and take the *agger*.[1] Artillery figured, too, in an exciting episode during the second battle of Bedriacum, A.D. 69. At first the Vitellian legions deployed their ordnance in the country beside the *Via Postumia*, but the trees and bushes deflected the bolts and shot, thus reducing their effectiveness. They then transferred the artillery to the road itself. A particularly large *ballista* belonging to the fifteenth legion began to hurl its shot from the causeway with devastating effect, but two of Antonius' soldiers, concealing their identity with captured Vitellian shields, slipped up to the engine and cut its sinew spring-cords.[2] Unfortunately, when the Vitellians were compelled to retreat in broken order along the *Via Postumia* back to Cremona, the pieces of artillery and their transport-wagons prevented the troops from re-forming.[3]

Yorkshire', in *Arch. Journ.* 89 (1932), 33, 46 f., 53, 57 f., 76. It was suggested that they were all practice-camps (*c.* A.D. 80–110).

[1] Tac. *An.* ii. 20.

[2] Tac. *Hist.* iii. 23; Dio, lxiv. 14. 2. Tacitus' sentence relating to the actual sabotage is by no means clear. The two soldiers '. . . vincla ac libramenta tormentorum abscidissent'. Editors have had trouble with the word 'tormentorum' which seems to indicate more than one piece of artillery, though only one engine, the large *ballista*, comes into the story. Therefore, Nipperdey wanted to delete it, Ritter read 'tormento'. Tacitus is not renowned for his care with technical terms, and neither *vincla* nor *libramenta* can be paralleled as such. *Vincla* could conceivably mean one of two things: the ropes of the pull-back system or the cords of the springs. Since repair of the withdrawal mechanism would take only a few minutes, whereas replacement of the springs would need several hours, and since Tacitus implies that the *ballista* was out of action for the rest of the battle, it is certain that the sinew-springs were severed. Dio's word for the cords, σχοινία, does mean spring-cords in another artillery context (Heron, *Bel.* W 81).

The *libramenta* present an even greater problem. At the simplest, they should be balancing weights. But technical writers give no hint of such things being necessary for *ballistae*. I think *libramenta* must be taken not as 'things which provide additional weight in order to balance the engine', but as 'components that apply additional tension to the springs in order to increase the propulsive force', that is, the *libramenta* are ἐπιζυγίδες, tightening-levers.

Vincla and *libramenta* go closely together. Each of the two daring soldiers slashed with his sword at the projecting end of one spring (the bottom ends, obviously, which could easily be reached). They cut through the sinew-cords (*vincla*, σχοινία), and the two lower tightening levers (*libramenta*, ἐπιζυγίδες) naturally fell out. The *ballista* was then immobilized for a matter of hours.

The word 'tormentorum' appears to be equivalent to 'tonorum' (τόνων), the two springs (see Vitr. x. 10. 6). It is possible, of course, that Tacitus actually wrote 'tonorum'.

There is no necessary connection between this *ballista* and the one which appears a little later in the defence of the Vitellian camp at Cremona (Tac. *Hist.* iii. 29). [3] Ibid. 25.

Thus, from Augustus to Trajan, artillery played a useful part in numerous operations. The idea of allotting ordnance to an army's major infantry divisions on a standard scale represents a remarkable step forward in the organization of artillery. But there was clearly much room for improvement, and, because the imperial army was almost entirely composed of long-term professionals and was not always engaged in actual fighting, there would be many opportunities for constructional development of artillery and for experiments in its tactical use.[1] Greater mobility was especially desirable,[2] particularly in the case of the smaller catapults which were most likely to be used in support of field operations. It is well known from the illustrations on Trajan's column that the Romans did succeed in producing, by his reign at the latest, a serviceable mobile carriage for small arrow-shooting machines.[3] But the full significance of this not really startling development can best be appreciated if we attempt to account for the fact that there was a complete change in artillery terminology between the first and fourth centuries A.D.

Roman machines bore exactly the same names in the early empire, at least until Tacitus' time, as they had in the republican period. The Romans called their arrow-firers *catapultae*. These were euthytones, and corresponded to the Greek καταπέλται ὀξυβελεῖς, the smaller ones being termed scorpions in both languages.[4] *Ballista* was the equivalent of καταπέλτης λιθοβόλος or πετροβόλος, being a palintone, two-armed stone-thrower.[5] It could be adapted for shooting bolts if exceptionally high performance was required.[6] Both *catapulta* and *ballista* may also denote the missiles hurled by the two types of machine.

In the fourth century A.D., however, the word *ballista* and its compounds, *arcuballista*, *carroballista*, and *manuballista*, signify arrow-shooting

---

[1] We need not take much notice of the complaint of the mutineers of A.D. 14 about 'sterilem pacem' (Tac. *An.* i. 17).

[2] Lack of mobility perhaps cost Cestius Gallus his artillery during his instructive retreat from Jerusalem in the autumn of A.D. 66 (Joseph. *BJ* ii. 546, 553).

[3] *TC* 104-5, 163-4. See Plates 9 to 13 at the end.

[4] Heron (*Bel.* W 74) seems to regard catapult and scorpion as synonymous; but all the other evidence suggests that the term scorpion was an alternative only for small catapults (cf. Vitr. x. 1. 3, on the difference between *organum* and *machina*).

[5] Normal Latin usage in the late republic and early empire in connection with these terms is amply demonstrated by the technical expert Vitruvius (x. 10 and 11). Although non-technical writers often employ vaguer words, especially *tormentum* (e.g. Caes. *BG* ii. 8; iv. 25; vii. 41 and 81; viii. 14. 40, and 41; *BC* 1. 17; ii. 9; iii. 51 and 56; Cic. *Tusc.* ii. 57; *Phil.* viii. 20; Tac. *An.* i. 56; ii. 6. 20, and 81; xiii. 39; *Hist.* iii. 20 and 23), they almost invariably observe the same strict system of nomenclature when they feel it necessary to be a little more precise (e.g. the scorpion, Caes. *BG* vii. 25).

[6] One of the most famous conversions of this sort was the work of the Massiliots in 49 B.C. (Caes. *BC* ii. 2). It appears from Sil. i. 335 that they rather specialized in it. On Massiliot ὀργανοποιία see Strabo, iv. 13.

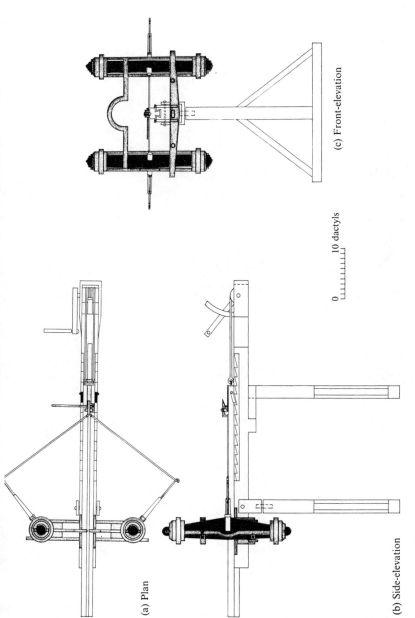

(c) Front-elevation

10 dactyls

0

(a) Plan

(b) Side-elevation

FIG. 8.1. Heron's *Cheiroballistra*

engines.[1] It is true that Ammianus employs *catapulta* twice. In the first case, where he indulges in a purple passage on the fighting qualities of the Gallic housewife, her fists being compared to catapult-bolts, he is merely offering a rather laboured echo of one of Plautus' catapult jokes, thus revealing his knowledge of Latin literature, but not of contemporary technical terms.[2] The second occurrence of the word may also be ascribed to Ammianus' liking for the old-fashioned turn of phrase, since he uses the good old formula 'catapultis ... atque ballistis'.[3] In view of his consistency in the use of *ballista* elsewhere, the only alternative explanation is that he simply means stone-throwers by his 'catapultis' here. After all, his regular word for the standard contemporary stone-thrower, the one-armed *onager*, is *scorpio*,[4] and everyone knows that *scorpio* denotes a small catapult.

The same uniformity is observable with regard to the fourth-century stone-thrower. The *onager* appears several times in Vegetius' Epitome.[5] We have just noted that Ammianus generally calls it a scorpion; he gives as a reason its resemblance in shape to the insect,[6] and states that *onager* is a more recent alternative name.[7] Of the old two-armed stone-throwing *ballista* there remains not a trace.

Heron's *Cheiroballistra* provides the key to the peculiar change in nomenclature. We have elsewhere attempted to show that this document gives instructions for building a machine of the same type as the pieces of artillery depicted on Trajan's Column.[8] Also, it has been demonstrated that the *cheiroballistra* could very easily be constructed in the palintone form, and no doubt was so constructed.[9] Because it was a palintone engine, expert artificers would call it a *ballista*. For a time, in and after Trajan's reign, the Roman army presumably had two sorts of *ballistae*—the new arrow-shooting engines with iron frames to hold the springs, and the old two-armed stone-throwers with wooden metal-plated frames. By the fourth century the two-armed stone-throwers had been replaced by the one-armed *onagri*. The Romans probably discovered by experiment that it was impossible to build efficient stone-throwers on the same principle as the *cheiroballistra*, employing all-metal frames.

---

[1] *Ballista*: Veg. *Mil.* ii. 10; iii. 3; iv. 9, 10, 18, 22, 28, and 44; Amm. xix. 1. 7; 5. 6; 7. 2, 5, 6, and 7; xx. 7. 2 and 10; 11. 20 and 22; xxiii. 4. 1; xxiv. 2. 13; 4. 16. *Carroballista*: Veg. *Mil.* ii. 25; iii. 14 and 24. *Arcuballista*: ibid. ii. 15; iv. 22. *Manuballista*: ibid. ii. 15; iv. 22.
[2] Amm. xv. 12. 1. On Ammianus' predilection for archaisms see E. von Nischer in Kromayer–Veith, *Heerwesen*, 470.
[3] Amm. xxiv. 2. 13.
[4] Ibid. xix. 2. 7; 7. 6 and 7; xx. 7. 10; xxiii. 4. 4; xxiv. 4. 16 and 28; xxxi. 15. 12.
[5] Veg. *Mil.* ii. 10 and 25; iii. 3 and 14; iv. 8, 9, 22, 28, and 44.
[6] Amm. xxiii. 4. 7.   [7] Ibid. xxiii. 4. 4 and 7; xxxi. 15. 12.
[8] See *Technical Treatises*, Heron's *Cheiroballistra*, § 1.   [9] Ibid. § 4.

At any rate, from *c.* A.D. 100 the Romans possessed the most powerful arrow-shooting engines ever produced in the ancient world, engines that were also the most suitable for use in the field.[1] They apparently made their début in the First Dacian War.[2] Probably most of the artillery which figures in Arrian's orders for his campaign against the Alani (A.D. 134) were *carroballistae*.[3] On the way to the battlefield the artillery was to take up position in the marching column behind the auxiliary cavalry units and infantry cohorts, immediately behind the *equites singulares* and legionary cavalry, but in front of the main body of legionary soldiers (*legg. XV Apollinaris, XII Fulminata*).[4] Arrian's orders stated that, when the army arrived at the battlefield, the tactical alignment would take the form of a crescent, the concavity pointing in the direction of the enemy. The artillery was deployed at each tip of the crescent 'so as to shoot at the enemy at the greatest possible range as he approached'. Other machines were deployed behind the main line of infantry.[5] In view of their somewhat exposed position, I think that the machines on the wings would be *carroballistae*. The other engines, protected by the infantry (over whose heads they were going to shoot!), would be stone-throwing *ballistae* and either static arrow-firing *ballistae* or old arrow-firing catapults. The whole army was to keep perfectly silent until the enemy came within range. Then everyone had to shout as loudly and formidably as possible. At the same time, the artillery, the auxiliary archers, and the other light troops, were supposed to put down a tremendous barrage.[6] Arrian goes so far as to express the hope that the enemy may not penetrate this barrage and reach the Roman infantry.[7] It is probable that Arrian's tactical dispositions for his battle with the Alani constituted one of the stock Roman plans during the second and third centuries A.D., and we can visualize many a conflict in which artillery was stationed on the flanks and behind the main line.

But a great deal would clearly depend on circumstances, and Vegetius' few hints about the tactical use of ordnance in the days of the *antiqua legio* indicate slightly different arrangements. He thought that the legion

[1] See *Technical Treatises*, Heron's *Cheiroballistra*, § 4.
[2] The tombstone of Vedennius (see Plate 1 at the end) shows that the old type of arrow-firing catapult was still important at the end of the first century A.D. Perhaps the arrow-shooting *ballista* figures so prominently on Trajan's Column because it was absolutely the latest thing.
[3] Arr. ἔκταξις κατὰ Ἀλανῶν, ed. A. G. Roos, *Flavii Arriani* Quae Exstant Omnia, ii (Leipzig, 1928), 177 ff.
[4] Arr. *Alan.* 5. Arrian's order of march is extraordinarily similar to that of Vespasian in Palestine as described by Josephus (*BJ* iii. 115–26). Vespasian's artillery appears to have been at exactly the same point in the column (ibid. 121).
[5] Arr. *Alan.* 19.   [6] Ibid. 25.   [7] Ibid. 26.

generally formed up in six parallel lines (*acies*). Behind the first line stood *tragularii* operating *manuballistae* (small torsion arrow-shooting engines) and *arcuballistae* (small non-torsion arrow-firers).[1] In the fifth line were some of the *carroballistae* and more *manuballistae*,[2] while the larger *carroballistae* with the greatest range took position right at the back.[3] The Romans used this system when the army had to be drawn up in a perfectly straight line, and it demonstrates another standard tactical plan.

It is noteworthy that Vegetius does not include legionary *onagri* in the above tactical arrangement, for the very good reason that they were not really suitable for use in the field. Arrian certainly employed the old stone-throwing *ballista* in his Alan campaign, so that stone-throwers were deployed in battle as long as this old type remained in service. It is impossible to discover at what precise period the *onager* took over as the standard heavy artillery within the legion. Strong arguments, based on evidence provided by the spade, suggest the existence at the fort of Bremennium (High Rochester, in Northumberland), about A.D. 220, of the peculiarly resilient platforms which *onagri* required.[4] We probably need not attach too much technical significance to the use of the word *ballistarium* in inscriptions which apparently record the construction and repair of this platform.[5] It may be, then, that one-armed stone-throwers were in service with the Roman army early in the third century. But what is artillery doing in an auxiliary fort? The Romans may have found the relatively simple *onager* a suitable machine to issue to auxiliary cohorts. On the other hand, the ordnance at Bremennium and at many more auxiliary forts may have been maintained and operated by legionary artillerymen on detached duty.

From the second and third centuries A.D. we have a few tenuous indications about the men who worked the artillery within the legions. They were called *ballistarii*,[6] and the *Digest* records a statement of Tarrutenius Paternus (*fl. c.* A.D. 150, ob. A.D. 183) including them among the *immunes*—men excused fatigues, guard-duties, and so on.[7] The epitaph of a certain Aelius Optatus, found near Novaria (Novara) in Cisalpine

---

[1] Veg. *Mil.* ii. 15.   [2] Ibid. iii. 14.   [3] Ibid. iii. 24.

[4] I. A. Richmond, 'The Romans in Redesdale', in *History of Northumberland*, xv (Newcastle, 1940), 97 ff. On the eastern version of the resilient platform see Amm. xxiii. 4. 5. On the *onager* in general see *Technical Treatises*, The Onager.

[5] *CIL* v. 1044–5 (A.D. 220) and 1046 (A.D. 225–35); *JRS* 27 (1937), 247: '. . . ballist(arium) a solo co(hors) I f(ida) Vardul(orum) Antonin(a) . . . fecit.'

[6] Veg. *Mil.* ii. 2; cf. Lyd. *Mag.* i. 46, who, describing the old legion, mentions βαλλιστράριοι καταπελτισταί.

[7] *Dig.* i. 6. 7 (6): 'naupegi, ballistrarii, specularii, fabri immunes sunt munerum graviorum.' I think Paternus originally wrote 'ballistarii'.

Gaul, tells us that he was a soldier in *legio XX* and apparently a *magister ballistarius*.[1] We have no further evidence as to the precise significance of this office, but we may tentatively conclude that Optatus was a senior and experienced artilleryman. An inscription on a bronze plaque from a vexillum, found at Novae (Sistow) and dated *c.* A.D. 300 by its editor on the basis of the letter-forms, was dedicated by Priscinius, a *ballistarius* of *legio I Italica*.[2] If the date is approximately correct, Priscinius must have been one of the last *ballistarii* in an ordinary legion, for shortly afterwards artillery and artillerymen were confined to special legions.

The Roman legionary *ballistarius* probably performed the same functions as the καταπαλταφέτης in the Hellenistic period.[3] It is unlikely that he constructed his own machines or carried out major repairs. The responsibility for these tasks lay, I think, with the *architecti*, though the *ballistarii* no doubt provided valuable semi-skilled assistance.[4] According to Vegetius each century allotted a section (*contubernium*) of eleven men to operate its *carroballista*.[5] But the illustrations on Trajan's Column show only two men working the arrow-firing *ballistae*, whether mobile or not.[6] We can easily justify a detachment of ten or eleven men for a stone-throwing *ballista* or an *onager*,[7] when we think of the manhandling involved not only in connection with the machine itself, but also in moving ammunition, and when we remember the force required to pull the spring or springs back. But I think two men would be quite sufficient for the *carroballista* in action. Even then, however, it was probably economic to entrust a complete *contubernium* with its care and maintenance.[8] I should estimate that there were two official *ballistarii* in each century possessing an arrow-shooting engine, with two understudies learning the job and ready to take over in emergency. The remaining members of their *contubernium* helped to look after the animals, the mobile carriage, and the engine itself, but were free for other duties when action commenced. In the century in each cohort that maintained the stone-thrower there may

---

[1] *CIL* v. 6632.

[2] W. Kubitschek, in *Jahreshefte des Österreichischen Archäologischen Institutes in Wien*, xxix. 1 (1934), 44–8: Πρισκείνιος βαλήστες (= ballistarius) λεγι(ῶνος) πρώτης 'Ιταλικῆς . . .

[3] See above, pp. 67 f.

[4] See above, p. 185, on Vedennius. An example of a legionary *architectus* is Q. Valerius Seius, buried at Carnuntum and described as 'mil(es) l(egionis) XV Ap(ollinaris) arci(tectus) . . .' (*Die römische Limes in Österreich*, xvi, 1926, 36).

[5] Veg. *Mil.* ii. 25.

[6] e.g. *TC* 104–5. 166.

[7] The *contubernium* perhaps comprised ten men in the second century A.D.: Veg. *Mil.* ii. 8 and 13.

[8] We can readily find tasks for two men to look after the mules or horses, two more to apply the inevitable spit and polish to the carriage, another to attend to the ammunition. The *ballistarii* would maintain the *ballista* itself and supervise the work of the others.

have been more than two *ballistarii*, and, when the machine was needed—which would not be so frequently as the arrow-firers—the presence of the whole section would be required.

The artificers who constructed and repaired artillery and other machines and buildings came under the orders of the *praefectus castrorum*,[1] who could also detail other legionaries, *ballistarii* among them when it was a question of making pieces of artillery, to assist his technical experts. But, in action, the *ballistarii* of a legion were under the direct tactical control of the *legatus legionis* or, if more than two legions were involved, of the governor of the province. Arrian clearly exercised such control over the artillery of two legions in Cappadocia. This being the case, there ought to be at least one artilleryman in each cohort with authority, a *principalis* who attended councils of war and then informed the other *ballistarii* of his cohort about the plan of campaign in general and the part their machines were to play in it. The evidence for a *principalis* of this sort in the legions is very slight indeed.

But the situation in the *Vigiles* may be similar, and we know a little more about artillery commands in this unit. In two nominal rolls of one cohort of *Vigiles*, one belonging to the year A.D. 205,[2] the other to A.D. 210,[3] we find four names to which one of the following rubrics is attached: OPB; OPTB; OP BA. The persons concerned appear to be *optiones ballistariorum* or *ballistarum*, and there were three of them in the cohort in A.D. 205. P. Julius Faustinus was a *vexillarius* in the earlier roll and *optio ball.* in the later one, therefore the latter post was senior to the former.[4] *Optiones* of the same type very probably existed in the legions, and an inscription set up between A.D. 92 and 96 possibly records one such *optio* in *legio X Domitiana*.[5]

The *Vigiles*, like the legions, are most likely to have had one machine per century.[6] Modern writers assume that their *ballistae* were stone-throwers; but in the third century, from which our scanty information comes,[7] *ballista* could easily denote an arrow-firer. What purpose did the artillery serve? Since the *Vigiles* in Rome fought fires, it has been proposed that they used *ballistae* (stone-throwers) to knock down safely from

[1] Veg. *Mil.* ii. 10. [2] *CIL* vi. 1057 (3) l. 39; (4) l. 6; (7) l. 1.
[3] Ibid. 1058 (4) l. 4.
[4] Ibid. l. 4. The *optio ball.* was thus a fairly important *principalis*.
[5] W. Vollgraff in *L'Antiquité classique*, 19 (1950), 165–7, and in *REA* 57 (1955), 291, n. 2: 'Or(atius) Avius o(ptio) b(allistariorum) . . .'.
[6] Domaszewski, *Rangordnung*, 10, thought they had three *ballistae* per cohort because there were three *optiones ball.* in the cohort roll for A.D. 205.
[7] Apart from the two nominal rolls dating to the early third century, an inscription of A.D. 362 possibly includes *ballistae* in a list of equipment belonging to the *Vigiles*; *CIL* vi. 3744 (= *CIL* vi. 31075), l. 9: *b(allistis)*.

a distance the walls of burning buildings that were in danger of collapsing.[1] Another ingenious and attractive suggestion is that they put vinegar, of which they are known to have had a stock, and which the ancients recognized as a chemical fire-extinguisher, into round vessels and then hurled them with the *ballistae* into the blaze.[2] But the supposition that the *ballistae* formed part of the fire-fighting equipment can only hold good if they were stone-throwers. On the whole, I favour the view that, whichever type of artillery they possessed, the *Vigiles* employed it for police work.

No records of *optiones ballistariorum* exist for the praetorian guard.[3] But the praetorians certainly had artillery and performed an important function in the maintenance of artillery standards throughout the imperial army. An inscription from Nicopolis near Alexandria records the demobilization of men of *Legio II Traiana Fortis* who commenced their service in A.D. 132/3 and obtained honourable discharge in A.D. 157.[4] In this list, third after a centurion and a *cornicularius* of the prefect of Egypt, there appears L. Furius Felix of Utica who is described as *evocatus ballistarum Augusti*.[5] Felix presumably spent sixteen years in the praetorian guard, specializing in shooting with, and maintaining, artillery. In other words, he was the equivalent of a legionary *ballistarius*. Being particularly efficient at his job, he was invited to remain in the army with the rank of *evocatus*, and was sent out to Egypt to instruct the *ballistarii* of the second Trajanic legion in the latest drill, methods of shooting, and care of their equipment.[6]

In a document recording the discharge of men from the praetorian guard in A.D. 144, the names of C. Suetonius Paullinus from Pisaurum and Q. Geminius Castus from Sora are preceded by the rubrics EVOB and EVOC B respectively.[7] They apparently received similar invitations to remain in the army as expert artillerymen. Hence, these three pieces of evidence provide a hint that the Romans had a system for preserving uniform artillery standards throughout the army, for passing on knowledge of the latest ordnance to the legions, and for communicating the

---

[1] Domaszewski, *Rangordnung*, 10.

[2] P. K. B. Reynolds, *The Vigiles of Imperial Rome* (London, 1926), 97.

[3] M. Durry, *Les Cohortes prétoriennes* (Paris, 1938), 103 n. 6.

[4] A. A. Aly, 'A Latin inscription from Nicopolis', in *Annals of the Faculty of Arts, Ain Shams University*, iii (Jan. 1955), 113 ff.

[5] The form *ballistarum* here prompted me to suggest earlier that the artillery *optio* may have been called *optio ballistarum* rather than *optio ballistariorum*.

[6] That an *evocatus* could be eventually discharged from the legion to which he was attached is shown by the career of the *librator* Nonius Datus (*c.* A.D. 150) who was *evocatus* and then *veteranus* of *Leg. III Aug.* (*CIL* viii. 2728).

[7] *CIL* vi. 2379a, iii, l. 57, and iv, l. 51.

most modern methods of operating drill. It seems to me that the three examples of *evocati ballistarum* occur a little too late to be directly associated with the introduction of the arrow-shooting *ballista*, which first appears in the Dacian wars.

To sum up the situation in the first three imperial centuries, the Roman army reached very high standards in artillery equipment and organization. In particular, after the introduction of the arrow-shooting *ballista* in its various forms at the beginning of the second century, and while the stone-throwing *ballista* remained in service, every Roman legion possessed substantial batteries of the most powerful artillery produced in the ancient world. There is very little direct evidence for the third century. But the introduction of the *onager* into general service, which may have occurred in the second century,[1] and of the non-torsion *arcuballista*,[2] both machines being of relatively simple construction, suggests a shortage of good artificers. In fact, the Roman Empire never had had enough of such men.[3] Similarly, as the third century progressed, it probably became increasingly hard to find men suitable for training as artillerymen (*ballistarii*), though, of course, good shots still existed. Zosimus records a most interesting story of a master artilleryman in the service of the brigand Lydius the Isaurian in the reign of Probus.[4] Apparently this man hardly ever missed his target. It must have been difficult, also, to maintain the full scale of allotment of artillery to the legions, except on paper. But I think that the factor most likely to reduce the effectiveness of artillery during this period was the increasing number of infantrymen in the army who were not sufficiently amenable to discipline and not intelligent enough to understand the benefits that artillery support could afford them.

In the fourth century the ordinary legions, so called, though they had nothing in common with the legions of the early empire, possessed no artillery whatsoever. Constantine, or whoever was responsible for this reform, obviously had little choice in the matter, though it seems a retrograde step. In connection with the siege of Amida (A.D. 359) Ammianus makes some frank remarks about two Magnentian legions recently brought to the east from Gaul, which were supposed to be assisting the besieged.[5] They were completely useless in siege-warfare in general and,

---

[1] If Schenk, *Vegetius*, 23, is right in his suggestion that the source for Vegetius's *antiqua legio* was Tarrutenius Paternus, the *onager* may have been in use in the time of the latter. On the other hand, it is possible that Vegetius translated Paternus' stone-throwing *ballista* into *onager*, the only stone-thrower he knew.

[2] Veg. *Mil.* ii. 15, mentions this engine in connection with the old type of legion.

[3] Cf. the career of Vedennius, above, p. 185; N.B. the generous treatment of the Byzantine technician Priscus by Septimius Severus (A.D. 196): Dio, lxxiv. 11. 1–3.

[4] Zos. i. 70.   [5] Amm. xix. 5. 2.

in particular, no help whatsoever in dealing with defensive machinery and defensive works ('cum neque in machinis neque in operum constructione iuvarent'). The Magnentian legions were probably not exceptions to the rule in the fourth century.

Special legions of *ballistarii* had to be raised from men who did understand machinery and were capable of operating and maintaining pieces of artillery. If these legions comprised 1,000 men, like the infantry legions of the same epoch, and if Vegetius is approximately right, as he may well be, in saying that eleven men formed the detachment working each arrow-shooting *ballista*, then a unit of *ballistarii* constituted an artillery regiment with about fifty pieces of ordnance.[1]

A few items preserved in the *Notitia Dignitatum* provide some idea, incomplete and not, of course, all valid for the entire fourth century, of the distribution of the artillery legions. Each mobile field army included one or two. The commander of the eastern field army (*magister militum per Orientem*) could call upon the *ballistarii seniores*,[2] who were a *legio comitatensis*, and upon the *ballistarii Theodosiaci*,[3] a *legio pseudocomitatensis*. Similarly, the commander in Thrace controlled the *ballistarii Dafnenses* and the *ballistarii iuniores*, both *legiones comitatenses*.[4] One unit, *ballistarii Theodosiani iuniores*, a *legio pseudocomitatensis*, was available to the commander in Illyricum.[5] Perhaps the original Constantinian establishment allotted two artillery legions, one called *ballistarii seniores*, the other *ballistarii iuniores*, to each mobile reserve army.[6] Because they were intended to support mobile forces, all these artillery units would be equipped primarily, if not exclusively, with *carroballistae*.

In Gaul the *Notitia* records the presence of one legion of *ballistarii*, a *legio pseudocomitatensis*, under the *magister equitum per Gallias*.[7] It is possibly

---

[1] From the period of the special artillery legions we have two inscriptions relating to *ballistarii*. The first (in *Syria*, 14, 1933, 167) simply records Χαλκίδιος βαλλ[ι]στάριος, without, of course, specifying a legion. The other was set up by Σίθρος . . . ἀρχιβαλι[στάριος] . . . whose post corresponds clearly to that of *magister ballistarius* in the old type of legion (see above, p. 192); *Revue Biblique*, 41 (1932), 400.

[2] *Not. Dig. Or.* vii. 8 = 48.

[3] Ibid. 21 = 57. The name suggests that this unit was formed in the last quarter of the fourth century under Theodosius I. But it may have replaced an earlier artillery legion which had been depleted or destroyed.

[4] Ibid. viii. 14 = 46; 15 = 47.   [5] Ibid. ix. 47; see above, n. 3.

[6] We are strongly reminded of an inscription from Old Paphos set up (in the latter half of the second century B.C.) by mercenary Lycian, possibly Ptolemaic, artillerymen (W. H. Buckler in *JHS* 55, 1935, 75 ff. and Launey, 833 and 1061–2). The expert gunners were divided into two units, τὸ τάγμα τῶν πρεσβυτέρων ἀφετῶν and τὸ τάγμα τῶν νεωτέρων, the distinction, it seems, being due to the greater experience of the former in catapult shooting. It is possible that the artillery units in the late Roman imperial army were similarly called *seniores* and *iuniores* according to their experience.

[7] *Not. Dig. Oc.* vii. 97.

this unit which Julian, newly appointed Caesar with special responsibility for the Gallic area (A.D. 356), picked up at Augustodunum (Autun) and used as his bodyguard through enemy-infested countryside on his way to Autessiodurum (Auxerre).[1] We find also in the *Notitia* mention of a prefect of artillery (*praefectus militum ballistariorum*) stationed at Bodobrica and under the *Dux Moguntiacensis.*[2] Although only one instance is confirmed, it may be that many frontier commanders (*duces*) had an artillery legion under their control. If so, frontier artillery units will have been equipped with a greater variety of engines—*manuballistae* (small arrow-firers which one man could operate, and very similar indeed to Heron's *cheiroballistra*), heavier static *ballistae* something like Anonymus' *fulminalis*,[3] as well as the mobile *carroballista.*

The artillery legionaries of the fourth century could no doubt maintain their machines in efficient working order, but they were constructed and given major overhauls in imperial workshops (*fabricae ballistariae*). The *Notitia* records only two of these for certain, both in Gaul; but there must have been others at strategic points throughout the empire. There was one at Augustodunum,[4] and it is probably no coincidence that Julian found the legion of *ballistarii* in winter quarters at that very place in A.D. 356. They would naturally winter beside their base workshop. The other definite *fabrica* for artillery was in Treveran territory and was surely placed there so that it could serve the artillery unit at Bodobrica.[5]

The legions of *ballistarii* do not appear to have had anything to do with the standard stone-thrower of the time, the *onager*. These engines were included in a category of machines generally indicated by the phrase garrison artillery (*tormenta muralia*), to which some static arrow-shooting engines of various sizes belonged, too. There is no specific information about the production of artillery of this type. It was perhaps not manufactured regularly, but constructed for a particular purpose and then stored in strategically chosen depots, when a defensive campaign was in prospect,[6] or collected at the point of concentration of an expeditionary force.[7]

The Romans still employed artillery in the usual ways, siege-warfare being its most prominent recorded sphere of activity. The defenders of

[1] Amm. xvi. 2. 5. [2] *Not. Dig. Oc.* xli. 23. [3] Anon. *de reb. bell.* 18.
[4] *Not. Dig. Oc.* xix. 33. [5] Ibid. 38.
[6] Constantius, as Caesar, established such a depot at Amida when Sapor's invasion was imminent (Amm. xviii. 9. 1: '. . . locatoque ibi conditorio muralium tormentorum'). *Tormenta muralia* were required for a Trajanic fort which was repaired (ibid. xvii. 1. 12). Ursicinus organized similar *castella* along the River Euphrates in A.D. 359 (ibid. xviii. 7. 6).
[7] Amm. xxi. 6. 6 (Constantius II's preparations at Antioch, early A.D. 361); xxiii. 3. 9 ff. (Julian's concentration at Callinicum in A.D. 363).

cities used *ballistae* and *onagri* against assaulting personnel and siege-engines.[1] Artillery covered the arrival of relief forces and the withdrawal of sallying parties into beleaguered towns.[2] Besiegers sought to keep the defenders' heads down so that they could proceed with approach-works in safety,[3] and their pieces of artillery were often placed in the upper storeys of siege-towers in order to achieve this purpose more effectively.[4]

We have absolutely no reason to suppose that Roman artillery in the last century of the western empire was much inferior in quality to earlier Greek or Roman ordnance. The arrow-shooting *ballista* was exactly the same type of machine (palintone) that had been the standard equipment of the army since the Dacian wars of Trajan. The *onager*, though not in the same class, as a piece of artillery, as the old two-armed stone-throwing *ballista*, nevertheless had certain points to recommend it. However, ordnance was probably in very short supply, and the organization of artillerymen in separate legions would not contribute to close co-operation between infantry and the machines. But the main trouble lay, I think, in the almost total lack of fighting men who really knew what engines of war could do for them and who knew how to make full use of them.

---

[1] Personnel: Amm. xix. 1. 7; 5. 6; 7. 4; xx. 7. 2; xxxi. 15. 12. Against siege-engines: Amm. xix. 7. 6–7 (*onagri* against Persian siege-towers); xx. 7. 10; 11. 13 (*ballistae* shooting flaming bolts against machinery; cf. Veg. *Mil.* iv. 18 and 22).

[2] Amm. xviii. 8. 13 (Ammianus managed to slip into Amida under cover of a barrage); xix. 6. 10 (the text here is damaged, but the sense seems clear as far as the artillery is concerned: the defending machines pretended to shoot, and the noise they made discouraged the pursuing enemy; at the same time, the sallying party was not subjected to a hail of bolts from its friends inside).

[3] e.g. Amm. xx. 11. 20; xxiv. 2. 13.   [4] e.g. especially Amm. xix. 7. 5.

APPENDIX 1

MODIFICATIONS IN THE DESIGN OF ARROW-SHOOTING CATAPULTS REFLECTED IN VITRUVIUS

VITRUVIUS' small arrow-shooting catapult or scorpion has one single centre-stanchion (*parastas media*) instead of the two separate centre-stanchions (μεσοστάται) that we find in earlier standard engines.

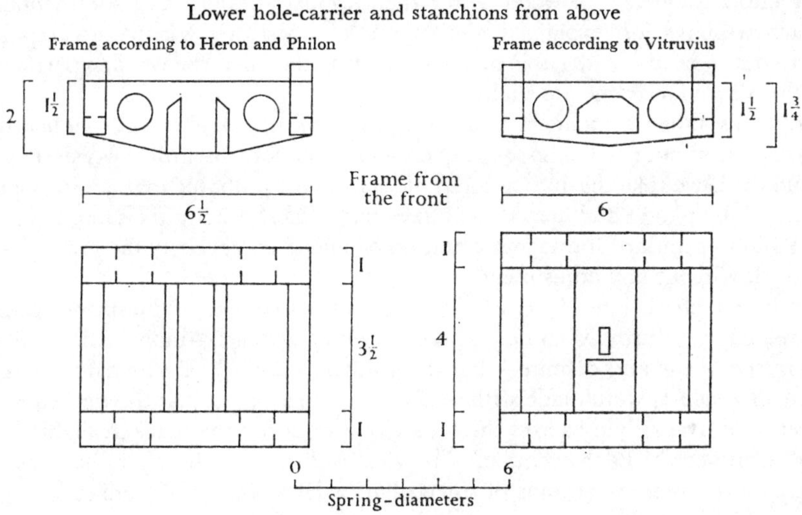

Lower hole-carrier and stanchions from above

Frame according to Heron and Philon   Frame according to Vitruvius

Frame from the front

FIG. 1. Comparison of euthytone frame of Heron and Philon with that of Vitruvius

Philon employed a prototype centre-stanchion of this sort for his novel wedge-machine.[1] He still started with two separate centre-stanchions, but they were thicker than usual and fitted flush against each other. It was necessary to leave two rectangular holes passing right through this composite centre-stanchion—an upper hole through which the slider could be pushed forward and through which the missile could fly out, and a lower socket that received the tenon at the front end of the case (σῦριγξ). The latter arrangement made a far simpler and firmer joint between frame and stock than in the standard artillery of Philon's time. It was possibly this design suggested by Philon that inspired later artificers to take over the composite centre-stanchion for standard machines and then to develop it into the single centre-stanchion.

But the single centre-stanchion required roughly twice as much wood as the

[1] Philon, *Bel.* 64. See *Technical Treatises*, Philon, nn. 79–82 and fig. 10.

two former separate stanchions combined; therefore, it was about twice as heavy. Further, for reasons to be discussed shortly, all Vitruvius' stanchions were 4 diameters high instead of Philon's 3½ diameters. This, too, means additional weight. Unless something is done by way of compensation, the stock of a Vitruvian catapult will not be able to balance the frame. Vitruvius' list of dimensions reveals that compensatory measures have in fact been taken.

The length of the hole-carriers (περίτρητα, tabulae) has been reduced from Philon's 6½ diameters to 6 diameters, and the breadth of the hole-carriers at their centres is now 1¾ diameters as compared with Philon's 2 diameters. The single Vitruvian centre-stanchion is only 1 diameter wide, whereas each of Philon's separate centre-stanchions (in standard catapults) was 1½ diameters wide. The frame of Philon's standard arrow-shooting engine contained about 29¾ cubic diameters of wood. After the various additions and subtractions which we have just explained, the volume of wood in a Vitruvian catapult turns out to be about 28 cubic diameters. Thus, in reality, the wooden portions of the Vitruvian frame are slightly lighter.

But his taller stanchions make the whole frame higher. Consequently Vitruvius' springs will also be higher and, therefore, a little heavier than Philon's. If we take this into account, it seems most probable that a Vitruvian frame, fully plated and armed, will have had almost exactly the same weight as Philon's standard frame and could be balanced by precisely the same type of stock without any adjustment.

Why has the height of the whole frame and, of course, of the springs been increased by Vitruvius' time? There is some evidence—unfortunately not altogether clear and definite—that the washers (modioli) of Vitruvius' stone-throwing ballista were made with oval holes at the top, so that the tightening-levers (epizygides) lying across them no longer reduced the space available for the spring-cord.[1] Each spring of Vitruvius' ballista will, therefore, have consisted of a few more strands of sinew than a Heronian or Philonian spring. Since it is reasonable to suppose that the washers of Vitruvius' arrow-shooting euthytones were designed in the same way, their springs will have been slightly thicker than in earlier catapults and would require an addition to their heights in order to re-establish the most effective relationship between thickness and height. If the above deductions are near the mark, the springs of a catapult of the design described by Vitruvius contained more sinew-cord than a Philonian arrow-firer of similar size and possessed greater power on that account.

A small piece of evidence, as typically brief as one would expect in Vitruvius' list of dimensions, strongly suggests that his catapult had curved arms.[2] Since the arm visible in the catapult illustrated on the Eumenes relief at Pergamum is plainly curved, this modification was apparently introduced early in the second century B.C.[3] Philon does not seem to know anything about

---

[1] Vitr. x. 11. 4. See *Technical Treatises*, Vitruvius, n. 26 and fig. 8.

[2] Vitr. x. 10. 5: 'bracchii . . . curvatura foraminum VIII'. See *Technical Treatises*, Vitruvius, n. 17.

[3] See Plate 3, below, and Droysen in *Alt. Perg.* ii. 119 ff. Droysen discusses in some detail

it. The curvature allowed the arms to be pulled back and to recoil through an angle of about 47 degrees.[1] The straight arms of Philon's arrow-shooting euthytones could only operate through an angle of about 35 degrees.[2] Thus, the springs of Vitruvius' euthytones could exert their force on the arms as they untwisted through an angle about one and one-third times greater. Because of this, and because the springs were larger, as we have seen, Vitruvius' arrow-shooting catapults must have been considerably more powerful than Philon's. It is difficult to say what this meant in terms of increased range; but we are perhaps justified in thinking of a superiority of 50 to 100 yards over the arrow-firers of Heron and Philon and of a corresponding improvement in striking power at lesser ranges.

There was one probable change in the mechanism of the stock. The components concerned are the ratchets and pawls. According to Heron, the early *gastraphetes* had a straight ratchet, a toothed iron beam, along each side of the case (σῦριγξ).[3] Two pawls, one on each side of the slider, worked in conjunction with the ratchets and locked the slider to the case when required. The non-torsion stone-throwers designed by Charon of Magnesia and Isidorus of Abydos incorporated straight ratchets of the same basic type.[4] Philon does not mention ratchets and pawls at all, though his machines must have had them. But Vitruvius offers a hint that the ratchets were slightly different in the latter half of the first century B.C. His *claviculae*, which I take to be the pawls, were fitted at the rear of the fixed portion of the stock (*canaliculus*) beside the windlass.[5] Therefore, he clearly envisaged the use of one, or possibly two, circular ratchets attached to the windlass, and corresponding pawls fitted to the beams (*regulae*) that hold the windlass at the rear of the stock.[6] Incidentally, the catapult illustrated on the Cupid gem reveals a pawl closely associated with the windlass so that this little machine, too, had circular ratchets.[7]

It is not possible to determine the period during which circular ratchets began to replace the straight variety. Perhaps the latter was never entirely superseded. The true *gastraphetes* had to be equipped with straight ratchets because it possessed no windlass. The evidence from Biton suggests that advanced non-torsion engines retained straight ratchets although they were fitted with windlasses.[8] The one-armed stone-thrower (μονάγκων, *onager*) obviously needed circular ratchets. Therefore, if Philon is not misleading us with his solitary passing reference to one-armed engines,[9] circular ratchets were employed in some pieces of artillery, at least, by about 200 B.C. Greek cranes

the measurements of the catapult there depicted, but, as he explains, the representation is not sufficiently accurate to enable any conclusions to be drawn.

[1] See *Technical Treatises*, Heron's *Cheiroballistra*, fig. 12a.

[2] See above, p. 21, Fig. 11.

[3] See *Technical Treatises*, Heron, n. 14 and fig. 5; Heron, *Bel.* W 79–81.

[4] Biton, W 45–6, W 50; see *Technical Treatises*, Biton, diag. 1.

[5] Vitr. x. 11. 8; see *Technical Treatises*, Vitruvius, fig. 14. He does not include ratchets and pawls in his description of the arrow-shooting catapult; they were almost certainly just the same as in his *ballista*.

[6] See *Technical Treatises*, Vitruvius, fig. 5.

[7] See Plate 2.   [8] Biton, W 46 and 50.   [9] Philon, *Pol.* 91. 36.

may well have possessed ratchet-mechanisms in the fifth century B.C., and these would necessarily have been of the circular type.[1] The application of the latter sort to artillery can have occasioned no difficulty and may have been accomplished at any time between the introduction of the winch for pulling back and about 200 B.C. My own practical experience has shown that both types of ratchet work with equal efficiency and involve roughly the same labour in their construction.

[1] The cranes which Conon used for dropping stones on Spartan ships as they tried to enter the harbour of Mytilene in 407 B.C. (D.S. xiii. 78. 7; 79. 2) most probably had ratchet devices so that they could hold large stones poised in the right position.

APPENDIX 2

MODIFICATIONS INCORPORATED IN VITRUVIUS' *BALLISTA*

WE have already noted (in Appendix 1) that Vitruvius' *ballista*, the palintone stone-thrower,[1] probably possessed washers of an improved design which enabled engineers to insert a substantially greater quantity of spring-cord in each spring. But this would lead to a significant increase in the total weight of the two separate palintone frames of his *ballista*, because the springs are now heavier. Therefore, the problem of balancing heavier frames with an ordinary stock arises here just as it did in the new arrow-shooting catapult.

There is only one noteworthy difference between the dimensions which Philon and Vitruvius provide for the components of the palintone frames. The height of each stanchion according to Vitruvius should be $5\frac{3}{16}$ spring-diameters as opposed to Philon's $5\frac{1}{2}$ (or, just possibly, $5\frac{7}{12}$) diameters. When all four stanchions were smaller by the amount indicated ($\frac{5}{16}$ of a diameter), a substantial volume of wood (and the corresponding iron plating, of course) would be saved. Vitruvius' springs would be reduced in height because of this arrangement, but, since they were thicker than Philon's springs, their total volume would still be appreciably greater than that of springs inserted in washers of the older type.

The theoretical volume of spring-cord in one spring of a 15-mina stone-thrower, built according to Philon's measurements and with the old washers, may be calculated as very nearly 12,000 cubic dactyls. One spring of the equivalent Vitruvian *ballista*, the twenty-pounder, fitted with the improved washers and with stanchions of reduced height, contains almost 16,000 cubic dactyls.[2] Thus, Vitruvius' *praeceptores* had managed to achieve a real advance in a matter which always engaged the attention of artificers. Philon, for example, lays great emphasis on the value of additional spring-cord in the

---

[1] Vitr. x. 11.

[2] These two figures for volume have been calculated as carefully as possible, but they are only theoretical because, in practice, it is impossible completely to fill up the holes in the washers and hole-carriers. Therefore, the actual volumes of Philonian and Vitruvian springs will be somewhat lower than the figures given here, but will still bear the same relationship to each other. The calculation of the volume of the Vitruvian spring is based on the assumption, which I believe we must inevitably make, that Vitruvius intended his spring-diameters to correspond as closely as possible to the Greek diameters. Thus, we cannot accept his list of weights of shot and diameters (x. 11. 3) as it stands. I have suggested (*Technical Treatises*, Vitruvius, n. 21) the possibility that Vitruvius' diameters were meant to be in *unciae* and not in digits. For the purpose of my calculation I took the diameter given in the text of Vitruvius for his twenty-pounder *ballista* to be 10 *unciae*, not 10 digits, and I regarded 10 *unciae* as the Roman equivalent of $12\frac{3}{4}$ dactyls.

springs: 'The man who wants to shoot far must try to put on as much spring-cord as possible'.[1] Vitruvian *ballista*-springs seem to have contained approximately one and one-third times the amount of cord which formed the springs of older stone-throwers of the same calibre. The *ballistae* for which they supplied the power will have possessed a noticeably better performance than stone-throwers of Philon's type, in spite of the fact that the necessary reduction in the height of the stanchions meant that the springs no longer had the optimum relationship between diameter and height. Military artificers presumably discovered that the sacrifice of height was of little importance when compared with the advantages afforded by the great increase in the quantity of resilient cord in each spring.

The greater power of Vitruvian *ballistae* has been suspected and suggested before, though for a different reason—briefly, as follows. In his list of calibres for stone-throwers Vitruvius supplies the weights of shot in Roman pounds and the corresponding diameters of the spring-hole, according to the text as we have it, in digits.[2] His diameters are consistently only about three-quarters of what they should be when calculated in accordance with the Greek formula for stone-throwers.[3] Hultsch and Drachmann, therefore, suggested that the springs of Roman machines must have been more powerful than the Greek and that the performance of a Greek stone-thrower could be matched by a Roman *ballista* of about three-quarters the size.[4]

When attempting to interpret Vitruvius' table of calibres, I suggested that Vitruvius really meant the diameters to be in *unciae* (twelfths of a Roman foot) and that, at some stage in the transmission of the text, a copyist misunderstood this and jumped to the conclusion that the figures for the diameters represent digits (sixteenths of a Roman foot). Vitruvius' diameters, if taken to be in *unciae* and not digits, correspond very closely to those worked out by means of the Greek formula. But we ought now to reconsider the relative merits of digits and *unciae*. It may turn out that the new design of the washers allows Vitruvius to use spring-holes with a diameter only about three-quarters of the diameter in the older engines and yet to put in just as much spring cord as before.

In the previous calculation of the volume of one spring in a Vitruvian twenty-pounder *ballista* I assumed that the diameter was ten *unciae*, not ten digits, and that *ten unciae* were roughly equivalent to twelve and three-quarter dactyls. If we now take the diameter to be 10 digits after all, we find that the theoretical volume of one spring in a twenty-pounder is 7,713 cubic digits, i.e. 6,792 cubic dactyls. On the other hand, we have already calculated that the volume of one spring in Philon's equivalent 15-mina stone-thrower was nearly 12,000 cubic dactyls. Thus, if Vitruvius meant his diameters to be in digits, his machines were greatly underpowered when compared with Philon's,

---

[1] Philon, *Bel.* 56.   [2] Vitr. x. 11. 3.

[3] For an account of the Greek formula, see Philon, *Bel.* 51. Vitruvius (x. 11. 1) indicates that he has the Greek formula in mind, though the passage where he does so is admittedly obscure.

[4] Hultsch in *RE* s.v. 'Arithmetica', col. 1087; for discussion of Drachmann's arguments and of Vitruvius' table of calibres, see *Technical Treatises*, Vitruvius, n. 21.

in spite of the advantage afforded by the improved washers. There is no evidence that Vitruvius' springs were made of better material than the older ones, or that there had been significant developments in the method of preparing sinew or hair. If anything, Roman production of spring-cord may have been inferior to the Greek. Therefore, I reaffirm my original proposal that Vitruvius intended the figures for the diameters of his *ballista*-springs to represent *unciae*. Except for the points mentioned, his stone-throwers were built to the same specification as earlier machines and owed their superiority simply to the new type of washer.

The most important single factor in the above interpretation of the differences between Philon's and Vitruvius' lists of dimensions is the need to preserve the balance of the pair of spring-frames and the stock. On general grounds, it is reasonable to regard a well-balanced machine as a more efficient piece of artillery than one which does not balance satisfactorily. There is fairly good evidence that ancient engineers thought so.[1] Nevertheless, it may be felt that, if the weight of the springs and frames is to be increased in order to produce greater power, the simplest method of restoring the balance would be to fix a neat and inconspicuous counterweight underneath the rear end of the stock. But this procedure violates another vital principle of construction which Greek and Roman artificers invariably tried to respect. That is to say, they always endeavoured to keep the total weight of any military machine, and also the weights of its components, to the absolute minimum.[2] The use of circular ratchets fitted to the windlass will have done something to ease the problem of balancing the heavier frames; but, apart from this, they pared down the frames by reducing the height of the stanchions to compensate for the heavier springs.

The new washers and the consequent adjustments to the frames were introduced in the period between Philon and Vitruvius. These changes may well have been devised by Agesistratus. The evidence is no more than circumstantial; but it is noteworthy that he achieved really outstanding performance with his machines and surpassed his predecessors by a considerable margin. His three-span arrow-firer (spring-diameter: 4 dactyls) had a range of about 700 yards, and a palintone machine specially adapted for shooting bolts hurled a missile 4 cubits long to a distance of about 800 yards.[3] Although we may be inclined to regard these impressive claims with suspicion, they could be due to Agesistratus' development of the improved washers.

We are also informed about another significant fact: Agesistratus' three-span catapult had 12 minae of spring-cord, probably sinew, in its springs. What was the weight of spring-cord in a Philonian catapult of this calibre? It is just possible to work this out. Philon says that the spring-cord in a stone-thrower's springs weighs about twenty-five times the stone-shot.[4] Therefore,

---

[1] Philon, *Bel.* 56.   [2] Heron, *Bel.* W 90 and 102; see *Technical Treatises*, Heron, n. 10.
[3] Ath. Mech. W 8.
[4] Philon, *Bel.* 54. This figure is not perhaps entirely above suspicion; but there is no sign of textual corruption, and it could well be correct.

the spring-cord in his 15-mina engine, in which each spring has a volume of about 12,000 cubic dactyls, weighs 375 minae. On this basis, we calculate that the spring-cord in a Philonian three-span catapult, in which each spring has a volume of 307 cubic dactyls, would weigh just over $9\frac{1}{2}$ minae. Agesistratus' heavier (12 minae) springs correspond exactly to what we would expect in an engine using the new washers.

Hultsch dated Agesistratus, together with his teacher, Apollonius, in the first half of the second century B.C.[1] However, since the washers of the Ampurias catapult are round like Philon's, and since this machine formed part of the Roman preparations in Spain during the second half of the second century B.C., it might be argued that Agesistratus could not have used or invented the improved washers before the end of that century or the early first century. Also Apollonius, under whom Agesistratus learned his trade, was remembered for one engineering feat only: he astonished onlookers by bringing stones of incredible size on ships into the harbour at Rhodes and unloading them on the mole.[2] Cichorius has demonstrated convincingly that these stones were intended for repairs to the Rhodian fortifications in the face of an impending siege, and that the siege in question was the one undertaken by Mithridates in 88 B.C., of which the Rhodians had advance notice.[3] Thus, Agesistratus will have been at his peak as a maker of catapults and will have devised or exploited the new washers about the second quarter of the first century B.C.

[1] In *RE* Suppl. i, s.v. 'Agesistratus (4)', col. 27; and *RE* s.v. 'Apollonius (113)', col. 160.
[2] Ath. Mech. W 8.   [3] Cichorius, *Römische Studien*, 272 f.

I. GENERAL

(All dates are B.C. unless otherwise indicated)

Accuracy (of shooting), 79 f., 93 f., 101.
Acragas, siege of (406), 48, 52.
Actium, 172.
advanced non-torsion catapults, 13 ff., 56, 63, 100.
Aegosthena, fortifications at, 134 ff., 151, 154, 160.
Aelius Optatus, artilleryman, 191 f.
Aemilius, L., Paullus, 166.
Aemilius, Q., Papus, 170.
Aeneas Tacticus, 100.
Aetolians, 77.
aerarium militare, 182.
Agathocles of Syracuse, 78, 144.
Agesistratus, noted artificer, 42, 70, 88 f., 95, 205 f.
Agrianians, 165.
Agrippa, M. Vipsanius, 172.
aiming, 92 f.; with earliest *gastraphetes*, 12, 16, 32; with torsion catapults, 39; helped by window, 70; in fortifications, 123, 128.
Alexander the Great, 73, 76, 78, 164, 179; *helepolis* designed for, 13, 50; engineers of, 58; besieges Halicarnassus, 60, 62, 101 f.; besieges Tyre, 61, 102 f., 117, 170; at Halicarnassus and Tyre, 66; at Gaza, 69, 95, 103 f.; on the Jaxartes, 97; uses field artillery, 165 ff., 177 f.
Alexandria, 84; formulae discovered at, 62; workshops at, 76 f., 175; Heptastadium, 171, 178.
Ambrossus (or Ambrysus), Boeotia, 126.
Amida, 195, 197 f.
Ammianus Marcellinus, 98, 189, 195, 198.
Ampurias, catapult from, 20, 29 f.
Ampurias, arsenal at, 174, 176.
Amyntas, Rhodian sea-captain, 106.
angle of depression, 39, 109, 113, 117 f.
angle of elevation, 68, 80, 91, 118, 139, 151, 153.
angle of projection, 80, 89 ff., 131.
Anonymus Byzantinus, 88.
Anticyra, 170.
Antigenes, soldier of Alexander, 101.
Antigonus I, 76, 169.
Antinous (in *Odyssey*), 10.
Antipater, 73.
Antium, 83.
Antonius, M., 169, 172.

Aous, R. (Aoi Stena), 166 f.
aperture, *see* window.
Appius Claudius Pulcher, at Syracuse, 108 f.
arbalest, 2.
Archelaus, Mithridatic commander, 111 f.
archers, 50 f., 104, 108, 110, 123, 127 f., 130, 138, 165 ff., 186, 190.
Archidamus, son of Agesilaus, 65.
Archimedes, three-talent stone-thrower of, 83, 91; in siege of Syracuse, 92, 97 f., 108 f., 115; and fortifications, 119, 122, 125.
architecti, 183, 185.
Argos, fortifications at, 144, 148, 162.
Ariarathes (or Arcathias), 111 f.
Aristotle, 71.
arm of catapult, 91; fitting of, 18, 31; movement of, 21 f.; heel of, 29; in Ctesibius' air-spring, 41; curved, 42, 200 f.
Arrhidaeus, besieges Cyzicus, 73.
Arrian, 102 f., 190 f., 193.
arrow-shooting *ballista*, 1, 91 f., 96, 188–90, 192–8.
Arsaces Epiphanes, 75.
arsenals, 175 f.; at Rhodes, 3; at Alexandria, 3; Macedonian, 59; New Carthage, 79; at Massilia, 112; at Athens, 137; at Ampurias (Emporiae), 174; at Rome, 184 f.; *fabricae*, 197.
Arsinoe, wife of Ptolemy II, 62 f.
Artemon of Clazomenae, 50.
artificer (μηχανοποιός, ὀργανοποιός, *architectus*), 68 ff., 73, 76, 78, 88, 96, 98, 106, 174, 177, 185, 192 f., 195.
artillerymen (καταπελταφέται, *ballistarii*), 75, 106, 132, 179; duties of, 67 f.; as instructors, 71 ff.; in Roman army, 191–7; Ptolemaic, 196.
Asine (Argolid), 148.
Assyrian siege-trains, 53.
Asteriscus, wins artillery competition, 74.
Athenaeus Mechanicus, 58, 88.
Athens, 17, 84, 105, 137; artillery stored at, 56 f.; Eretrian catapults at, 58, 60; torsion engines at, 61; first artillery at, 65 f., 116; history of artillery at, 67 ff.; Sulla's siege of, 111.
Athens–Peiraeus, 99, 110 f.
Attalus I of Pergamum, 13, 177.
Atticus, T. Pomponius, 179.

II. AUTHORS AND PASSAGES

(Italic figures indicate page numbers in this work)

III. INSCRIPTIONS

(Italic figures indicate page numbers in this work)

IV. GREEK

V. LATIN

PLATE 1

The catapult on Vedennius' tombstone

PLATE 2

a. The Cupid Gem, greatly enlarged (*c.* 6 : 1)

b. Line-drawing to clarify the Cupid Gem

PLATE 3

Catapult in the balustrade relief at Pergamum

PLATE 4

Full-scale reconstruction of a three-span catapult

PLATE 5

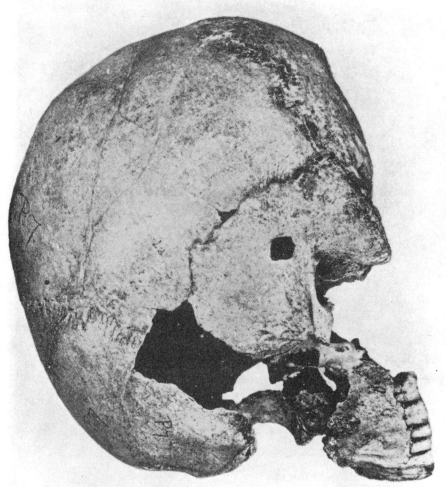

The skull from Maiden Castle

PLATE 6

Full-scale reconstruction of Heron's *Cheiroballistra*—front view

PLATE 7

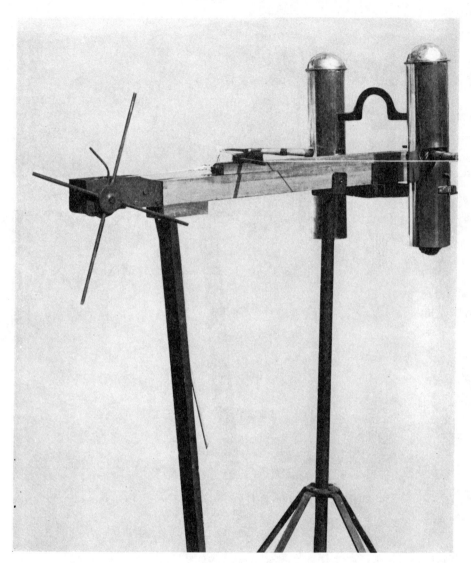

Full-scale reconstruction of Heron's *Cheiroballistra*—side view

PLATE 8

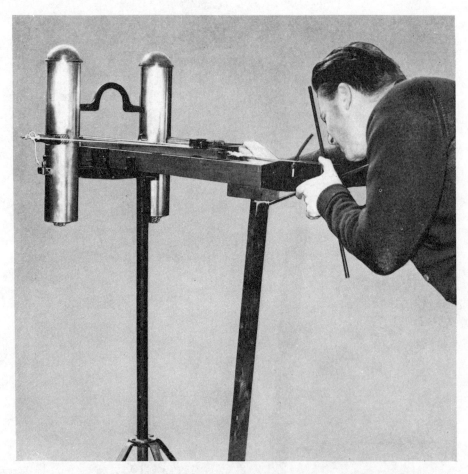

Full-scale reconstruction of Heron's *Cheiroballistra*—from the rear

PLATE 9

PLATE 10

Trajan's Column 163–4

PLATE 11

Trajan's Column 165

PLATE 12

Trajan's Column 166

PLATE 13

Trajan's Column 169

PLATE 14

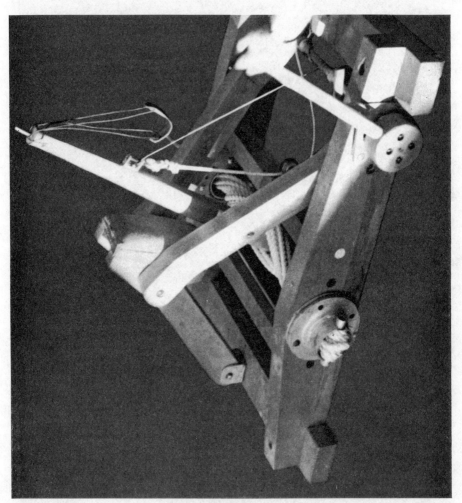

Small-scale reconstruction of an *onager*

OTHER TITLES IN THIS HARDBACK REPRINT PROGRAMME FROM SANDPIPER BOOKS LTD (LONDON) AND POWELLS BOOKS (CHICAGO)

ISBN 0–19–	Author	Title
8143567	ALFÖLDI A.	The Conversion of Constantine and Pagan Rome
6286409	ANDERSON George K.	The Literature of the Anglo-Saxons
8228813	BARTLETT & MacKAY	Medieval Frontier Societies
8111010	BETHURUM Dorothy	Homilies of Wulfstan
8142765	BOLLING G. M.	External Evidence for Interpolation in Homer
9240132	BOYLAN Patrick	Thoth, the Hermes of Egypt
8114222	BROOKS Kenneth R.	Andreas and the Fates of the Apostles
8203543	BULL Marcus	Knightly Piety & Lay Response to the First Crusade
8216785	BUTLER Alfred J.	Arab Conquest of Egypt
8148046	CAMERON Alan	Circus Factions
8148054	CAMERON Alan	Porphyrius the Charioteer
8148348	CAMPBELL J.B.	The Emperor and the Roman Army 31 BC to 235
826643X	CHADWICK Henry	Priscillian of Avila
826447X	CHADWICK Henry	Boethius
8219393	COWDREY H.E.J.	The Age of Abbot Desiderius
8148992	DAVIES M.	Sophocles: Trachiniae
825301X	DOWNER L.	Leges Henrici Primi
814346X	DRONKE Peter	Medieval Latin and the Rise of European Love-Lyric
8142749	DUNBABIN T.J.	The Western Greeks
8154372	FAULKNER R.O.	The Ancient Egyptian Pyramid Texts
8221541	FLANAGAN Marie Therese	Irish Society, Anglo-Norman Settlers, Angevin Kingship
8143109	FRAENKEL Edward	Horace
8201540	GOLDBERG P.J.P.	Women, Work and Life Cycle in a Medieval Economy
8140215	GOTTSCHALK H.B.	Heraclides of Pontus
8266162	HANSON R.P.C.	Saint Patrick
8224354	HARRISS G.L.	King, Parliament and Public Finance in Medieval England to 1369
8581114	HEATH Sir Thomas	Aristarchus of Samos
8140444	HOLLIS A.S.	Callimachus: Hecale
8212968	HOLLISTER C. Warren	Anglo-Saxon Military Institutions
8223129	HURNARD Naomi	The King's Pardon for Homicide – before AD 1307
8140401	HUTCHINSON G.O.	Hellenistic Poetry
9240140	JOACHIM H.H.	Aristotle: On Coming-to-be and Passing-away
9240094	JONES A.H.M	Cities of the Eastern Roman Provinces
8142560	JONES A.H.M.	The Greek City
8218354	JONES Michael	Ducal Brittany 1364–1399
8271484	KNOX & PELCZYNSKI	Hegel's Political Writings
8225253	LE PATOUREL John	The Norman Empire
8212720	LENNARD Reginald	Rural England 1086–1135
8212321	LEVISON W.	England and the Continent in the 8th century
8148224	LIEBESCHUETZ J.H.W.G.	Continuity and Change in Roman Religion
8141378	LOBEL Edgar & PAGE Sir Denys	Poetarum Lesbiorum Fragmenta
9240159	LOEW E.A.	The Beneventan Script
8241445	LUKASIEWICZ, Jan	Aristotle's Syllogistic
8152442	MAAS P. & TRYPANIS C.A .	Sancti Romani Melodi Cantica
8142684	MARSDEN E.W.	Greek and Roman Artillery—Historical
8142692	MARSDEN E.W.	Greek and Roman Artillery—Technical
8148178	MATTHEWS John	Western Aristocracies and Imperial Court AD 364–425
8223447	McFARLANE K.B.	Lancastrian Kings and Lollard Knights
8226578	McFARLANE K.B.	The Nobility of Later Medieval England
8148100	MEIGGS Russell	Roman Ostia
8148402	MEIGGS Russell	Trees and Timber in the Ancient Mediterranean World
8142641	MILLER J. Innes	The Spice Trade of the Roman Empire
8147813	MOORHEAD John	Theoderic in Italy
8264259	MOORMAN John	A History of the Franciscan Order
8116020	OWEN A.L.	The Famous Druids
8131445	PALMER, L.R.	The Interpretation of Mycenaean Greek Texts
8143427	PFEIFFER R.	History of Classical Scholarship (vol 1)
8143648	PFEIFFER Rudolf	History of Classical Scholarship 1300–1850
8111649	PHEIFER J.D.	Old English Glosses in the Epinal-Erfurt Glossary
8142277	PICKARD–CAMBRIDGE A.W.	Dithyramb Tragedy and Comedy
8269765	PLATER & WHITE	Grammar of the Vulgate
8213891	PLUMMER Charles	Lives of Irish Saints (2 vols)
820695X	POWICKE Michael	Military Obligation in Medieval England
8269684	POWICKE Sir Maurice	Stephen Langton
821460X	POWICKE Sir Maurice	The Christian Life in the Middle Ages
8225369	PRAWER Joshua	Crusader Institutions
8225571	PRAWER Joshua	The History of The Jews in the Latin Kingdom of Jerusalem
8143249	RABY F.J.E.	A History of Christian Latin Poetry

8143257	RABY F.J.E.	A History of Secular Latin Poetry in the Middle Ages (2 vols)
8214316	RASHDALL & POWICKE	The Universities of Europe in the Middle Ages (3 vols)
8154488	REYMOND E.A.E & BARNS J.W.B.	Four Martyrdoms from the Pierpont Morgan Coptic Codices
8148380	RICKMAN Geoffrey	The Corn Supply of Ancient Rome
8141076	ROSS Sir David	Aristotle: Metaphysics (2 vols)
8141092	ROSS Sir David	Aristotle: Physics
8142307	ROSTOVTZEFF M.	Social and Economic History of the Hellenistic World, 3 vols.
8142315	ROSTOVTZEFF M.	Social and Economic History of the Roman Empire, 2 vols.
8264178	RUNCIMAN Sir Steven	The Eastern Schism
814833X	SALMON J.B.	Wealthy Corinth
8171587	SALZMAN L.F.	Building in England Down to 1540
8218362	SAYERS Jane E.	Papal Judges Delegate in the Province of Canterbury 1198–1254
8221657	SCHEIN Sylvia	Fideles Crucis
8148135	SHERWIN WHITE A.N.	The Roman Citizenship
9240167	SINGER Charles	Galen: On Anatomical Procedures
8113927	SISAM, Kenneth	Studies in the History of Old English Literature
8642040	SOUTER Alexander	A Glossary of Later Latin to 600 AD
8222254	SOUTHERN R.W.	Eadmer: Life of St. Anselm
8251408	SQUIBB G.	The High Court of Chivalry
8212011	STEVENSON & WHITELOCK	Asser's Life of King Alfred
8212011	SWEET Henry	A Second Anglo-Saxon Reader—Archaic and Dialectical
8148259	SYME Sir Ronald	History in Ovid
8143273	SYME Sir Ronald	Tacitus (2 vols)
8200951	THOMPSON Sally	Women Religious
8201745	WALKER Simon	The Lancastrian Affinity 1361–1399
8161115	WELLESZ Egon	A History of Byzantine Music and Hymnography
8140185	WEST M.L.	Greek Metre
8141696	WEST M.L.	Hesiod: Theogony
8148542	WEST M.L.	The Orphic Poems
8140053	WEST M.L.	Hesiod: Works & Days
8152663	WEST M.L.	Iambi et Elegi Graeci
822799X	WHITBY M. & M.	The History of Theophylact Simocatta
8206186	WILLIAMSON, E.W.	Letters of Osbert of Clare
8114877	WOOLF Rosemary	The English Religious Lyric in the Middle Ages
8119224	WRIGHT Joseph	Grammar of the Gothic Language